MACMILLAN WORK OUT SERIES

Physical Chemistry

D. J. Shaw
and
H. E. Avery

MACMILLAN

First published 1989
Reprinted 1990, 1991

Published by
MACMILLAN EDUCATION LTD
Houndmills, Basingstoke, Hampshire RG21 2XS
and London
Companies and representatives
throughout the world

Typeset by TecSet Ltd,
Wallington, Surrey

Printed in Hong Kong

British Library Cataloguing in Publication Data
Shaw, D. J.
Work out physical chemistry.
1. Physical chemistry—Questions & answers—
For colleges
I. Title   II. Avery, H. E.
541.3'076
ISBN 0–333–45869–9

Contents

Acknowledgements

We wish to thank the Royal Society of Chemistry, the Universities of Birmingham, Bristol, Brunel, Durham, Leeds, Liverpool, Manchester, Nottingham, Salford and Sheffield, and Liverpool Polytechnic for permission to publish extracts from their examination papers. In a few cases, we have amended original material so as to conform with the principles outlined in Chapter 1. We also wish to thank Butterworth and Co. for permission to make use of a small amount of material from our book *Basic Physical Chemistry Calculations*.

Finally, we wish to thank Dr H. Morris and Mr G. D. Shaw, for a number of helpful suggestions concerning Chapter 8, and our wives, Ann and Elizabeth, for their help in preparing the manuscript and checking the text.

General Introduction

The Nature and Purpose of This Book

This book is primarily intended for students in the early stages of a chemistry degree or equivalent course. It covers most of the physical chemistry found in first-year syllabuses and much second-year material as well. The book should also prove useful for students of related subjects in the physical and life sciences and for ambitious 'A' Level students who wish to extend and broaden their knowledge of physical chemistry, particularly if intending to sit an 'S' Level chemistry examination.

It is not intended as a substitute for a textbook of physical chemistry. Following a short introductory chapter on units and methods of expression, the subsequent chapters cover the major areas of physical chemistry. Each chapter contains sections in which basic theory is set out in a concise fashion. Factual material and experimental detail are kept to a minimum. The text should provide not only a base for clarifying and consolidating the fundamentals of physical chemistry, but also a convenient revision aid. Most physical chemistry examinations are heavily weighted with numerical problems and this book seeks to give the reader familiarity and practice in methods of solving these. Simple examples are given in the main text to illustrate points as they arise. Each chapter contains a selection of worked examples, some covering a single topic and some of wider and more ambitious content. Students may care to attempt these before inspecting the worked answer. At the end of each chapter there are some unworked examples, with answers provided at the end of the book. Some of the numerical examples are taken from past examination papers. Since, in most cases, only part of the question is quoted, it would be misleading to assume that these questions always reflect the standard required in a particular examination.

The book builds on the physicochemical topics covered in *Work Out Chemistry 'A' Level*. The basic concepts of thermodynamics are extended and applied to phase equilibria and solutions. Chemical kinetics includes rate theory and an introduction to complex reactions. Electrochemistry is divided into a study of the nature of and processes in electrolyte solutions and a study of electrode processes. The book concludes with introductions to two topics that may be new to most students, 'Surface chemistry and colloids' and 'Molecular structure and spectroscopy'.

Background Knowledge

The reader is assumed to be reasonably familiar with the following topics:

(a) Perfect (ideal) and real gases; perfect gas equation ($pV = nRT$). Dalton's law of partial pressures ($p_{total} = p_A + p_B + \ldots$). Basic characteristics of solid, liquid and gaseous states. Existence and consequences of van der Waals' forces and hydrogen bonding.

(b) Simple kinetic theory of gases; kinetic interpretation of thermodynamic temperature. Distribution of energy amongst molecules.

(c) Stoichiometric equations. Mole concept and Avogadro constant.

(d) Law of mass action and its use to formulate expressions for equilibrium constants. Le Chatelier's principle.

(e) Factors affecting the rate of a reaction.

(f) Acids and bases; dissociation of water; pH; buffer solutions; dissociation constants; solubility product. Oxidation and reduction. Electrolysis.

(g) Logarithms and exponentials. Basic calculus and algebra.

Revision

Obtain copies of your syllabus and a selection of past examination papers. Most universities/polytechnics/colleges have provision for this. Ascertain as far as you can the relevance of past questions to your year of study; there may have been syllabus and/or staff changes since then. Identify as clearly as possible the subject areas that you need to study and the breadth and depth of knowledge that is expected from you. Much of this should be self-evident, but if in any doubt do not hesitate to ask your lecturers, who, in general, will be only too pleased to help.

It is essential that you own a textbook of physical chemistry; there are several excellent ones available. Also on the market is a selection of monographs on specific areas of physical chemistry; you should purchase and/or make library use of some of these. In general, your choice of textbooks will be dictated by the recommendations of your lecturers.

It is essential that your study programme be spread over the whole of the academic year. An appropriate number of hours per week should be set aside for reviewing, understanding and, if necessary, supplementing your lecture material. Leaving this work to a concentrated effort during the last few weeks before the examination is a well known recipe for disaster. The final period of revision should be for 'fine tuning'. Work in a place where you are as free as possible from external distractions. One hour of solid, well organised work is far more useful than several hours of vague, uncoordinated effort. Remember that the brain has a limited capacity for reception during a long study period.

Resist the temptation to bias revision towards your favourite subject area, but strive for reasonably even coverage. If anything, you should bias your study time to your weaker subjects.

Spend a fair proportion of your study time in an active role, writing things down, attempting problems, etc., rather than in the more passive role of just reading. Where possible, have a very brief pre-read, without bothering too much about the detail, before you attend the lecture(s) on a particular subject. Do not attempt to take copious notes during a lecture; just get enough down on paper for future revision purposes and devote as much effort as possible actually to listening to and trying to understand the lecturer. You can then use this book plus your textbook(s) and your brief lecture notes to produce a clear and fuller set of notes. The act of writing is a very effective learning method.

Examinations

Make sure that you are familiar with the rules. Scan through the paper first and tick off or put a question mark against those questions you are likely to attempt.

Do the question that you feel you can answer best first; this should help to build up confidence.

Before writing your answer to a descriptive question, pencil in proposed sub-headings and formulate a suitable order. This should help at a very early stage to confirm your selection of the question. It should also make the resulting account easier to write, and it will read better. It may even save time and will act as a partial insurance against forgetfulness at a later stage.

Divide your time fairly evenly between questions, especially those of a descriptive nature. The first few marks in these questions tend to be quite easy to obtain, but for the last few marks a situation of diminishing returns usually exists. It follows that it is bad technique to spend excessive time on an already good answer for a possible extra mark or two if this puts at risk the award of several easy marks on another question.

The examination paper is likely to contain several calculations and may be constructed so that you are forced to attempt one or more of these. When it comes to a choice between calculation and descriptive material, confidence is the important factor. For the able and well prepared student, calculations allow high (even full) marks to be obtained and can often be done in a relatively short time. If you do get into a hopeless muddle, do not ponder over it for too long, but move on to another question. Many questions involve descriptive material followed by a calculation and if you feel uncertain about the calculation (especially if it carries a high mark) and need to test it out, it may be a good idea to try this part first. Sometimes you will know how to set about a calculation, but the detail defeats you. If you state clearly what you were trying to do and indicate the type of answer that you would have expected, a moderate mark is still possible. Alternatively, you might obtain the wrong answer because of an undetected arithmetic slip. If the answer is obviously wrong, say so and indicate, with reason(s) if possible, the type of answer that you would have expected. The loss of marks in such circumstances should be small. Finally, with calculations, be careful with powers of 10 and do not forget units.

1 The Language of Physical Science

1.1 Quantities and Units

In any physical science the use of standardised methods of expression offers obvious advantages in enabling us to communicate clearly and unambiguously. Such a scheme exists and is outlined in this chapter. It is based on a coherent set of units, known as the SI (abbreviation for Système International d'Unités).

1.2 SI Units

The SI is based on the seven independent physical quantities shown in Table 1.1, the first six of which are of particular interest to physical chemists. The choice of the magnitude of these units is arbitrary, but in practice is based on a combination of natural and historical considerations.

Table 1.1

Physical quantity	Symbol(s)	Basic SI unit	Unit symbol
Length	$l, a, b, h,$ r, s etc.	metre	m
Mass	m	kilogram	kg
Time	t	second	s
Electric current	I	ampere	A
Thermodynamic temperature	T	kelvin	K
Amount of substance	n	mole	mol
Luminous intensity	I_v	candela	cd

The mole is of particular relevance to physical chemistry. It is defined as the amount of substance of a system that contains in it as many specified elementary entities as there are carbon atoms (i.e. 6.0225×10^{23}) in 0.012 kg of ^{12}C. These elementary entities may be atoms, molecules, ions, electrons, etc., or specified groups of such particles (see comment on molar quantities). The factor 6.0225×10^{23} mol^{-1} is known as Avogadro's constant.

The SI also includes two fundamental quantities with dimensionless units, given in Table 1.2.

Other physical quantities can be expressed in SI units that are derived from the above fundamental units by appropriate multiplication and/or division and without the introduction of any numerical factors (including powers of 10). In this

Table 1.2

Physical quantity	Symbols	SI unit	Unit symbol
Plane angle	$\alpha, \beta, \gamma, \theta, \phi$	radian	rad
Solid angle	ω, Ω	steradian	sr

sense, the SI is a coherent system of units. Some of these derived units are given special names and symbols, mostly after well known scientists, as in Table 1.3; others are listed in Table 1.4.

Table 1.3 Derived SI units with special names

Physical quantity	Symbol(s)	Name of SI unit	Unit symbol	Definition
Frequency	ν, f	hertz	Hz	s^{-1}
Force	F	newton	N	$kg\ m\ s^{-2}$
Energy (all forms)	E, ϵ, U, V, w, etc.	joule	J	$N\ m = C\ V = kg\ m^2\ s^{-2}$
Pressure	p	pascal	Pa	$N\ m^{-2} = kg\ m^{-1}\ s^{-2}$
Power	P	watt	W	$J\ s^{-1} = V\ A = kg\ m^2\ s^{-3}$
Electric charge	Q	coulomb	C	$A\ s$
Electric potential difference	E, ψ, ϕ, η, etc.	volt	V	$J\ C^{-1} = kg\ m^2\ s^{-3}\ A^{-1}$
Electric resistance	R	ohm	Ω	$V\ A^{-1} = kg\ m^2\ s^{-3}\ A^{-2}$
Electric conductance	G	siemens	S	Ω^{-1}
Electric capacitance	C	farad	F	$C\ V^{-1} = kg^{-1}\ m^{-2}\ s^4\ A^2$
Inductance	L, M	henry	H	$V\ A^{-1}\ s = kg\ m^2\ s^{-2}\ A^{-2}$
Magnetic flux	ϕ	weber	Wb	$V\ s = kg\ m^2\ s^{-2}\ A^{-1}$
Magnetic induction	B	tesla	T	$Wb\ m^{-2} = kg\ s^{-2}\ A^{-1}$
Luminous flux	ϕ	lumen	lm	$cd\ sr$
Illumination	E	lux	lx	$lm\ m^{-2} = cd\ sr\ m^{-2}$

Table 1.4 Some other derived SI units

Physical quantity	Symbol(s)	Definition	SI unit
Area	A	$\int l\ dh$	m^2
Volume	V	$\int A\ dh$	m^3
Velocity	u, v, c	ds/dt	$m\ s^{-1}$
Angular velocity	ω	$d\theta/dt$	$rad\ s^{-1}$
Momentum	p	mu	$kg\ m\ s^{-1}$
Angular momentum	L	rp	$kg\ m^2\ s^{-1}$
Acceleration	a, g	du/dt	$m\ s^{-2}$
Moment of inertia	I	$I_z = \int (x^2 + y^2)\ dm$	$kg\ m^2$
Weight	G, W	mg	N
Density	ρ	m/V	$kg\ m^{-3}$
Specific volume	v	V/m	$m^3\ kg^{-1}$
Shear stress	τ	F/A	$N\ m^{-2}$
Dynamic viscosity	η	$\tau_{xz} (du_x/dz)^{-1}$	$kg\ m^{-1}\ s^{-1}$
Diffusion coefficient	D	$(-dm/dt)(A\ dc/dx)^{-1}$	$m^2\ s^{-1}$

Quantity	Symbol	Definition	Unit
Surface tension	γ, σ	dw/dA (rev)	$N\,m^{-1}$
Molecular mass	m		kg
Molar mass	M	m/n	$kg\,mol^{-1}$
Molar volume	V_m	V/n	$m^3\,mol^{-1}$
Relative atomic mass	A_r	(see § 1.5.8)	dimensionless
Relative molecular mass	M_r	(see § 1.5.8)	dimensionless
Work	w	Fs	J
Quantity of heat	q		J
Internal energy	U		J
Enthalpy	H	$U + pV$	J
Gibbs free energy	G	$H - TS$	J
Entropy	S	(see § 2.8.2)	$J\,K^{-1}$
Heat capacity	C_V	$(\partial U/\partial T)_V$	$J\,K^{-1}$
Heat capacity	C_p	$(\partial H/\partial T)_p$	$J\,K^{-1}$
Molar gas constant	R	$\lim_{p\to0} pV_m/T$	$J\,K^{-1}\,mol^{-1}$
Boltzmann constant	k	R/N_A	$J\,K^{-1}$
Avogadro constant	N_A, L	(see § 1.2)	mol^{-1}
Concentration of substance B	$c_B, [B]$	n_B/V	$mol\,m^{-3}$
Molality of solute B	m_B	n_B/m_A	$mol\,kg^{-1}$
Mole fraction of substance B	x_B	$n_B/\Sigma n_B$	dimensionless
Stoichiometric coefficient of substance B	ν_B	products +ve, reactants −ve	dimensionless
Degree of dissociation	α		dimensionless
Molar internal energy	U_m	U/n	$J\,mol^{-1}$
Molar enthalpy	H_m	H/n	$J\,mol^{-1}$
Molar heat capacity	$C_{V,m}, C_{p,m}$	$C_V/n, C_p/n$	$J\,K^{-1}\,mol^{-1}$
Molar entropy	S_m	S/n	$J\,K^{-1}\,mol^{-1}$
Molar Gibbs free energy	G_m	G/n	$J\,mol^{-1}$
Partial molar volume of substance B	V_B	$(\partial V/\partial n_B)_{T,p,n_C,\ldots}$	$m^3\,mol^{-1}$
Chemical potential of substance B	μ_B	$(\partial G/\partial n_B)_{T,p,n_C,\ldots}$	$J\,mol^{-1}$
Fugacity	p^*, f	(see § 2.7.3)	Pa
Relative activity of component B	a_B	(see § 1.5.3)	dimensionless
Activity coefficient of component B	y_B, γ_B, f_B	(see § 1.5.3)	dimensionless
Osmotic pressure	Π		Pa
Equilibrium constant*	K_c	$\Pi (c_B)^{\nu_B}$	$(mol\,m^{-3})^{\Sigma \nu_B}$
Equilibrium constant	K_p	$\Pi (p_B)^{\nu_B}$	$Pa^{\Sigma \nu_B}$
Standard equilibrium constant	$K_c^{\ominus}$, etc.	$\Pi (c_B y_B/c^{\ominus})^{\nu_B}$, etc. (see § 1.5.3)	dimensionless
Electric field strength	E	$d\psi/dx$	$V\,m^{-1}$
Charge density	ρ	Q/V	$C\,m^{-3}$
Electric current density	j	I/A	$A\,m^{-2}$
Permittivity	ϵ	(see § 1.4)	$F\,m^{-1}$
Relative permittivity	ϵ_r	ϵ/ϵ_0	dimensionless
Permeability	μ	(see § 1.4)	$H\,m^{-1}$
Relative permeability	μ_r	μ/μ_0	dimensionless
Dipole moment of a molecule	μ		$C\,m$
Elementary charge	e		C
Charge number of an ion i (+ve or −ve)	z_i		dimensionless
Faraday constant	F	$N_A e$	$C\,mol^{-1}$
Electric conductivity	κ	j/E	$S\,m^{-1}$
Molar conductivity	Λ	κ/c	$S\,m^2\,mol^{-1}$

*In the definitions of equilibrium constants Π represents a product; and in the units Σ represents a sum.

Table 1.4 (*cont'd*)

Physical quantity	Symbol(s)	Definition	SI unit
Transport number of ion i	t_i		dimensionless
Mobility of a charged particle	u	v/E	$m^2\ s^{-1}\ V^{-1}$
Extent of reaction	ξ	$(n_B - n_{B,0})/\nu_B$	mol
Rate of a reaction	J	$(d\xi/dt)/V$ $= (d[B]/dt)/\nu_B$	$mol\ m^{-3}\ s^{-1}$
Rate constant of a $(n+1)$th-order reaction	k, k_r		$s^{-1}\ (mol\ m^{-3})^{-n}$
Activation energy of a reaction	$E_a, E^{\ddagger}$		$J\ mol^{-1}$
Collision number	Z		$m^{-3}\ s^{-1}$
Refractive index	n		dimensionless
Planck constant	h	ϵ/ν	J s
Wavelength	λ		m
Wavenumber	$\bar{\nu}, \sigma$	$1/\lambda$	m^{-1}
Transmittance	T	I/I_0	dimensionless
Decadic absorbance	A	$-\log_{10} T$	dimensionless
Molar decadic absorption coefficient	ϵ	A/lc	$m^2\ mol^{-1}$

(a) Quantity symbols are always printed in *italic* (sloping) type, whereas unit symbols are printed in roman (upright) type. In ordinary handwriting, of course, this distinction will not be present.

(b) Full stops are not used between units to represent multiplication, but units are spaced to avoid possible confusion, such as between $1\ m\ s^{-1}$ (one metre per second) and $1\ ms^{-1}$ (interpretable as one reciprocal millisecond). $10^{-3}\ s^{-1}$ unambiguously represents the latter quantity.

(c) Plural forms for unit symbols are not used, e.g. 2 kg, and not 2 kgs.

(d) The use of a single slash for expressing divided units (e.g. $m\ s^{-1}/V\ m^{-1}$ for ionic mobility, rather than $m^2\ s^{-1}\ V^{-1}$) is permissible, but the simple use of positive and negative powers is preferable. More than one slash in a derived unit (e.g. m/s/V/m for ionic mobility) should never be used owing to the ambiguity created.

1.2.1 Prefixes for SI Units

The SI permits the use of prefixes (Tables 1.5 and 1.6) to denote decimal fractions and multiples of basic SI units and derived SI units with special names. These prefixes confer factors of 10^{3n}, except around unity where additional prefixes are available to denote 10^{-2}, 10^{-1}, 10 and 10^2. Compound prefixes should not be

Table 1.5

Factor	Prefix	Symbol
10^{-1}	deci	d
10^{-2}	centi	c
10^{-3}	milli	m
10^{-6}	micro	μ
10^{-9}	nano	n
10^{-12}	pico	p
10^{-15}	femto	f
10^{-18}	atto	a

Table 1.6

Factor	Prefix	Symbol
10	deka	da
10^2	hecto	h
10^3	kilo	k
10^6	mega	M
10^9	giga	G
10^{12}	tera	T
10^{15}	peta	P
10^{18}	exa	E

used. These prefixes, though not absolutely necessary, are obviously convenient in avoiding the use of inconveniently large and small numerical values and sometimes help to facilitate an appreciation of the magnitudes of physical quantities, as illustrated below:

(a) The H—Br bond length in hydrogen bromide is 1.42×10^{-10} m, or 0.142 nm (nanometre), or 142 pm (picometre).

(b) The concentration of an aqueous solution of potassium chloride is 100 mol m^{-3}, or 0.1 mol dm^{-3}. The latter is the more convenient of these alternatives because (i) 1 m^3 is in considerable excess of the scale of a typical laboratory experiment, (ii) it is numerically the same as the obsolete but still loosely used term 'molar concentration' (mol l^{-1}), and (iii) it is numerically similar to molality expressed in moles per kilogram (mol kg^{-1}).

1.2.2 Non-SI Units

Table 1.7 lists a selection of units that are defined exactly in terms of the SI, but are not coherent with the SI. Some of these units are decimal fractions or multiples of the corresponding SI unit and some are non-decimal with respect to the corresponding SI unit.

Some of these units, e.g. dyne, erg, poise, maxwell, gauss and calorie, are obsolete. Some represent sloppy usage and have no respectable place in physical science: e.g. the symbol μ for the so-called micron means 10^{-6} and not 10^{-6} m; likewise, the symbol M for molar concentration stands for 10^{+6} (mega) and not mol dm^{-3}.

The atmosphere plays a central (albeit inconvenient) role in physical chemistry in view of its role as a standard state.

Some non-SI units, such as the minute, tonne, bar, degree Celsius and the litre enjoy everyday usage.

Table 1.7   Non-SI units

Physical quantity	Name of unit	Unit symbol	Definition
Length	angstrom	Å	10^{-10} m
Length	micron	μ	10^{-6} m $= \mu$m
Volume	litre	l	10^{-3} m^3 = dm^3
Mass	tonne	t	10^3 kg = Mg
Force	dyne	dyn	10^{-5} N
Energy	erg	erg	10^{-7} J
Pressure	bar	bar	10^5 Pa
Dynamic viscosity	poise	P	10^{-1} kg m^{-1} s^{-1}
Concentration	molar	M	mol dm^{-3}
Magnetic flux	maxwell	Mx	10^{-8} Wb
Magnetic induction	gauss	G	10^{-4} T
Energy	thermochemical calorie	cal	4.184 J
Pressure	atmosphere	atm	1.01325×10^5 Pa
Pressure	millimetre of mercury	mmHg	13.5951×9.80665 Pa $= 133.32239$ Pa
Pressure	torr	Torr	$1.01325 \times 10^5/760$ Pa $= 133.32237$ Pa
Temperature	degree Celsius	°C	$\theta_C = T - 273.15$ K

It is often convenient to express experimental data in non-SI units in view of the method of measurement. However, non-SI units should generally be avoided when recording physical quantities that have been calculated from experimental data. For example, if a mercury manometer has been used to follow the progress of a second-order gas-phase reaction at constant temperature and volume which takes place over a timescale of many minutes, it is convenient, and quite permissible, to tabulate pressures in millimetres of mercury (mmHg) with the corresponding reaction times in minutes (min); however, the calculated rate constant should be expressed in SI units, such as $Pa^{-1} s^{-1}$ or $(mol \ dm^{-3})^{-1} s^{-1}$, and not in non-SI $mmHg^{-1} min^{-1}$.

1.3 Calculations

Numerical calculations play an important role in undergraduate physical chemistry courses. Most experimental data require appropriate numerical processing and a significant proportion of a typical physical chemistry examination will be devoted to calculations.

To perform such calculations correctly, a sound grasp of the underlying physicochemical principles is obviously required. Beyond this, however, the simple mechanics of performing a calculation often presents difficulty. This can be avoided by adhering to a simple rule to use only basic SI units.

Since the SI is a coherent system of units, it follows that, when performing a numerical calculation, no thought of conversion factors is necessary if the physical quantities in question are expressed in basic SI units. When presented with prefixed SI units in a numerical calculation, a conversion factor of an appropriate power of 10 may be necessary to obtain the final answer in the desired unit. If the data are presented in prefixed SI units or non-SI units, the risk of miscalculation will be minimised if conversion to basic SI units is made before substitution into the appropriate equation(s). The final answer will then automatically appear in the appropriate basic SI unit(s). The following examples illustrate this point:

(a) Use the relationship $E = N_A hc\bar{\nu}$ to calculate the molar energy that corresponds to a wavenumber $\bar{\nu}$ of 2360 cm^{-1}. Substituting $N_A = 6.0225 \times 10^{23}$ mol^{-1}, $h = 6.6256 \times 10^{-34}$ J s, $c = 2.9979 \times 10^8$ m s^{-1} and $\bar{\nu} = 2360 \times 10^2$ m^{-1} automatically gives the value of E in the basic SI unit for molar energy, which is J mol^{-1}, i.e.

$$E = 6.0225 \times 10^{23} \times 6.6256 \times 10^{-34} \times 2.9979 \times 10^8 \times 2.360 \times 10^2$$

$$= 28230 \text{ J mol}^{-1}$$

If desired, this can then be expressed as $E = 28.23$ kJ mol^{-1}.

(b) Calculate the potential ψ such that the relationship $e\psi = kT$ is valid at 25°C. Substituting $e = 1.6021 \times 10^{-19}$ C, $k = 1.3805 \times 10^{-23}$ J K^{-1} and $T = 298.15$ K automatically gives the value of ψ in the basic SI unit for electric potential difference, which is the volt, i.e.

$$\psi = \frac{1.3805 \times 10^{-23} \times 298.15}{1.6021 \times 10^{-19}} = 0.0257 \text{ V}$$

If desired, this can then be expressed as $\psi = 25.7$ mV.

1.4 Electrical and Magnetic Quantities and Units — Rationalisation

In the SI, electrical and magnetic units are based on the fundamental units of metre, kilogram, second and ampere, and equations are rationalised.

The force F between charges Q_1 and Q_2 separated by a distance r in a medium of permittivity ϵ is given by the rationalised expression

$$F = Q_1 Q_2 / 4\pi \epsilon r^2$$

Since Q has the dimension [current] [time], ϵ has the dimension [length]$^{-3}$ [mass]$^{-1}$ [time]^4 [current]^2. The permittivity of a vacuum, ϵ_0, in accordance with the above equation is equal to 8.8542×10^{-12} kg^{-1} m^{-3} s^4 A^2.

The relative permittivity of a medium, ϵ/ϵ_0, can be referred to as the dielectric constant D of the medium if it is independent of electric field strength.

The above equation differs from the old traditional Coulomb inverse-square-law equation by the inclusion of the factor 4π. The reason for including 4π is so that its occurrence or otherwise in derived expressions might be in accord with geometric expectation, and not vice versa. For example, the equation for a parallel-plate capacitor, where the occurrence of 4π would not be expected from geometric considerations, is $\sigma = \epsilon E/4\pi d$ in the old non-rationalised form and $\sigma = \epsilon E/d$ in rationalised form; whereas the equation for an isolated spherical capacitor, where the occurrence of 4π is expected from geometric considerations, is $Q = \epsilon a E$ in non-rationalised form and $Q = 4\pi \epsilon a E$ in rationalised form.

The force F between electric currents I_1 and I_2 in parallel conductors of length l separated by a distance d in a medium of permeability μ is given by the rationalised expression

$$F = 2\mu I_1 I_2 l / 4\pi d$$

Permeability, therefore, has the dimension [length] [mass] [time]$^{-2}$ [current]$^{-2}$, and the permeability of a vacuum, μ_0, in accordance with the above equation is equal to $4\pi \times 10^7$ kg m s^{-2} A^{-2}.

The quantities ϵ_0 and μ_0 are related by the expression $\epsilon_0 \mu_0 = c_0^{-2}$, where c_0 is the velocity of light in a vacuum.

1.5 Methods of Expression

1.5.1 Superscripts and Subscripts

Some commonly used superscripts and subscripts are listed below.

Superscripts

•	pure substance
⊖	standard value of a property (e.g. $p^{\ominus} = 1$ atm, $c^{\ominus} = 1$ mol dm^{-3})
∞	limiting value at infinite dilution
‡	transition state

Subscripts

A	solvent
B, etc.	solute(s)
B, C, etc.	components of a mixture

i	typical ionic species
$+$, $-$	+ve or −ve ion
m	molar quantity, mixing
f	formation
p, T, V, etc.	constant pressure, temperature, volume, etc.

1.5.2 Tables and Graphs

The value of a physical quantity is expressed as the product of a pure number and a unit, e.g.

$p = 1.013 \times 10^5$ Pa $T = 298.15$ K

Such expressions can be processed just like any other algebraic expression, e.g.

$p/\text{Pa} = 1.013 \times 10^5$ $T/\text{K} = 298.15$
$p/10^5$ Pa $= 1.013$ $\text{K}/T = 0.003354$
$\log_{10}(p/\text{Pa}) = 5.0056$ $10^3 \text{ K}/T = 3.354$
$\log_{10}(p/10^5 \text{ Pa}) = 0.0056$

To avoid repetition of the unit symbol, and, if relevant, repetition of a power of 10, it is good practice to tabulate data in the form of pure numbers of convenient magnitude. It follows that column headings should be dimensionless and should include an appropriate power of 10 where necessary. Table 1.8, which refers to the vapour pressure of tetrachloromethane at various temperatures, illustrates this point.

Table 1.8

$\theta_C/°C$	p/mmHg	T/K	$p/10^5$ Pa	$10^3 \text{ K}/T$	$\log_{10}(p/\text{Pa})$
20	91	293.15	0.121	3.411	4.083
40	216	313.15	0.288	3.193	4.459
60	451	333.15	0.601	3.002	4.779
80	843	353.15	1.124	2.832	5.051

The same considerations apply to the labelling of graphs, as illustrated in Fig. 1.1. A sensible and easy scale should be chosen so as to use a reasonably high proportion of the total area of the graph paper (usually an A4 sheet). The slope of a straight-line graph (as it appears on the graph paper, as opposed to the actual slope) should be close to unity (45°) and certainly not greater than 2 or less than 0.5. The slope (and intercept, if required) of a straight-line plot plus the corresponding standard deviation(s) are best computed using the method of least squares, but the result should be checked against that from the actual graph.

1.5.3 Logarithmic Relationships and Standard States

Since only pure numbers can be converted into the corresponding logarithm, it follows that in physicochemical equations such as

$\Delta G^{\ominus} = - RT \ln K^{\ominus}$

and

$\mu = \mu^{\ominus} + RT \ln a$

$K^{\ominus}$ and a must be dimensionless.

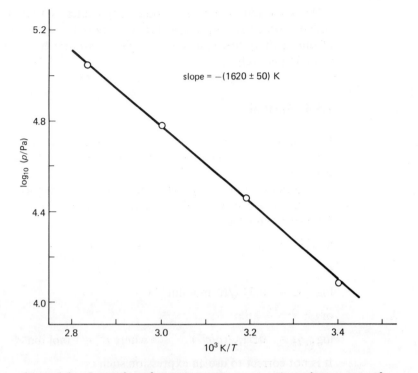

Figure 1.1   Logarithm of vapour pressure versus reciprocal temperature for tetrachloromethane.

For the first of these examples, consider the gas-phase reaction

$$N_2(g) + 3H_2(g) \rightleftharpoons 2NH_3(g)$$

for which

$$K_p = \frac{(p_{NH_3})^2}{(p_{N_2})(p_{H_2})^3}$$

and has the dimension $[\text{pressure}]^{-2}$. Now consider

$$K_p^{\ominus} \ (\text{or } K_{p/p^{\ominus}}) = \frac{(p_{NH_3}/p^{\ominus})^2}{(p_{N_2}/p^{\ominus})(p_{H_2}/p^{\ominus})^3}$$

$$= \frac{(p_{NH_3}/\text{atm})^2}{(p_{N_2}/\text{atm})(p_{H_2}/\text{atm})^3}$$

where $p^{\ominus} = 1$ atm. $K_p^{\ominus}$ is dimensionless, but numerically equal to K_p expressed in the unit atm^{-2}.

Relative activity a is defined by expressions such as

$$a = \frac{c}{c^{\ominus}} y \qquad \text{and} \qquad a = \frac{m}{m^{\ominus}} \gamma$$

where c represents concentration, m molality, and y and γ are the corresponding activity coefficients. $c^{\ominus}$ and $m^{\ominus}$ are arbitrarily chosen standard values of concentration and molality (1 mol dm^{-3} and 1 mol kg^{-1}), respectively. It can be seen that a, $c/c^{\ominus}$, y, $m/m^{\ominus}$ and γ are all dimensionless. In many physical chemistry texts activity is often defined by convenient, but dimensionally incorrect, expressions such as

$$a = cy \qquad \text{and} \qquad a = m\gamma$$

An important concept in thermodynamics is that of standard state of unit activity, which is simply the state of affairs for which $a = 1$. The standard states of unit activity for liquids and solids are arbitrarily taken as pure liquid and pure solid, respectively.

1.5.4 Equations

Equations that relate physical quantities to one another should not imply the choice of any particular set of units (including the SI), as illustrated by the following example.

According to the Debye–Hückel theory, the mean ionic activity coefficient of a 1–1 electrolyte in very dilute aqueous solution at 25°C is given by any of the following expressions:

$$\log_{10} \gamma_{\pm} = -A \sqrt{c} \qquad \text{where } A = 0.51 \ (\text{mol dm}^{-3})^{-1/2}$$

or

$$\log_{10} \gamma_{\pm} = -0.51 \sqrt{(c/\text{mol dm}^{-3})}$$

or

$$\log_{10} \gamma_{\pm} = -0.51 \sqrt{(c/c^{\ominus})} \qquad \text{where } c^{\ominus} = 1 \text{ mol dm}^{-3}$$

It is not correct to use an expression such as

$$\log_{10} \gamma_{\pm} = -0.51 \sqrt{c}$$

The left-hand side of this equation is dimensionless, whereas the right-hand side has the dimension [concentration]$^{1/2}$. The equation is, therefore, dimensionally invalid.

1.5.5 Specific Quantities

The adjective 'specific' denotes an extensive quantity divided by the mass of substance; for example, the specific volume of a substance is its volume divided by its mass. When an extensive quantity is denoted by a capital letter, the corresponding specific quantity can be denoted by the corresponding lower-case letter; for example,

$$v = V/m \qquad c_p = C_p/m$$

1.5.6 Molar Quantities

The adjective 'molar' denotes an extensive property divided by the amount of substance; for example, $H_m = H/n$. The SI unit for amount of substance is the mole, one mole of substance being 6.0225×10^{23} specified elementary units (cf. Avogadro constant).

The subscript m, which denotes a molar quantity, may be dropped when the appropriate unit is quoted; for example, $\Delta H^{\ominus}_{298\,K} = 50.0 \text{ kJ mol}^{-1}$ unambiguously refers to a standard molar enthalpy change at 298 K and a subscript m is unnecessary.

Correct notation for thermochemical equations is, for example,

$$H_2(g) + \tfrac{1}{2}O_2(g) \rightarrow H_2O(l) \qquad \Delta H^{\ominus}_{298\,K} = -286 \text{ kJ mol}^{-1}$$

$$2H_2(g) + O_2(g) \rightarrow 2H_2O(l) \qquad \Delta H^{\ominus}_{298\,K} = -572 \text{ kJ mol}^{-1}$$

(not -286 kJ and -572 kJ respectively). The first of the above reactions is between 1 mol of $H_2(g)$ and 1 mol of $\frac{1}{2}O_2(g)$ to give 1 mol of $H_2O(l)$, and the second reaction is between 1 mol of $2H_2(g)$ and 1 mol of $O_2(g)$ to give 1 mol of $2H_2O(l)$; i.e. they are consistently per one mole (hence kJ mol^{-1} in both cases). The difference between these reactions is the factor of 2 in the size of the elementary units and, consequently, in the magnitude of ΔH. The quoted value of a quantity such as ΔH of a reaction, strictly speaking, therefore, is meaningless unless the stoichiometric equation to which the value refers is also quoted.

The prefix Δ refers to a finite increment; thus $\Delta H = -286$ kJ mol^{-1} refers to an increase in enthalpy of minus 286 kJ mol^{-1} which is the same as a decrease in enthalpy of 286 kJ mol^{-1}.

1.5.7 Conductance and Conductivity

Conductance denotes the reciprocal of resistance, whereas conductivity is the reciprocal of resistivity and denotes the ratio of current density to electric field strength, i.e. conductivity is a quantity with the dimension [resistance]$^{-1}$ [length]$^{-1}$. In view of the definition of the adjective 'specific' (see Section 1.5.5), the terms 'specific conductance' and 'specific conductivity' have no useful meaning.

Molar conductivity is defined as conductivity divided by concentration and is stated, for example, as follows:

$\Lambda^\infty(Na_2SO_4, aq) = 0.026$ S m^2 mol^{-1} at 25°C

$\Lambda^\infty(\frac{1}{2}Na_2SO_4, aq) = 0.013$ S m^2 mol^{-1} at 25°C

1.5.8 Relative Atomic and Molecular Masses

Relative atomic mass and relative molecular mass (sometimes rather loosely called 'atomic weight' and 'molecular weight', respectively) are dimensionless quantities defined as the ratio of the average mass per atom or molecule (natural isotopic composition being assumed unless otherwise stated) to 1/12 of the mass of an atom of the nuclide ^{12}C. For example,

$A_r(Cl) = 35.453$ $\qquad$ $M_r(HCl) = 36.461$

$M_r(H_2SO_4) = 98$ $\qquad$ $M_r(\frac{1}{2}H_2SO_4) = 49$

For crystalline substances, the term 'molecule' has little meaning, and $M_r(NaCl) = 58.443$ is an example of a relative formula mass.

A_r and M_r must not be confused with molar mass (symbol M), which has the dimension [mass] [amount of substance]$^{-1}$ and is numerically equal to (A_r or M_r) $\times 10^{-3}$ if expressed in the unit kg mol^{-1}. As an example of possible confusion between these terms, the equation giving the average velocity of a gas molecule is $c = (8RT/\pi M)^{0.5}$, where M is the molar mass (not, as sometimes incorrectly stated, the relative molecular mass, which would make the equation dimensionally invalid).

1.5.9 Solution Concentrations

Correct notation would, for example, be as follows:

$c(KMnO_4, aq) = 0.1$ mol dm^{-3}

or (for the purpose of considering titration in acid solution) this could be written in the equivalent form:

$$c\left(\tfrac{1}{5}KMnO_4, aq\right) = 0.5 \text{ mol dm}^{-3}$$

1.5.10 Wavenumbers

In spectroscopy, a convenient parameter is the so-called 'wavenumber', which is the reciprocal of the wavelength and, therefore, has the dimension $[\text{length}]^{-1}$. The quantity should not, as is sometimes the practice, be referred to as a frequency or an energy. For example, the fundamental vibration wavenumber for molecular nitrogen is 2360 cm^{-1}; therefore, the wavelength is $1/(2360 \text{ cm}^{-1}) = 4.237 \times 10^{-4}$ cm, and the frequency is $2.998 \times 10^{10} \text{ cm s}^{-1} \times 2360 \text{ cm}^{-1} = 7.075 \times 10^{13} \text{ s}^{-1}$ (see also the energy calculation in Section 1.3).

2 Chemical Thermodynamics

2.1 Introduction

Thermodynamics sets out to describe and correlate the directly observable properties of substances.

Chemical thermodynamics is concerned with chemical and phase changes, and in particular with

(a) the direction of spontaneous change,
(b) the conditions for equilibrium,
(c) the energy change during a chemical process, and
(d) the dependence of the above on variables such as temperature and pressure.

Thermodynamics is in no way concerned with the rate of attainment of equilibrium. It will (at least in principle) give the answer to the question 'How far?', but not to the question 'How fast?'.

Classical thermodynamics adopts a macroscopic approach. It does not enquire into mechanism. It exists independently of any proposed model of the structure of matter and is, therefore, universally applicable. One does not even need to know that matter is made up of atoms and molecules in order to construct the framework of classical thermodynamics. Conversely, classical thermodynamics offers nothing to our fundamental knowledge and understanding of the microscopic structure of matter.

Notwithstanding this, the atomic picture and how atomic events add up to give macroscopic phenomena give a deeper meaning to thermodynamic concepts. This subject is called statistical mechanics (or statistical thermodynamics), since it deals with mechanisms and since the impossibility of specifying the state of each particle necessitates the use of statistical methods. In certain respects, thermodynamics can only be understood properly through the general principles that are formulated from statistical considerations. In a typical undergraduate course, statistical mechanics tends to be treated at minimal level in the first year, simply as a means to back up a fuller treatment of classical thermodynamics. It tends to be treated more fully at a later stage, often in the final year and usually as a subject in its own right.

The chapter(s) on classical thermodynamics in most physical chemistry textbooks may at first intimidate the average student. There are probably two major reasons for this — the basic concepts and the mathematics. Both difficulties tend to be more imaginary than real!

Classical thermodynamics has an experimental base. To a large extent, it involves the derivation of equations that relate physical quantities to one another. Often this permits the calculation of quantities that are not amenable to direct measurement from other quantities that are more easily measured. For example, the difference between the heat capacities at constant pressure and constant volume, C_p and C_V, for any system is given by

$$C_p - C_V = \left(\frac{\partial V}{\partial T}\right)_p \left[p + \left(\frac{\partial U}{\partial V}\right)_T\right]$$

All of the above terms, except for $(\partial U/\partial V)_T$ can be measured directly. It follows that measurement of these quantities together with the use of the above equation allows an evaluation of the difficult quantity, $(\partial U/\partial V)_T$.

The average textbook chapters will contain many such equations, but only a limited number of key relationships (not including the above example) need be committed to memory.

An increasing number of chemistry undergraduates tend to be weak in mathematics and find physical chemistry in general and thermodynamics in particular apparently difficult on this account. Whilst some basic mathematical ability is essential, for the most part all that is required is a reasonable grasp of fairly straightforward calculus and algebra. The most complex operation at the level of this book is the integration of $1/x$ to give the natural logarithm of x (i.e. $\ln x$).

Classical thermodynamics involves a fairly liberal use of partial differentials and these may be unfamiliar to the reader. They are really quite simple. Consider the relationship

$$dH = T\,dS + V\,dp$$

This equation gives the infinitesimal change dH in the enthalpy of a system at temperature T and volume V which would result from infinitesimal changes dS and dp in entropy and pressure, respectively. The equation represents a potentially complex situation in which three quantities (H, S and p) could vary at the same time. To simplify matters, physical chemists will usually strive to study situations in which there are only two variables. Therefore, for the special case of constant pressure ($dp = 0$) the above equation reduces to $dH = T\,dS$, and for constant entropy ($dS = 0$) it reduces to $dH = V\,dp$. In each case, the introduction of a special condition means restriction to only part of the full differential expression — known as a partial differential. The partial differentials of the above equation are expressed as follows:

$$\left(\frac{\partial H}{\partial S}\right)_p = T \qquad \text{and} \qquad \left(\frac{\partial H}{\partial p}\right)_S = V$$

The use of curly ∂ indicates a partial differential and subscript, p or S, refers to the quantity that is being kept constant.

In the previous equation for $C_p - C_V$, the quantity $(\partial V/\partial T)_p$ would refer to the rate of change of volume with temperature for a system (i.e. its coefficient of expansion) under a condition of constant pressure.

For convenience, the present chapter concentrates mainly on general thermodynamics. Thermodynamic aspects of more specific subject areas (phase equilibria, solutions of non-electrolytes, solutions of electrolytes and electrochemical cells) are treated in separate chapters.

2.2 The Laws of Thermodynamics

The framework of classical thermodynamics consists of a collection of logical deductions, which are based on the four so-called 'laws of thermodynamics'. These are broad generalisations based on experience and frustration. On the one hand, there exists no absolute proof of their truth, but, on the other hand, there eixsts no evidence to lead one to disbelieve them.

Everything derived from the laws of thermodynamics is true, subject to the restrictions of any approximations made. The usefulness of such thermodynamic relationships is only as good as the quality of the experimental data input.

The zeroth law introduces the concept of temperature.

The first law is the law of conservation of energy in its broadest sense.

The second law deals with the direction of spontaneous change (and hence position of equilibrium) in macroscopic systems and introduces the concept of entropy.

The third law deals with the impossibility of attaining the absolute zero of temperature.

2.3 Thermodynamic Terminology

It is important for the reader to be clear as to the meaning of certain terms before getting down to a serious study of any thermodynamics text.

- **System** That portion of matter that is selected for investigation.
- **Surroundings** Everything outside the system that can be affected by changes within the system.
- **Isolated system** A system that cannot exchange energy or mass with its surroundings.
- **Closed system** A system that does not exchange mass with its surroundings.
- **Open system** A system that may exchange mass with its surroundings.
- **Phase** A system, or part of a system, that is homogeneous and has definite boundaries.
- **Diathermal** Allowing exchange of heat energy.
- **Adiabatic** No exchange of heat energy.
- **Isothermal** Constant temperature.
- **Isobaric** Constant pressure.
- **Isochoric** Constant volume.
- **Heat** Disorganised energy.
- **Work** Organised energy (mechanical, chemical, light, etc.).
- **Thermodynamic state of a system**
  (i) *Macrostate* Complete description of the system in terms of observable properties, such as temperature, pressure, volume and amount of substance.
  (ii) *Microstate* Complete description of the system (necessarily statistical) in terms of molecular properties, such as translational, rotational, vibrational and electronic energies.
- **State function** A property of a system (e.g. temperature, pressure, volume, internal energy, enthalpy, entropy, free energy) that has a unique value when the system is in a particular thermodynamic state, i.e. its value is independent of any previous history of the system.
- **Extensive property** Proportional to the amount of material present, e.g. volume, energy and entropy.
- **Intensive property** Independent of amount of material present, e.g. temperature, pressure, refractive index and chemical potential.
- **Independent variables (degrees of freedom)** The minimum number of state functions whose values must be known to give a complete description of the thermodynamic macrostate of a system; e.g. the macrostate of a gas is specified if any three of pressure, temperature, volume and amount of substance are known.
- **Equation of state** An equation that gives the value of a state function in terms of independent variables of the system; e.g. the equation of state of a

perfect gas is $pV = nRT$. Knowledge of the equation of state plus a method of calculating the energy of a substance permits, in principle, through thermodynamics, the calculation of all other physical properties of the substance.

- **Equilibrium** A system is in a state of equilibrium if its macrostate remains constant, provided that the conditions external to the system remain unaltered.
- **Process** Any transformation of a system from one equilibrium state to another over an interval of time. Transfer of energy may be involved.
- **Path of a process** The specific series of equilibrium states through which the system passes during the process.
- **Reversible process** A process (necessarily quasi-static) in which dissipation of work as heat is absent.
- **Irreversible process** A process in which work is dissipated as heat, as a result of which according to the second law, the system and surroundings cannot be returned to their original state.

2.4 Sign Convention

In thermodynamics attention is always focused on the **system**. Thus, for the reaction

$$C(s) + O_2(g) \rightarrow CO_2(g)$$

the system consists of reactants and products, $C(s)$, $O_2(g)$ and $CO_2(g)$. This reaction is exothermic, i.e. the system loses enthalpy and the surroundings gain enthalpy, and therefore ΔH is negative.

2.5 The Zeroth Law of Thermodynamics

If two systems are separately in thermal equilibrium with a third system, then they must also be in thermal equilibrium with each other. The state function called **temperature** is thus introduced such that two systems in thermal equilibrium are said to be at the same temperature.

2.5.1 Empirical Temperature Scales

To establish a particular empirical scale of temperature, a system with suitable thermometric properties is selected and a convenient method of assigning numerical values for the temperatures of its isotherms is adopted.

The thermometric property that is selected may, for example, be the expansion of a liquid such as mercury (with a linear temperature dependence assumed), or the change in the resistance of a semiconductor (with an exponential temperature dependence assumed). In the Celsius empirical scale, the temperatures at which water freezes and boils (both at 1 atm) are arbitrarily assigned values of $0°C$ and $100°C$, respectively.

2.5.2 Perfect Gas Celsius Temperature Scale

Comparisons of the various Celsius scales show that the smallest differences occur between those based on the expansion of gases, and the consistency between these scales becomes absolute in the limit as $p \to 0$; the Celsius temperature θ_C is thus given by

$$\theta_C = \lim_{p \to 0} \frac{V - V_{ice}}{V_{steam} - V_{ice}} \times 100 \qquad (2.1)$$

2.5.3 Absolute (Kelvin) Temperature

If the magnitude of unit temperature interval is chosen to be the same on perfect gas Celsius and Kelvin scales, the Kelvin temperature T is given by

$$T = T_{ice} + \theta_C \qquad (2.2)$$

The Kelvin temperature of the ice point on the perfect gas scale is given by

$$T_{ice} = \lim_{p \to 0} \frac{V_{ice}}{V_{steam} - V_{ice}} \times 100$$

The experimental value of T_{ice} thus determined is 273.15 K.

However, definition of absolute temperature in terms of equation (2.2) is unsatisfactory, since uncertainty in the exact value of T_{ice} leads to the same magnitude of uncertainty in temperatures close to the absolute zero.

This difficulty is overcome by defining the perfect gas temperature scale with reference to only one arbitrarily fixed point. The temperature chosen for this fixed point is that of water at its triple point (the temperature at which ice, water and water vapour coexist under the natural vapour pressure). The value arbitrarily assigned to this temperature is

$$T_{tr} = 273.16 \text{ K} \qquad (2.3)$$

Since, for a perfect gas, $pV \propto T$, then

$$T = T_{tr} \lim_{p \to 0} \left[\frac{(pV)}{(pV)_{tr}} \right] \qquad (2.4)$$

Temperatures determined in this way are called 'thermodynamic temperatures', because of the unique significance in thermodynamics of the absolute zero temperature, which is now explicitly one of the fixed points of the Kelvin scale. The best available measurements (at present) make the Kelvin and Celsius temperature intervals identical, $T_{tr} = 273.16$ K having been chosen so that they would be identical.

2.5.4 Commonly Used Thermometers

For reasons of convenience, gas thermometers are rarely used and their main purpose lies in the accurate establishment of secondary reference temperatures (usually using helium gas); e.g. standard boiling point of oxygen = 90.18 K, standard melting point of silver = 1233.9 K. More convenient thermometers (liquid expansion, resistance, thermocouple, semiconductor, etc.) are calibrated against these standard points.

The choice of thermometer for a particular temperature measurement depends predominantly on the magnitude of the temperature (see Fig. 2.1), but also depends on factors such as sample size, response time and sensitivity.

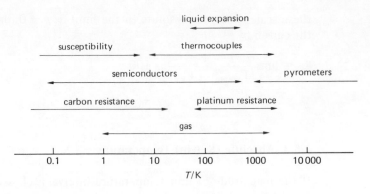

Figure 2.1 The useful ranges of different kinds of thermometer.

2.6   The First Law of Thermodynamics

The first law of thermodynamics is a statement of the law of conservation of energy. Although energy may be converted from one form to another, it cannot be created or destroyed; i.e. whenever a quantity of one kind of energy disappears, an equivalent amount of other forms of energy must be produced. The first law of thermodynamics can be stated in the concise form: **The energy of an isolated system is constant.**

2.6.1 Analytical Formulation

If a quantity of heat q is transferred from the surroundings to a system, and an amount of work w is done on the system (e.g. by compressing it), then the sum of these energy inputs will contribute to an increase ΔU in the internal energy of the system, i.e.

$$\Delta U = q + w \tag{2.5}$$

2.6.2 Internal Energy, U

The internal energy of a system is the energy associated with the translation, rotation and vibration of the molecules, electronic energy, interaction energy and any other form of energy associated with the structure of the system. Internal energy is a state function.

2.6.3 Work Done on a System Due to Volume Change

Consider a gas confined in a cylinder fitted with a weightless and frictionless piston. By applying an external pressure p_{ext}, the piston is pushed down through a distance dh (Fig. 2.2). The force on the piston is $p_{ext}A$, and therefore the work done, đw, is given by

$$đw = p_{ext}A\ dh = -p_{ext}\ dV$$

where dV is the increase in the volume of the gas (i.e. đw is negative for expansion and positive for compression). For an infinitesimal change, p_{ext} is only infinitesimally greater than p, the pressure of the gas, and therefore

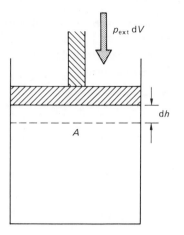

Figure 2.2

$$đw = - p \, dV \tag{2.6}$$

For a finite change

$$w = - \int_1^2 p \, dV \tag{2.7}$$

This integral is equal to the area under the p–V curve, the value of which depends on the route taken. For example, as illustrated in Fig. 2.3,

$-w$ (route A) $> -w$ (route B)

Owing to this path dependence, $đw$ is referred to as an inexact differential and is denoted as such by using the differential symbol, $đ$. Therefore, for a cyclic process,

$$\oint đw \neq 0$$

Since internal energy is a state function, the change in internal energy on going from one state to another is independent of the route taken, i.e.

$$\oint dU = 0$$

and dU is referred to as an exact differential.

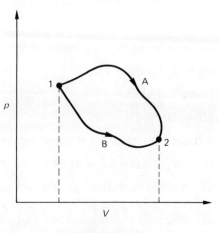

Figure 2.3

Since w is route-dependent and ΔU route-independent, then q must be route-dependent and $đq$ is an inexact differential.

The analytical formulation of the first law of thermodynamics, therefore, takes the differential form

$$dU = đq + đw \qquad (2.8)$$

2.6.4 Work Done During Isothermal Expansion

(a) Against a constant external pressure

$$w = -\int_1^2 p \, dV = -p \, (V_2 - V_1) = -p \, \Delta V \qquad (2.9)$$

(b) Reversibly (for a perfect gas)

$$w = -\int_1^2 p \, dV$$

For a perfect gas, $pV = nRT$, i.e. $p = nRT/V$. Therefore

$$w = -nRT \int_1^2 (1/V) \, dV$$

$$= -nRT \ln \left(\frac{V_2}{V_1} \right) = -nRT \ln \left(\frac{p_1}{p_2} \right) \qquad (2.10)$$

2.6.5 Enthalpy, H

Equation (2.5) can be rewritten as

$$q = \Delta U - w$$

For a process carried out at constant pressure where the only work done on the system is 'pV' work, i.e. $w = -p \, \Delta V$, then

$$q_p = \Delta U + p \, \Delta V$$

$$= (U_2 + pV_2) - (U_1 + pV_1) \qquad (2.11)$$

U, p and V are state functions, and therefore $U + pV$ is a state function, which (for convenience) is represented by a single symbol, H, and is called **enthalpy**.

Enthalpy is, therefore, defined by the expression

$$H = U + pV \qquad (2.12)$$

Differentiating this expression gives

$$dH = dU + p \, dV + V \, dp \qquad (2.13)$$

Under conditions of constant pressure, $dp = 0$, and equation (2.13) reduces to

$$dH = dU + p \, dV \qquad (2.14)$$

A finite increment in enthalpy is given by

$$H_2 - H_1 = \Delta H = \Delta U + \Delta(pV) \qquad (2.15)$$

which under conditions of constant pressure reduces to

$$\Delta H = q_p = \Delta U + p \, \Delta V$$

which resembles equation (2.11).

2.6.6 Heat Capacity, C

By definition

$$C = đq/dT \tag{2.16}$$

Since $đq$ is an inexact differential, C is an indefinite quantity unless the path of the process is specified.

Constant volume:

$$C_V = (\partial U/\partial T)_V \tag{2.17}$$

Constant pressure:

$$C_p = (\partial H/\partial T)_p \tag{2.18}$$

Substituting $H = U + pV$ gives

$$C_p - C_V = d(pV)/dT$$

which for one mole of perfect gas ($pV = RT$) gives

$$C_p - C_V = R \tag{2.19}$$

2.6.7 Adiabatic Expansion of a Perfect Gas

An adiabatic process is one in which no heat enters or leaves the system, i.e. $q = 0$. Adiabatic conditions can be approached by thermal insulation of the system, e.g. by containing it in a Dewar vessel.

Since $đq = 0$, equation (2.8) becomes

$$dU - đw = 0$$

Therefore

$$C_V\, dT + p\, dV = 0$$

For one mole of perfect gas, $p = RT/V$ and $R = C_p - C_V$. Therefore

$$C_V \frac{dT}{T} + R \frac{dV}{V} = C_V \frac{dT}{T} + (C_p - C_V) \frac{dV}{V} = 0$$

Integrating (assuming C_V and C_p to be temperature-independent) gives

$$C_V \ln T + (C_p - C_V) \ln V = \text{constant}$$

Dividing by C_V and putting $C_p/C_V = \gamma$,

$$\ln T + (\gamma - 1) \ln V = \text{constant}$$

i.e.

$$TV^{(\gamma-1)} = \text{constant} \tag{2.20}$$

or, since $pV = RT$,

$$pV^\gamma = \text{constant} \tag{2.21}$$

and

$$p^{(1-\gamma)} T^\gamma = \text{constant} \tag{2.22}$$

[Note: Worked Example 2.13.1 covers all of the first-law material to this point.]

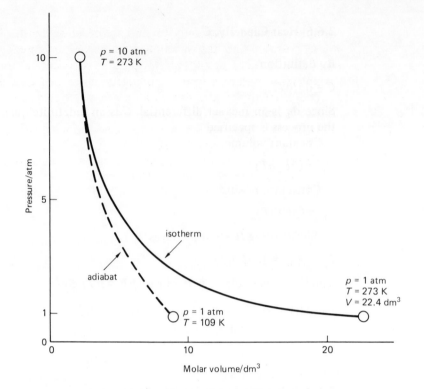

Figure 2.4 Reversible isothermal and adiabatic expansions of one mole of perfect gas from 10 atm and 273 K to 1 atm. γ is taken as equal to 1.40 and temperature-independent.

2.7 Thermochemistry

Thermochemistry is the specific application of the first law of thermodynamics to the study of chemical reactions. It deals with the measurement or calculation of the heat absorbed or given out during chemical processes and is, therefore, a subject of immediate practical importance. Thermochemistry provides data from which the relative internal energy or enthalpy contents of substances can be deduced. This aspect implies that thermochemistry is basic to the study of chemical bonding. Thermochemistry also provides data that are necessary for the thermodynamic study of chemical equilibrium.

2.7.1 Experimental Considerations

Only a few of the many possible chemical reactions are such that ΔH can be determined directly and accurately. For precise calorimetric study, a reaction must be fast, complete and clean.

Combustion reactions are of outstanding suitability in this respect and most of the available thermochemical data relating to organic compounds originate from combustion experiments. Heats of combustion (initially as ΔU) are usually determined using a bomb calorimeter. A weighed sample is placed in a cup within the reaction chamber, which is then filled with oxygen at high pressure (20 atm or more) to facilitate rapid and complete reaction. The bomb is immersed in a water chamber, which is carefully insulated from the surroundings, i.e. the whole set-up is as near as possible an adiabatic calorimeter. A fine wire in contact with the sample is heated electrically to start the reaction and the temperature rise of the water surrounding the reaction chamber is measured. The apparatus can be calibrated by measuring the temperature rise resulting from the combustion of a sample with a known heat of combustion, e.g. benzoic acid, or by measuring the temperature rise resulting from a known electrical energy input. An accuracy of 0.01% is attainable.

Other reactions that are amenable to calorimetric study include hydrogenation reactions and reactions in solution.

Enthalpies of dissociation, etc., can be calculated from electronic and/or vibrational spectra (see Chapter 8).

ΔH values can be obtained from e.m.f. measurements (see Chapter 6).

2.7.2 Relation between ΔU and ΔH

Equation (2.15) is given as

$$\Delta H = \Delta U + \Delta(pV)$$

$\Delta(pV)$ is of appreciable magnitude only when gases are involved. If perfect gas behaviour is assumed, i.e. $pV = nRT$, then

$$\Delta H = \Delta U + (\Delta n)RT \tag{2.23}$$

where Δn = (amount of gaseous products) − (amount of gaseous reactants).

Example 2.1

$$2CO(g) + O_2(g) \rightarrow 2CO_2(g)$$

A bomb calorimeter determination shows that for this reaction at constant volume and at 298 K, 563 500 J mol^{-1} of heat is evolved, i.e. $\Delta U_{298\,K}$ = −563 500 J mol^{-1}. We have

$$\Delta n = 2 - (2 + 1) = -1$$

Therefore,

$$\Delta H_{298\,K} = -563\,500 - (8.314 \times 298)$$
$$= -565\,980 \text{ J mol}^{-1} \qquad \blacksquare$$

2.7.3 Thermochemical Equations

Enthalpies of reaction depend on the physical states (solid, liquid or gas) of the reagents, and these must, therefore, be specified. This is usually done by adding (s), (l) or (g) after the formula of the compound. For example,

$$H_2(g) + \tfrac{1}{2}O_2(g) \rightarrow H_2O(g) \qquad \Delta H^{\ominus}_{298\,K} = -241.8 \text{ kJ mol}^{-1}$$
$$H_2(g) + \tfrac{1}{2}O_2(g) \rightarrow H_2O(l) \qquad \Delta H^{\ominus}_{298\,K} = -285.8 \text{ kJ mol}^{-1}$$

In the case of solids, specification of the crystal form is sometimes necessary. For example,

$$C(\text{graphite}) + O_2(g) \rightarrow CO_2(g) \qquad \Delta H^{\ominus}_{298\,K} = -393.5 \text{ kJ mol}^{-1}$$
$$C(\text{diamond}) + O_2(g) \rightarrow CO_2(g) \qquad \Delta H^{\ominus}_{298\,K} = -395.4 \text{ kJ mol}^{-1}$$

The symbol (aq) is used in aqueous solution reactions and denotes the presence of sufficient water for the solution in question to have negligible enthalpy of dilution.

Some thermochemical equations often appear in alternative forms, which are simple multiples of one another; this is discussed in Section 1.5.6.

Heats of reaction depend on temperature. The temperature is usually indicated by a subscript, or is bracketed; e.g. $\Delta U_{298\,K}$, $\Delta H_{298\,K}$, $\Delta H(298\,K)$, $\Delta H(500\,K)$. To facilitate tabulation and usage of data, experimental values of ΔU and ΔH are usually corrected to $\Delta H_{298\,K}$ and recorded as such.

Heats of reaction also depend on pressure (gases) and concentration (solutions). Again, to facilitate tabulation and usage of data, experimental values of ΔU and ΔH are corrected to values that would apply if the reactants and products were all in their standard states. A standard heat change is denoted by the superscript $^{\ominus}$. The standard states normally adopted are:

Gases: fugacity = 1 atm (i.e. pressure ≈ 1 atm)
Solutes: activity = 1 (relative to a standard concentration of 1 mol dm^{-3} or a standard molality of 1 mol kg^{-1})
Liquids: pure liquid
Solids: pure solid

2.7.4 Hess' Law — Indirect Determination of Heats of Reaction

In accord with the first law of thermodynamics, ΔH of a reaction is independent of the route taken. As a consequence of this, thermochemical equations can be treated algebraically.

Example 2.2

$$C(g) + O_2(g) \rightarrow CO_2(g) \qquad \Delta H^{\ominus}_{298\,K} = -393.5 \text{ kJ mol}^{-1}$$

$$CO(g) + \tfrac{1}{2}O_2(g) \rightarrow CO_2(g) \qquad \Delta H^{\ominus}_{298\,K} = -283.0 \text{ kJ mol}^{-1}$$

Subtracting $C(s) + \tfrac{1}{2}O_2(g) \rightarrow CO(g) \qquad \Delta H^{\ominus}_{298\,K} = -110.5 \text{ kJ mol}^{-1}$

Direct calorimetric determination of ΔH for the formation of CO(g) would be complicated, since unreacted C(s) and $CO_2(g)$ are inevitable additional products.

■

2.7.5 Enthalpy of Formation, $\Delta_f H$

The enthalpy of formation of a compound is the enthalpy change when the compound is made up from its elements.

Compilation of thermochemical data for each reaction for which data are available would be quite unwieldy. It is, however, feasible and convenient to compile thermochemical data for each compound for which data are available. Standard enthalpies of formation $\Delta_f H^{\ominus}$ are suitable quantities in this respect. From these data, it is an easy matter (see equation (2.24)) to calculate the standard enthalpy change of any reaction involving the listed compounds.

Only differences in enthalpy (or in internal energy) can be measured. Therefore, quantities such as these are meaningful only when compared with some reference state. It is customary to assign zero enthalpy (and internal energy) to the stable phase of all elements at 1 atm and at the temperature under consideration. This arbitrary assignment is allowed on account of there being conservation of atomic species in chemical reactions. It follows that the standard enthalpy of a compound at a given temperature is equal to its standard enthalpy of formation at that temperature.

Example 2.3

$$CH_3OH(g) + 1\tfrac{1}{2}O_2(g) \rightarrow CO_2(g) + 2H_2O(l) \qquad \Delta H^{\ominus}_{298\ K} = -763.9 \text{ kJ mol}^{-1}$$

$$C(\text{graphite}) + O_2(g) \rightarrow CO_2(g) \qquad \Delta H^{\ominus}_{298\ K} = -393.5 \text{ kJ mol}^{-1}$$

$$H_2(g) + \tfrac{1}{2}O_2(g) \rightarrow H_2O(l) \qquad \Delta H^{\ominus}_{298\ K} = -285.8 \text{ kJ mol}^{-1}$$

The standard enthalpy of formation of $CH_3OH(g)$ at 298 K is the same as ΔH at 298 K for the reaction

$$C(\text{graphite}) + 2H_2(g) + \tfrac{1}{2}O_2(g) \rightarrow CH_3OH(g)$$

and is, therefore, given by

$$\Delta_f H^{\ominus}_{298\ K}(CH_3OH) = (-393.5) + 2 \times (-285.8) - (-763.9)$$
$$= -201.2 \text{ kJ mol}^{-1} \qquad \blacksquare$$

To calculate $\Delta H^{\ominus}$ for a reaction, the following equation is used:

$$\Delta H^{\ominus} = \Delta_f H^{\ominus}(\text{products}) - \Delta_f H^{\ominus}(\text{reactants}) \qquad (2.24)$$

Example 2.4

$\Delta_f H^{\ominus}_{298\ K}$ for $CH_3OH(g)$ and $CO(g)$ are equal to -201.2 and -110.5 kJ mol^{-1}, respectively. Calculate $\Delta H^{\ominus}_{298\ K}$ for the reaction

$$CO(g) + 2H_2(g) \rightarrow CH_3OH(g)$$

We have

$$\Delta H^{\ominus}_{298\ K} = (-201.2) - [-110.5 + (2 \times 0)]$$
$$= -90.7 \text{ kJ mol}^{-1} \qquad \blacksquare$$

2.7.6 Enthalpy of Formation of Ions in Solution

It is not possible to study single ionic species in isolation. For example, the study of $Na^+(aq)$ ions cannot be undertaken without involving a neutralising amount of anions.

By convention,

$$\Delta_f H^{\ominus}(H^+(aq)) = 0 \qquad \text{(at all temperatures)} \qquad (2.25)$$

On this basis, enthalpies of formation of single ion types can be evaluated.

Example 2.5

$$\tfrac{1}{2}H_2(g) + \tfrac{1}{2}Cl_2(g) \rightarrow HCl(g) \qquad \Delta H^{\ominus}_{298\ K} = -92.3 \text{ kJ mol}^{-1}$$

$$HCl(g) + (aq) \rightarrow H^+(aq) + Cl^-(aq) \qquad \Delta H^{\ominus}_{298\ K} = -75.1 \text{ kJ mol}^{-1}$$

Therefore,

$$\tfrac{1}{2}H_2(g) + \tfrac{1}{2}Cl_2(g) + (aq) \rightarrow H^+(aq) + Cl^-(aq) \qquad \Delta H^{\ominus}_{298\ K} = -167.4 \text{ kJ mol}^{-1}$$

i.e.

$$\Delta_f H^{\ominus}_{298\ K}(H^+(aq)) + \Delta_f H^{\ominus}_{298\ K}(Cl^-(aq)) = -167.4 \text{ kJ mol}^{-1}$$

and so

$$\Delta_f H^{\ominus}_{298\ K}(Cl^-(aq)) = -167.4 \text{ kJ mol}^{-1}$$

Likewise,

$$K(s) + \tfrac{1}{2}Cl_2(g) \rightarrow KCl(s) \qquad \Delta H^{\ominus}_{298\ K} = -435.9\ kJ\ mol^{-1}$$

$$KCl(s) + (aq) \rightarrow K^+(aq) + Cl^-(aq) \qquad \Delta H^{\ominus}_{298\ K} = +17.2\ kJ\ mol^{-1}$$

Therefore,

$$\Delta_f H^{\ominus}_{298\ K}(K^+(aq)) + \Delta_f H^{\ominus}_{298\ K}(Cl^-(aq)) = -418.7\ kJ\ mol^{-1}$$

giving

$$\Delta_f H^{\ominus}_{298\ K}(K^+(aq)) = -418.7 - (-167.4)$$
$$= -251.3\ kJ\ mol^{-1} \qquad\qquad\qquad \blacksquare$$

$\Delta H^{\ominus}$ for a reaction involving ions can be calculated on this basis using equation (2.24).

Example 2.6

$$Ca^{2+}(aq) + CO_2(g) + H_2O(l) \rightarrow CaCO_3(s) + 2H^+(aq) \qquad (at\ 298\ K)$$

$$\Delta H^{\ominus} = \Delta_f H^{\ominus}(CaCO_3(s)) + 2 \times \Delta_f H^{\ominus}(H^+(aq)) - \Delta_f H^{\ominus}(Ca^{2+}(aq))$$
$$-\Delta_f H^{\ominus}(CO_2(g)) - \Delta_f H^{\ominus}(H_2O(l))$$
$$= (-1206.9) + (2 \times 0) - (-543.0) - (-393.5) - (-285.8)$$
$$= 15.4\ kJ\ mol^{-1} \qquad\qquad\qquad \blacksquare$$

2.7.7 Temperature Dependence of ΔH (Kirchhoff Equation)

$$\Delta H = H(products) - H(reactants)$$

Therefore, differentiating with respect to temperature at constant pressure,

$$\left(\frac{\partial \Delta H}{\partial T}\right)_p = \left(\frac{\partial H(products)}{\partial T}\right)_p - \left(\frac{\partial H(reactants)}{\partial T}\right)_p$$
$$= C_p(products) - C_p(reactants)$$
$$= \Delta C_p \qquad\qquad\qquad (2.26)$$

If C_p is taken as being temperature-independent,

$$\Delta H(T_2) - \Delta H(T_1) = \Delta C_p(T_2 - T_1) \qquad\qquad\qquad (2.27)$$

In practice, heat capacities are temperature-dependent. It is customary to fit heat capacity–temperature data (e.g. using the method of least squares) into equations such as $C_p = A + BT$ or $C_p = a + bT + cT^2$.

Example 2.7

$$N_2(g) + 3H_2(g) \rightarrow 2NH_3(g) \qquad \Delta H^{\ominus}_{300\ K} = -92.4\ kJ\ mol^{-1}$$

Estimate $\Delta H^{\ominus}_{800\ K}$ for this reaction, given that the average values of C_p over the temperature range 300 to 800 K for $N_2(g)$, $H_2(g)$ and $NH_3(g)$ are 30.2, 29.4 and 42.6 J K^{-1} mol^{-1}, respectively.

$$\Delta H^{\ominus}_{800\ K} - \Delta H^{\ominus}_{300\ K} = \Delta C_p(800 - 300)\ K$$
$$= [(2 \times 42.6) - 30.2 - (3 \times 29.4)] \times 500\ J\ mol^{-1}$$
$$= -16\,600\ J\ mol^{-1}$$

Therefore,

$$\Delta H_{800\,K}^{\ominus} = -92.4 - 16.6 = -109.0 \text{ kJ mol}^{-1}$$

∎

2.7.8 Bond Enthalpies

The enthalpies of formation (or of rupture) of chemical bonds can be estimated from thermochemical data.

Ideally, consideration of bond energies should relate to zero thermodynamic temperature, where there is no thermal excitation of vibrational energy; however, at 298 K this thermal excitation term is sufficiently small to permit meaningful calculation of bond energies from thermochemical data relating to this temperature.

For diatomic molecules the bond energy is the same as the enthalpy of dissociation, and this can be determined, for example, from vibrational spectroscopic data; e.g.

$$H_2(g) \rightarrow 2H(g) \qquad \Delta H_{298\,K}^{\ominus} = 436 \text{ kJ mol}^{-1}$$

Ionisation energies can be determined from electronic spectra; e.g.

$$Na(g) \rightarrow Na^+(g) + e \qquad \Delta H_{298\,K}^{\ominus} = 490 \text{ kJ mol}^{-1}$$

Calculation of bond energies in organic compounds requires knowledge of the enthalpy of sublimation (i.e. atomisation) of carbon (graphite). This quantity, unfortunately, is not amenable to measurement with the accuracy associated with most other thermochemical determinations. The currently accepted value is

$$C(\text{graphite}) \rightarrow C(g) \qquad \Delta H_{298\,K}^{\ominus} = 713 \text{ kJ mol}^{-1}$$

Armed with these and other appropriate ΔH values, it is possible to calculate bond enthalpies.

Example 2.8

Consider the C—H bond enthalpies in methane:

$$\Delta_f H_{298\,K}^{\ominus}(CH_4(g)) = -75 \text{ kJ mol}^{-1}$$

$$\Delta_f H_{298\,K}^{\ominus}(H(g)) = 218 \text{ kJ mol}^{-1}$$

$$\Delta_f H_{298\,K}^{\ominus}(C(g)) = \Delta_s^g H_{298\,K}^{\ominus}(C)^* = 713 \text{ kJ mol}^{-1}$$

Therefore

$$CH_4(g) \rightarrow C(g) + 4H(g) \qquad \Delta H_{298\,K}^{\circ} = 713 + (4 \times 218) \quad (-75)$$
$$= 1660 \text{ kJ mol}^{-1}$$

The average C—H bond enthalpy in CH_4 is, therefore, given by

$$E(C—H) = 1660/4 = 415 \text{ kJ mol}^{-1}$$

Likewise, other thermochemical bond enthalpies can be determined; for example,

$$\Delta_f H_{298\,K}^{\ominus}(C_2H_6(g)) = -85 \text{ kJ mol}^{-1}$$

---

*The symbol $\Delta_s^g H_{298\,K}^{\ominus}(C)$ is not as complicated as it may appear. It simply represents the increase in enthalpy when carbon is sublimed ((s) to (g)) at 298 K and under standard conditions.

Therefore

$$C_2H_6(g) \rightarrow 2C(g) + 6H(g) \qquad \Delta H_{298\,K}^{\ominus} = (2 \times 713) + (6 \times 218) - (-85)$$

$$= 2819\ \text{kJ mol}^{-1}$$

If $E(C{-}H)$ is assumed to be the same as in CH_4, then

$$E(C{-}C) = 2819 - (6 \times 415) = 329\ \text{kJ mol}^{-1} \qquad\qquad \blacksquare$$

The thermochemical bond enthalpy of a particular bond type (e.g. C—C) is not, in general, constant, but varies within small limits from compound to compound owing to environmental differences. Average values (where appropriate) are given in Table 2.1.

Table 2.1   Thermochemical bond enthalpies (kJ mol^{-1})

H—H	436	O—H	465	C—H	415	C—F	485
H—F	563	O—O	140	C—C	345	C—Cl	335
H—Cl	432	O=O	495	C—O	355	C—Br	280
H—Br	366	S—S	215	C—N	305		
H—I	299	S—H	340	C—S	280		
F—F	153	N—H	390	C=C	615	Si—H	320
Cl—Cl	243	N—N	160	C≡C	810	Si—O	450
Br—Br	193	N=N	420	C=O	710	Si—Si	220
I—I	151	N≡N	945				

ΔH of a reaction can be estimated as

$$\Delta H = \sum(\text{bond enthalpies of reactants}) - \sum(\text{bond enthalpies of products}) \qquad (2.28)$$

Generally, ΔH so calculated should agree within the limits of experimental error with ΔH calculated from enthalpies of formation. Significant differences between such values are sometimes observed where factors such as resonance and strain energy are involved.

2.7.9 Lattice Energies, Born–Haber Cycle

The first law of thermodynamics can be applied to a cyclic process of the type

where

$\Delta_c H$	= enthalpy of formation of crystalline MX from gaseous ions
$\Delta_i H(M)$	= enthalpy of ionisation of M (ionisation potential)
$\Delta_i H(X)$	= enthalpy of ionisation of X (negative of electron affinity)
$\Delta_s^g H(M)$	= enthalpy of sublimation of M
$\Delta_d H(X_2)$	= enthalpy of dissociation of $X_2(g)$
$\Delta_f H(MX)$	= enthalpy of formation of MX(s)

The lattice energy is then given by

Lattice energy $= -\Delta_c H$

$$= -\Delta_f H(MX) + \Delta_s^g H(M) + \tfrac{1}{2}\Delta_d H(X_2) + \Delta_i H(M) + \Delta_i H(X)$$

For example, substituting the respective values relating to potassium chloride, we obtain

$$-\Delta_c H = -(-435) + 88 + (\tfrac{1}{2} \times 226) + 410 + (-368)$$

$$= 678 \text{ kJ mol}^{-1}$$

A theoretical calculation of the binding energy in a purely ionic crystal can be made via electrostatic theory. When this calculated lattice energy deviates markedly from the Born–Haber value, non-ionic contributions are indicated.

2.8 The Second Law of Thermodynamics

The second law of thermodynamics is concerned with the direction of spontaneous change and, therefore, with equilibrium.

2.8.1 Heat and Work

Work (organised energy) can be converted into an equivalent amount of heat (disorganised energy) continuously and indefinitely. But heat cannot be converted continuously and indefinitely into work with 100% efficiency.

2.8.2 Entropy, S

Naturally occurring (spontaneous) processes are never entirely free of friction and other forms of energy dissipation to heat. In view of the above conclusions concerning heat–work interconversion, it follows that such processes are thermodynamically irreversible.

Given any spontaneous process, the final state differs from the initial state, and the initial state cannot be reinstated without external change. Taking interest only in the initial and final states (and not in the route between them) there is, therefore, a state function that always changes in the same sense during a spontaneous process.

Such a state function is now introduced and called **entropy** (symbol, S). Changes in entropy in an isolated system will (arbitrarily) be defined as being zero for reversible processes and positive for irreversible (spontaneous) processes, i.e.

$$\Delta S \underset{R}{\overset{I}{\gtreqless}} 0 \tag{2.29}$$

or, in the limit for small changes

$$dS \underset{R}{\overset{I}{\gtreqless}} 0 \tag{2.30}$$

The second law of thermodynamics can now be stated as follows: **The entropy of an isolated system tends to its maximum (equilibrium) value.**

For a non-isolated system in which a quantity of heat $đq$ is transferred from the surroundings to the system, it can be shown (e.g. from the equations describing the Carnot cycle) that

$$dS \underset{R}{\overset{I}{\gtreqless}} đq/T \tag{2.31}$$

which for an isolated system ($đq = 0$) reduces to equation (2.30).

2.8.3 Combination of the First and Second Laws of Thermodynamics

Equation (2.8) is

$$dU = đq + đw$$

For a reversible process, we have (equation (2.6))

$$đw = -p \, dV$$

and

$$đq = T \, dS \tag{2.32}$$

Therefore,

$$dU = T \, dS - p \, dV \tag{2.33}$$

Although derived on the basis of a reversible process, equation (2.33) contains in it only state functions and is, therefore, applicable to any process. Now we use equation (2.13)

$$dH = dU + p \, dV + V \, dp$$

Therefore, from equations (2.13) and (2.33),

$$dH = T \, dS + V \, dp \tag{2.34}$$

2.8.4 Calculation of Entropy Changes

Rearranging equation (2.34)

$$dS = \frac{dH}{T} - \frac{V \, dp}{T} = \frac{C_p \, dT}{T} - \frac{V \, dp}{T}$$

For one mole of perfect gas, $pV = RT$, and therefore

$$dS = C_p \frac{dT}{T} - R \frac{dp}{p} \tag{2.35}$$

$$= C_p \, d \ln T - R \, d \ln p \tag{2.36}$$

For any material at constant pressure, integration of equations (2.35) or (2.36) gives

$$\Delta S = S_2 - S_1 = \int_1^2 (C_p/T) \, dT = \int_1^2 C_p \, d \ln T \tag{2.37}$$

If C_p is temperature-independent,

$$\Delta S = C_p \ln (T_2/T_1) \tag{2.38}$$

If C_p is temperature-dependent, the integral in equation (2.37) can be evaluated graphically from a plot of C_p/T against T, or of C_p against $\ln T$; or the integral can be calculated if an equation giving C_p in terms of T is known.

Example 2.9

The graph in Fig. 2.5 is of C_p/T versus T for rhombic sulphur up to its normal melting point of 368.6 K. The area under the curve between 0 and 368.6 K gives the molar entropy change between these temperatures, i.e.

$$S^{\ominus}_{368.6 \, K} - S^{\ominus}_0 = 36.9 \, J \, K^{-1} \, mol^{-1}$$

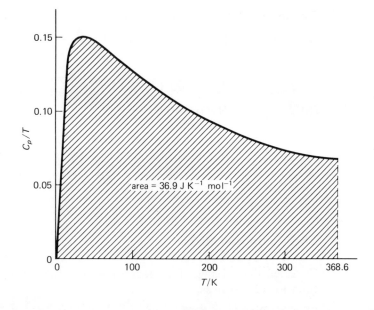

Figure 2.5

Example 2.10

Calculate the entropy change when one mole of oxygen at a constant pressure of one atmosphere is heated from 300 to 400 K, given that $C_p^{\ominus}(O_2)/J\ K^{-1}\ mol^{-1} = 25.8 + 0.012T/K$ in this temperature range.

$$\Delta S^{\ominus} = \int_{300\ K}^{400\ K} (C_p^{\ominus}/T)\ dT = \int_{300\ K}^{400\ K} [(25.8/T) + 0.012]\ dT$$

$$= 25.8 \ln(400/300) + 0.012(400 - 300)$$

$$= 7.42 + 1.20 = 8.62\ J\ K^{-1}\ mol^{-1}$$

For a perfect gas at constant temperature, integration of equations (2.35) or (2.36) gives

$$\Delta S = S_2 - S_1 = -\int_1^2 R\ d\ln p$$

$$= -R \ln\left(\frac{p_2}{p_1}\right) = +R \ln\left(\frac{p_1}{p_2}\right) = +R \ln\left(\frac{V_2}{V_1}\right) \tag{2.39}$$

Example 2.11

One mole of perfect gas is expanded to twice its original volume at constant temperature, therefore

$$\Delta S = R \ln 2 = 0.693R = 5.8\ J\ K^{-1}\ mol^{-1}$$

If a system changes phase,

$$\Delta_{\alpha}^{\beta} S = \Delta_{\alpha}^{\beta} H/T \tag{2.40}$$

31

Example 2.12

(a) $\Delta_s^l H_{273.15\,K}^{\ominus}(H_2O) = 6.01$ kJ mol^{-1}

Therefore,

$\Delta_s^l S_{273.15\,K}^{\ominus}(H_2O) = 6010/273.15 = 22.0$ J K^{-1} mol^{-1}

(b) $\Delta_l^g H_{373.15\,K}^{\ominus}(H_2O) = 40.6$ kJ mol^{-1}

Therefore,

$\Delta_l^g S_{373.15\,K}^{\ominus}(H_2O) = 40\,600/373.15 = 108.8$ J K^{-1} mol^{-1} ∎

2.8.5 Entropy of Mixing

Consider the mixing of perfect gases at constant temperature. Integration of equation (2.36) gives

$$S = S' - R \ln p$$

where S' is an integration constant.

The total entropy of a collection of different perfect gases (all at pressure p) before mixing is given by

$$S_1 = \sum n_i (S_i' - R \ln p)$$

After mixing, the partial pressure of the ith gas is given by

$$p_i = n_i p / \sum n_i = x_i p$$

where x represents mole fraction. The total entropy after mixing is, therefore, given by

$$S_2 = \sum n_i [S_i' - R \ln (x_i p)]$$

and the entropy change on mixing is given by

$$\Delta_m S = S_2 - S_1 = - R \sum (n_i \ln x_i) \qquad (2.41)$$

The same expression can be derived for the entropy of mixing to form any ideal mixture.

Since $x_i < 1$, $\ln x_i$ is always negative and $\Delta_m S$ is always positive.

Example 2.13

Calculate $\Delta_m S$ when 1 mol of O_2 (g, 1 atm) is mixed with 4 mol of N_2 (g, 1 atm) at constant temperature.

$n(O_2) = 1$ $x(O_2) = 0.2$

$n(N_2) = 4$ $x(N_2) = 0.8$

Therefore,

$\Delta_m S = - R (\ln 0.2 + 4 \ln 0.8)$

$\quad\quad\quad = 2.50R = 20.8$ J K^{-1} mol^{-1} ∎

2.9 Statistical Basis of Entropy

In many instances it is impossible to predict with certainty the outcome of a particular event. However, if a number of similar events are considered, a statement based on statistical considerations becomes possible. Moreover, the larger the sample the closer its behaviour as a whole is likely to be to that predicted statistically.

In general, the number of molecules in a system is so large that its macroscopic behaviour to all intents and purposes coincides with that predicted from a statistical consideration of molecular behaviour.

The second law of thermodynamics is based on this fact and, consequently, it applies only to systems containing a large number of elementary units (e.g. molecules).

Consider a system that contains a very large number of molecules and investigate either exchanges of energy between the molecules (conduction) or changes in the positions of the molecules (diffusion). Of all the possible energy or position distributions (microstates), those which coincide (within the limits of experimental detection) with the statistically most probable distribution astronomically outnumber all other distributions.

For example, consider a perfect gas distributed between two bulbs A and B of equal volume and connected to one another. At equilibrium, each molecule in turn has an equal chance of being in A or B and all of the possible distributions of molecules between A and B (microstates) have equal probability. However, the number of microstates in which the excess of molecules in one bulb over the number in the other bulb is sufficient to permit the measurement of a pressure difference is a quite discountably small fraction of the total number of microstates.

Similarly with energy distributions, the number of microstates in a macroscopic system that coincide within the limits of experimental significance with the statistically most probable microstate* is astronomically large compared with the number of other microstates, though, again, all microstates have equal probability of occurrence.

The temperature of a system is related to its molecular energies. Exchange of energy between molecules takes place continuously and, at equilibrium, the energy distribution is, within experimental limits, the statistically most probable distribution. This is an uneven distribution, from which it follows that different molecules have different 'temperatures'. The measurement of temperature, however, involves interaction of the thermometer (a large object) with a large number of the molecules of the system, with inevitable averaging. If a thermally isolated metal bar is initially hot at one end and cold at the other end, heat will flow spontaneously from the hot end to the cold end until a uniform temperature is attained. This is because the number of microstates in which the energy distribution is (within the limits of experimental detection) the same throughout the sample astronomically exceeds the number of microstates in which the energy distribution is at a higher level one end compared with that at the other end.

2.9.1 The Boltzmann–Planck Equation

The entropy of an isolated system tends to its maximum (equilibrium) value. It follows that any other quantity that changes unidirectionally during a spontaneous

---

*For example, the Boltzmann distribution

$n_i = n_0 \exp[-(\epsilon_i - \epsilon_0)/kT]$

process can be related to entropy. Probability is such a quantity. In statistical mechanics entropy is related to the so-called 'thermodynamic probability'. Thermodynamic probability W is defined as the number of microstates that correspond to a particular macrostate. Therefore,

$S = f(W)$

To ascertain the general nature of this relationship, consider combining systems A and B, with entropies S_A and S_B, and thermodynamic probabilities W_A and W_B. Since entropies add and probabilities multiply,

$S_{AB} = S_A + S_B = f(W_A \times W_B)$

The relationship between S and W is, therefore, of the form

$$S = S_0 + k^* \ln W \tag{2.42}$$

where S_0 and k^* are constants.

S_0 is arbitrarily put equal to zero. This means that the entropy of a perfectly crystalline material at absolute zero temperature (for which $W = 1$ and $\ln W = 0$) is made equal to zero (see third law of thermodynamics, in the following section).

To deduce the value of k^*, consider the isothermal expansion of a perfect gas. If α is the thermodynamic probability for one molecule in unit volume, then the probability for this molecule in volume V is αV, and the probability for N_A molecules in volume V is $(\alpha V)^{N_A}$. If the isothermal expansion is carried out from volume V_1 to volume V_2 then

$$S_2 - S_1 = k^* \ln \left(\frac{W_2}{W_1} \right) = k^* \ln \left(\frac{(\alpha V_2)^{N_A}}{(\alpha V_1)^{N_A}} \right) = k^* N_A \ln \left(\frac{V_2}{V_1} \right)$$

But, from classical thermodynamics (equation (2.39)), the isothermal expansion of one mole (N_A molecules) of perfect gas gives

$$S_2 - S_1 = R \ln (V_2/V_1)$$

Therefore, $k^* = R/N_A$, i.e. k^* is the Boltzmann constant k, and

$$S = k \ln W \tag{2.43}$$

Equation (2.43) gives the entropy of any given macrostate. At equilibrium, $W = W_{max}$, therefore,

$$S = k \ln W_{max} \tag{2.44}$$

But, for a system containing a very large number of molecules, $\ln W_{max}$ is not significantly different from $\ln W_{total}$, where W_{total} is the sum of the thermodynamic probabilities for all possible macrostates. W_{total} can, in effect, be calculated from molecular parameters, and this provides a method for determining so-called 'statistical entropies' by way of the relationship

$$S = k \ln W_{total} \tag{2.45}$$

2.10   The Third Law of Thermodynamics

The third law of thermodynamics is concerned with the limiting behaviour of systems as the temperature approaches absolute zero.

Very low temperatures are attained by successive adiabatic demagnetisations, but the nature of this process is such that absolute zero temperature can only be approached, but not actually reached.

2.10.1 Nernst Heat Theorem

Adiabatic demagnetisation uses an entropy change to produce cooling. If any such entropy difference existed down to absolute zero temperature, it should be possible to use it to reduce the temperature to (or even below) absolute zero. Accepting that absolute zero temperature is unattainable, the third law of thermodynamics can be stated in the form: **The entropies of all systems in a state of thermodynamic equilibrium at absolute zero temperature are the same.** That is

$$\Delta S_0 = 0 \tag{2.46}$$

On the basis of the molecular interpretation of entropy (Section 2.9), it is convenient (though arbitrary) to state the third law of thermodynamics in the following modified form (suggested by Planck): **The entropy of all systems in a state of thermodynamic equilibrium at absolute zero temperature is equal to zero.** That is

$$S_0 = 0 \tag{2.47}$$

In addition,

$$C_{V,0} = C_{p,0} = 0 \tag{2.48}$$

2.10.2 Third-Law (Thermal) Entropies

The third law of thermodynamics in the form of equation (2.47) makes it possible to obtain entropies of chemical compounds from calorimetric measurements, as now illustrated.

Example 2.14

The thermal entropy of nitrogen can be obtained as follows:

$S^{\ominus}_{10\,K} - S_0$ (extrapolation) $= 1.92 \ \text{J K}^{-1} \ \text{mol}^{-1}$

$S^{\ominus}_{35.61\,K} - S^{\ominus}_{10\,K} \ \left(\int (C_p/T)\,\mathrm{d}T \right) = 25.25 \ \text{J K}^{-1} \ \text{mol}^{-1}$

$\Delta^{\beta}_{\alpha} S^{\ominus} = 228.9/35.61 \qquad = 6.43 \ \text{J K}^{-1} \ \text{mol}^{-1}$

$S^{\ominus}_{63.14\,K} - S^{\ominus}_{35.61\,K} \ \left(\int (C_p/T)\,\mathrm{d}T \right) = 23.38 \ \text{J K}^{-1} \ \text{mol}^{-1}$

$\Delta^{l}_{s} S^{\ominus} = 720.9/63.14 \qquad = 11.42 \ \text{J K}^{-1} \ \text{mol}^{-1}$

$S^{\ominus}_{77.32\,K} - S^{\ominus}_{63.14\,K} \ \left(\int (C_p/T)\,\mathrm{d}T \right) = 11.41 \ \text{J K}^{-1} \ \text{mol}^{-1}$

$\Delta^{g}_{l} S^{\ominus} = 5535.0/77.32 \qquad = 72.13 \ \text{J K}^{-1} \ \text{mol}^{-1}$

$S^{\ominus}_{298.15\,K} - S^{\ominus}_{77.32\,K} \ \left(\int (C_p/T)\,\mathrm{d}T \right) = 40.12 \ \text{J K}^{-1} \ \text{mol}^{-1}$

Total: $\qquad S^{\ominus}_{298.15\,K} \quad = 192.1 \ \text{J K}^{-1} \ \text{mol}^{-1}$ ∎

Thermal and statistical entropies are consistent, except in those cases where frozen-in disorder causes the thermal entropy to be low.

2.11 Free-Energy Functions

The universal criterion for equilibrium has already been established (equation (2.30)), i.e.

$$\mathrm{d}S \text{(isolated system)} \underset{R}{\overset{I}{\gtrless}} 0$$

or

$$\mathrm{d}S\text{(system)} + \mathrm{d}S\text{(surroundings)} \underset{R}{\overset{I}{\gtrless}} 0$$

This criterion, however, has limited direct application; in most practical situations, the system under consideration is not isolated from its surroundings. Criteria for equilibrium that involve consideration of only the system must, therefore, be sought.

For a process at constant temperature and constant pressure (see equation (2.31)),

$$\mathrm{d}S\text{(surroundings)} \underset{R}{\overset{I}{\gtrless}} \mathrm{d}H\text{(surroundings)}/T$$

$$\underset{R}{\overset{I}{\gtrless}} - \mathrm{d}H\text{(system)}/T$$

Therefore,

$$\mathrm{d}H\text{(system)}/T - \mathrm{d}S\text{(system)} \underset{R}{\overset{I}{\lessgtr}} 0$$

or

$$(\mathrm{d}H - T\,\mathrm{d}S)\text{(system)} \underset{R}{\overset{I}{\lessgtr}} 0$$

Since an isothermal process is being considered,

$$\mathrm{d}(H - TS)\text{(system)} \underset{R}{\overset{I}{\lessgtr}} 0 \tag{2.49}$$

Likewise, for a process at constant temperature and constant volume,

$$\mathrm{d}(U - TS)\text{(system)} \underset{R}{\overset{I}{\lessgtr}} 0 \tag{2.50}$$

$U - TS$ and $H - TS$ are state functions which (in view of their considerable importance as criteria of spontaneity and equilibrium in terms of properties of the system only) are given special names.

2.11.1 Helmholtz Function (or Helmholtz Free Energy), A

This is

$$A = U - TS \tag{2.51}$$

For a process at constant temperature and constant volume (equation (2.50)),

$$\mathrm{d}A\text{(system)} \underset{R}{\overset{I}{\lessgtr}} 0$$

i.e. $\mathrm{d}A$ is negative for a spontaneous change and zero at equilibrium.

2.11.2 Gibbs Function (or Gibbs Free Energy), G

This is

$$G = H - TS \tag{2.52}$$

$$= U + pV - TS \tag{2.53}$$

For a process at constant temperature and constant pressure (equation (2.49)),

$$dG(\text{system}) \underset{R}{\overset{I}{\lessgtr}} 0$$

i.e. dG is negative for a spontaneous change and zero at equilibrium.

2.11.3 Development of Equations Involving Gibbs Free Energy

Differentiating (2.53) gives

$$dG = dU + p\,dV + V\,dp - T\,dS - S\,dT \tag{2.54}$$

Substituting equation (2.33)

$$dU = T\,dS - p\,dV$$

gives

$$dG = V\,dp - S\,dT \tag{2.55}$$

for which the partial differentials are

$$\left(\frac{\partial G}{\partial p}\right)_T = V \tag{2.56}$$

and

$$\left(\frac{\partial G}{\partial T}\right)_p = -S \tag{2.57}$$

2.11.4 Variation of Gibbs Free Energy with Pressure

From equation (2.56), for an isothermal process,

$$dG = V\,dp$$

In order to integrate this equation, the variation of V with p (i.e. the equation of state) for the substance in question must be known.

For solids and liquids the isothermal compressibility

$$\kappa = \frac{1}{V}\left(\frac{\partial V}{\partial p}\right)_T$$

is small. Therefore, to a reasonable approximation

$$\Delta G = V\,\Delta p \tag{2.58}$$

For one mole of perfect gas, $pV = RT$, and therefore

$$dG = RT\,dp/p$$

which on integration between the limits p and $p^{\ominus}$ (where $p^{\ominus}$ is a standard pressure) gives

$$G - G^{\ominus} = RT \ln (p/p^{\ominus}) \tag{2.59}$$

or, putting $p^{\ominus}$ equal to its customary value of one atmosphere,

$$G = G^{\ominus} + RT \ln (p/\text{atm})$$

2.11.5 Variation of Free Energy with Temperature (Gibbs–Helmholtz Equation)

From equations (2.57) and (2.52)

$$\left(\frac{\partial G}{\partial T}\right)_p = -S = \frac{G-H}{T} \tag{2.60}$$

or

$$\left(\frac{\partial \Delta G}{\partial T}\right)_p = \frac{\Delta G - \Delta H}{T}$$

which can be developed to the useful form

$$\left[\frac{\partial}{\partial T}\left(\frac{\Delta G}{T}\right)\right]_p = -\frac{\Delta H}{T^2}$$

2.11.6 Standard Free Energies of Formation

The free energy of formation of a compound is equal to the increase in free energy when the compound is made up from its elements.

As with enthalpy, only differences in free energy can be determined. Therefore, free energy itself is a meaningful quantity only when referred to some reference (or standard) state. It is customary (as with enthalpy) to assign zero Gibbs free energy to the stable phase of all elements at 1 atm and at the temperature under consideration. It follows that the standard free energy of a compound at a given temperature is equal to its standard free energy of formation at that temperature.

To calculate $\Delta G^{\ominus}$ for a reaction, we use

$$\Delta G^{\ominus} = \sum \Delta_f G^{\ominus}(\text{products}) - \sum \Delta_f G^{\ominus}(\text{reactants}) \tag{2.61}$$

Alternatively, using $\Delta G^{\ominus} = \Delta H^{\ominus} - T\,\Delta S^{\ominus}$, $\Delta G^{\ominus}$ for a reaction may be calculated from

$$\Delta G^{\ominus} = \sum \Delta_f H^{\ominus}(\text{products}) - \sum \Delta_f H^{\ominus}(\text{reactants})$$
$$- T[\sum S^{\ominus}(\text{products}) - \sum S^{\ominus}(\text{reactants})] \tag{2.62}$$

Example 2.15

From the following data, calculate $\Delta G^{\ominus}_{298\,K}$ for the reaction

$$2H_2S(g) + SO_2(g) \rightarrow 2H_2O(l) + 3S(s)$$

	$H_2S(g)$	$SO_2(g)$	$H_2O(l)$	$S(s)$
$\Delta_f H^{\ominus}_{298\,K}/\text{kJ mol}^{-1}$	−22.2	−296.6	−285.8	0
$S^{\ominus}_{298\,K}/\text{J K}^{-1}\text{ mol}^{-1}$	205.6	247.9	70.1	31.9

$$\Delta G^{\ominus}_{298\,K} = [(2 \times -285.8) + (3 \times 0)] - [(2 \times -22.2) + (-296.6)]$$
$$- 298 \times 10^{-3} \times \{[(2 \times 70.1) + (3 \times 31.9)] - [(2 \times 205.6) + 247.9]\}$$
$$= -104.5 \text{ kJ mol}^{-1} \qquad \blacksquare$$

The free energies of ions in aqueous solution are calculated in relation to the conventional standard.

$$\Delta_f G^{\ominus}(H^+(aq)) = 0 \qquad \text{(at all temperatures)} \qquad (2.63)$$

This is, of course, the convention of assigning a value of zero (at all temperatures) to the potential of a standard hydrogen electrode. Indeed, standard free energies of formation of ions are usually tabulated in the form of standard electrode potentials (see Chapter 6).

2.12   Chemical Equilibrium

2.12.1   Law of Mass Action, Equilibrium Constants, Reaction Isotherm

The law of mass action states that the velocity with which a chemical change takes place is proportional to the product of the active masses of the interacting substances, active mass being that part of the substance which is effective in a reaction.

Consider a reaction between perfect gases in which forward and reverse reactions take place in single steps:

$$aA + bB \rightleftharpoons cC + dD$$

The active mass of a perfect gas is proportional to its pressure. Therefore, according to the law of mass action, the velocities, $v(+)$ and $v(-)$, of forward and reverse reactions are given by

$$v(+) = k(+)(p_A)^a(p_B)^b$$

$$v(-) = k(-)(p_C)^c(p_D)^d$$

where $k(+)$ and $k(-)$ are the respective rate constants.

At equilibrium, $v(+) = v(-)$, and therefore

$$\frac{k(+)}{k(-)} = \frac{(p_C)^c(p_D)^d}{(p_A)^a(p_B)^b} = K$$

In fact, most reactions do not take place in a single step (a point very much emphasised in the kinetics chapter (Chapter 4)), and so the relationship $k(+)/k(-) = K$ is somewhat meaningless. However, this does not affect the validity of the relationship

$$\frac{(p_C)^c(p_D)^d}{(p_A)^a(p_B)^b} = K \qquad (2.64)$$

since this expression relates only to the equilibrium state and not to the reaction mechanism by which equilibrium is established. K is called the **equilibrium constant**.

From equation (2.59), we have for a perfect gas

$$G = G^{\ominus} + RT \ln p$$

where p is expressed in the unit that conforms with the chosen standard state (i.e. in standard atmospheres; 1 atm = 1.013×10^5 Pa).

For an infinitesimal displacement of the above reaction from its state of equilibrium,

$$dG = (dG_C + dG_D) - (dG_A + dG_B)$$

$$= [dn_C(G_C^{\ominus} + RT \ln p_C) + dn_D(G_D^{\ominus} + RT \ln p_D)]$$

$$- [dn_A(G_A^{\ominus} + RT \ln p_A) + dn_B(G_B^{\ominus} + RT \ln p_B)] \qquad (2.65)$$

39

If the system is at equilibrium, $dG = 0$. Therefore, since dn_A, dn_B, dn_C and dn_D must be proportional to the stoichiometric coefficients a, b, c and d, respectively,

$$0 = [c(G_C^\ominus + RT \ln p_C) + d(G_D^\ominus + RT \ln p_D)]$$
$$- [a(G_A^\ominus + RT \ln p_A) + b(G_B^\ominus + RT \ln p_B)]$$

which rearranges to

$$RT \ln \left(\frac{(p_C)^c (p_D)^d}{(p_A)^a (p_B)^b} \right) = (aG_A^\ominus + bG_B^\ominus) - (cG_C^\ominus + dG_D^\ominus) \tag{2.66}$$

where the values of p are equilibrium pressures.

The right-hand side of equation (2.66) is a constant equal to $-\Delta G^\ominus$, where $\Delta G^\ominus$ is the standard free-energy change for the complete reaction at the temperature in question.

It follows that $(p_C)^c (p_D)^d / (p_A)^a (p_B)^b$ is also a constant, i.e. the equilibrium constant, $K_p^\ominus$. Therefore, equation (2.66) can be written in the form

$$\Delta G^\ominus = -RT \ln K_p^\ominus \tag{2.67}$$

2.12.2 Equilibrium Constants

The general symbol for equilibrium constant is K. Subscripts p, c, etc., may be added to indicate that K is calculated in terms of pressures, concentrations, etc.

Since for a perfect gas, $pV = nRT$, then $p = (n/V) RT = c(RT)$, where c represents concentration. Therefore

$$K_p = K_c (RT)^{\Delta n} \tag{2.68}$$

where Δn = (amount of products) − (amount of reactants).

Example 2.16

$$N_2 O_4 (g) \rightleftharpoons 2NO_2 (g) \qquad K_p (298 \text{ K}) = 0.144 \text{ atm}$$

Calculate $K_c (298 \text{ K})$.

$n = 2 - 1 = 1$. Therefore

$$K_p = 0.144 \text{ atm} = 0.144 \times 1.013 \times 10^5 \text{ N m}^{-2}$$
$$= K_c \times RT = K_c \times 8.314 \times 298 \text{ J mol}^{-1}$$

giving

$$K_c = 5.9 \text{ mol m}^{-3} = 5.9 \times 10^{-3} \text{ mol dm}^{-3} \qquad \blacksquare$$

If the reactants and products do not behave ideally, K as given in an expression such as equation (2.64) will not be a true constant. A true equilibrium constant (the thermodynamic equilibrium constant) is obtained only when calculated in terms of effective concentrations (activities) or effective pressures (fugacities), etc. The equation $\Delta G^\ominus = -RT \ln K^\ominus$ (known as the standard reaction isotherm, or the van't Hoff isotherm) then holds generally. The numerical values of the (dimensionless) activities used to calculate K relate to the standard state to which $\Delta G^\ominus$ refers. For example, the activities of solutes are usually calculated relative to a standard concentration of 1 mol dm^{-3}. Activity is then related to concentration by the expression

$$a = \frac{c}{c^\ominus} y = \frac{c}{\text{mol dm}^{-3}} y \tag{2.69}$$

where y is a dimensionless factor called the **activity coefficient**. The corresponding $\Delta G^{\ominus}$ is the value of ΔG when reactants at unit activity (i.e. $cy = 1$ mol dm^{-3}) react to give products at unit activity.

Example 2.17

Calculate $K^{\ominus}$ (298 K) for the reaction

$$2H_2 S(g) + SO_2 (g) \rightleftharpoons 2H_2 O(l) + 3S(s)$$

for which $\Delta G^{\ominus}(298$ K$) = -104.5$ kJ mol^{-1} (see Example 2.15).

$$\ln K^{\ominus} = \frac{-\Delta G^{\ominus}}{RT} = \frac{104\,500}{8.314 \times 298}$$

giving

$$K^{\ominus}(298 \text{ K}) = 2 \times 10^{18}$$

i.e. the equilibrium is well over to the right.

The $H_2 O(l)$ and $S(s)$ are in their standard states of unit activity (i.e. pure liquid and pure solid, respectively) during this reaction. The equilibrium pressures of the gases will be so low that perfect gas behaviour can be assumed. Therefore, since their standard states relate to a standard pressure of one atmosphere, a non-thermodynamic equilibrium 'constant', i.e.

$$K_p (298 \text{ K}) = 2 \times 10^{18} \text{ atm}^{-3}$$

may be quoted. ∎

2.12.3 Variation of Equilibrium Constant with Temperature

$$\Delta G^{\ominus} = \Delta H^{\ominus} - T \Delta S^{\ominus}$$

$$\Delta G^{\ominus} = -RT \ln K^{\ominus}$$

Combining these expressions gives

$$\ln K^{\ominus} = \frac{\Delta S^{\ominus}}{R} - \frac{\Delta H^{\ominus}}{RT} \tag{2.70}$$

This is one of the most important equations in thermodynamics. It allows calculation of the equilibrium constant of a reaction at a selected temperature from enthalpy and entropy data.

The so-called van't Hoff isobar is the differential form of this equation, i.e.

$$\left(\frac{\partial \ln K^{\ominus}}{\partial T} \right)_p = \frac{\Delta H^{\ominus}}{RT^2} \tag{2.71}$$

Enthalpy and entropy data relating to 298 K tend to be readily available. In applying equation (2.70) it is frequent practice to assume $\Delta H^{\ominus}$ and $\Delta S^{\ominus}$ to be independent of temperature, and to use $\Delta H^{\ominus}_{298 \text{ K}}$ and $\Delta S^{\ominus}_{298 \text{ K}}$ for all values of T under consideration. The variations of $\Delta H^{\ominus}$ and $\Delta S^{\ominus}$ with temperature (equations (2.26)/(2.27) and (2.38)) both depend on the magnitude of $\Delta C_p^{\ominus}$, which is usually small. Since the right-hand terms in equation (2.70) have opposite signs, it follows that any errors due to assuming temperature-independent $\Delta H^{\ominus}$ and $\Delta S^{\ominus}$ will, in any case, partly cancel one another. The assumption of temperature-independent $\Delta H^{\ominus}$ and $\Delta S^{\ominus}$ is, therefore, generally an acceptable one, except, possibly, at very high temperatures.

Example 2.18

For the reaction

$$C_2H_4(g) + H_2O(g) \rightleftharpoons C_2H_5OH(g)$$

$\Delta H_{298\,K}^{\ominus} = -44.6\ \text{kJ mol}^{-1}$ and $\Delta S_{298\,K}^{\ominus} = -125.6\ \text{J K}^{-1}\ \text{mol}^{-1}$. Hence, calculate the temperature at which $K^{\ominus} = 1$.

$$\ln 1 = 0 = \frac{-125.6}{8.314} - \frac{-44\,600}{8.314T}$$

giving

$$T = 355\ \text{K}$$ ■

2.12.4 Equilibrium Constant and Extent of Reaction

For a reaction with a single reactant (or with reactants in stoichiometric proportions), the yield can conveniently be represented by α, the fraction of reactant(s) converted to product(s). The relative amounts of reactant(s) and product(s) are, therefore, given in terms of α. For example

$$COCl_2(g) \rightleftharpoons CO(g) + Cl_2(g)$$

$$1 - \alpha \qquad \alpha \qquad \alpha$$

In this particular case, these 'proportions' add to $1 + \alpha$. By dividing throughout by $1 + \alpha$, they can be made to add to unity, and so become mole fractions. If it is assumed for this gas-phase reaction that the partial pressure of each component of the reaction mixture is proportional to its mole fraction, these partial pressures will be as follows:

$$COCl_2(g) \rightleftharpoons CO(g) \qquad + Cl_2(g)$$

$$\left(\frac{1-\alpha}{1+\alpha}\right)p \qquad \left(\frac{\alpha}{1+\alpha}\right)p \qquad \left(\frac{\alpha}{1+\alpha}\right)p$$

where p is the total pressure of the reaction mixture. Therefore, if the system is at equilibrium,

$$K_p = \frac{p_{CO} \times p_{Cl_2}}{p_{COCl_2}} = \frac{[\alpha/(1+\alpha)]\,p \times [\alpha/(1+\alpha)]\,p}{[(1-\alpha)/(1+\alpha)]\,p}$$

$$= \frac{\alpha^2 p}{(1-\alpha)(1+\alpha)} = \frac{\alpha^2 p}{1-\alpha^2}$$

Similar expressions relating equilibrium yield and total pressure can be derived for other gas-phase reactions. The nature and complexity of such expressions depend on stoichiometry, but will take the general form

$$K_p = f(\alpha)p^{\Delta n} \tag{2.72}$$

Example 2.19

For the above reaction, $K_p(500\ \text{K}) = 0.64$ atm. Calculate the pressure of the reaction mixture to give 40% dissociation of $COCl_2(g)$ at equilibrium.

$$K_p = 0.64\ \text{atm} = \frac{\alpha^2 p}{1-\alpha^2} = \frac{(0.4)^2 p}{1-(0.4)^2}$$

giving

$p = 3.36$ atm ∎

A similar treatment in terms of α applies to solution reactions, as illustrated, in particular, in Chapter 5.

If there is more than one reactant, they will often not be in stoichiometric proportions and consideration of the reaction in terms of α becomes meaningless. A term that is applicable generally, extent of reaction ξ (xi), is introduced:

$$\xi = (n_B - n_{B,0})/\nu_B \tag{2.73}$$

Example 2.20

For the reaction

$$N_2(g) + 3H_2(g) \rightleftharpoons 2NH_3(g)$$

the initial reaction mixture consists of N_2 (4 mol), H_2 (5 mol) and NH_3 (1 mol), and at a certain stage, reaction has taken place (in accord with the above stoichiometry) so that these amounts are now N_2 (3 mol), H_2 (2 mol) and NH_3 (3 mol). Calculate the extent of reaction.

	N_2	H_2	NH_3
$n_{B,0}$/mol	4	5	1
n_B/mol	3	2	3
ν_B	−1	−3	+2

$$\xi = \frac{n(N_2) - n_0(N_2)}{\nu(N_2)} = \frac{n(H_2) - n_0(H_2)}{\nu(H_2)} = \frac{n(NH_3) - n_0(NH_3)}{\nu(NH_3)}$$

$$= \frac{3-4}{-1} \text{ mol} \qquad = \frac{2-5}{-3} \text{ mol} \qquad = \frac{3-1}{+2} \text{ mol} \qquad = 1 \text{ mol} \quad ∎$$

As illustrated, ξ is an unambiguous term in that its value does not depend on which reactant/product is selected for attention in considering the progress of the reaction.

The rate of a reaction J can be expressed with similar unambiguity as

$$J = d\xi/dt \tag{2.74}$$

2.13 Worked Examples

2.13.1 Isothermal and Adiabatic Expansion

A monatomic gas (assumed ideal) initially at 298 K and 2 atm is expanded to a final pressure of 1 atm:

(a) isothermally and reversibly,
(b) isothermally against a constant pressure of 1 atm,
(c) adiabatically and reversibly,
(d) adiabatically against a constant pressure of 1 atm.

Calculate for each of these expansions:

(i) the final temperature of the gas,
(ii) ΔU, the increase in the internal energy of the gas,
(iii) w, the work done on the gas,

(iv) q, the heat absorbed by the gas,

(v) ΔH, the increase in the enthalpy of the gas.

Answer

In the answers to these questions, subscripts 1 and 2 will be used to denote initial and final states, respectively; therefore, $p_1 = 2$ atm, $p_2 = 1$ atm, $T_1 = 298$ K.

(a) *Reversible isothermal expansion*

(i) (ii) Since the expansion is isothermal, $T_2 = T_1 = 298$ K and $\Delta U = 0$.

(iii) $w = - RT \ln (V_2/V_1) = - RT \ln (p_1/p_2)$
$= - 8.314 \times 298 \times \ln 2$ J mol^{-1}
$= - 1720$ J mol^{-1}

(iv) $q = \Delta U - w = 0 - (- 1720) = + 1720$ J mol^{-1}

(v) $\Delta H = \Delta U + \Delta(pV)$, but, since T remains constant, $\Delta(pV) = 0$, and, since $\Delta U = 0$ then $\Delta H = 0$.

(b) *Rapid isothermal expansion*

(i) (ii) Again, since the expansion is isothermal, $T_1 = T_2 = 298$ K and $\Delta U = 0$.

(iii) $w = - p_2(V_2 - V_1)$

$= - p_2 \left(\dfrac{RT}{p_2} - \dfrac{RT}{p_1} \right) = - RT \left(1 - \dfrac{p_2}{p_1} \right)$

$= - 8.314 \times 298 \times (1 - 0.5)$ J mol^{-1}

$= - 1240$ J mol^{-1}

[Note: w(reversible) $< w$(rapid).]

(iv) $q = \Delta U - w = 0 - (- 1240) = + 1240$ J mol^{-1}

(v) $\Delta H = \Delta U + \Delta(pV) = 0$

(c) *Reversible adiabatic expansion*

(iv) By definition, for an adiabatic process, $q = 0$.

(i) For the reversible adiabatic expansion or compression of a perfect gas, $p^{1-\gamma} T^{\gamma}$ is constant (equation (2.22)), where $\gamma = C_p/C_V$. For a monatomic gas C_V reflects translational kinetic energy changes only and is, therefore, equal to $1.5R$ and independent of temperature. Therefore, $C_p = C_V + R = 2.5R$, and $\gamma = 1.67$.

$p_1^{1-\gamma} T_1^{\gamma} = p_2^{1-\gamma} T_2^{\gamma}$

or

$T_2 = T_1(p_1/p_2)^{(1-\gamma)/\gamma} = 298 \times 2^{-0.4}$ K
$= 226$ K

(ii) $\Delta U = C_V(T_2 - T_1) = 1.5 \times 8.314 \times (226 - 298)$ J mol^{-1}
$= - 900$ J mol^{-1}

(iii) $\Delta U = q + w$, and therefore, since $q = 0$, $w = \Delta U = - 900$ J mol^{-1}.

(v) $\Delta H = C_p(T_2 - T_1) = 2.5 \times 8.314 \times (226 - 298)$ J mol^{-1}
$= - 1500$ J mol^{-1}

(d) *Rapid adiabatic expansion*

(iv) Again, since the expansion is adiabatic, $q = 0$ and $\Delta U = w$.

(i) For expansion against a constant pressure p_2, $w = -p_2(V_2 - V_1)$, and therefore

$$\Delta U = w = C_V(T_2 - T_1) = -p_2(V_2 - V_1)$$

Substituting RT/p for V and $1.5R$ for C_V gives

$$1.5R(T_2 - T_1) = -p_2 \left(\frac{RT_2}{p_2} - \frac{RT_1}{p_1} \right)$$

i.e.

$$1.5(T_2 - 298\ \text{K}) = -T_2 + 298\ \text{K}/2$$

giving

$$T_2 = 238\ \text{K}$$

(ii) $\Delta U = C_V(T_2 - T_1) = 1.5 \times 8.314 \times (238 - 298)\ \text{J mol}^{-1}$
$= -750\ \text{J mol}^{-1}$

(iii) Since $q = 0$, $w = \Delta U = -750\ \text{J mol}^{-1}$.

(v) $\Delta H = C_p(T_2 - T_1) = 2.5 \times 8.314 \times (238 - 298)\ \text{J mol}^{-1}$
$= -1250\ \text{J mol}^{-1}$

These results are summarised in the following table.

Type of expansion	T_2/K	ΔU/J mol^{-1}	w/J mol^{-1}	q/J mol^{-1}	ΔH/J mol^{-1}
Reversible isothermal	298	0	-1720	$+1720$	0
Rapid isothermal	298	0	-1240	$+1240$	0
Reversible adiabatic	226	-900	-900	0	-1500
Rapid adiabatic	238	-750	-750	0	-1250

2.13.2 Enthalpy of Formation

The increase in temperature (at around 25°C) arising from the combustion of 0.950 g of o-toluic acid ($M_r = 136.15$) in a bomb calorimeter can be duplicated by the application of 27.02 kJ of electrical energy. Given that the standard enthalpies of formation of $H_2O(l)$ and $CO_2(g)$ are -285.8 and -393.5 kJ mol^{-1}, respectively, at 298 K, calculate the standard enthalpy of formation of o-toluic acid.

Answer

$$\Delta_c U = \frac{-27.02 \times 136.15}{0.950} = -3872.4\ \text{kJ mol}^{-1}$$

where subscript c represents combustion.

$$C_8H_8O_2(s) + 9O_2(g) \rightarrow 8CO_2(g) + 4H_2O(l)$$

Therefore, $\Delta n = 8 - 9 = -1$ and

$$\Delta_c H = \Delta_c U - RT = -3872.4 - \frac{8.314 \times 298}{1000}\ \text{kJ mol}^{-1}$$

$$= -3874.9\ \text{kJ mol}^{-1}$$

$$\Delta_c H = 8\Delta_f H(CO_2(g)) + 4\Delta_f H(H_2O(l)) - \Delta_f H(C_8H_8O_2(s))$$

Therefore,

$$\Delta_f H(C_8H_8O_2(s)) = [8 \times (-393.5)] + [4 \times (-285.8)] - (-3874.9)$$

$$= -416\ \text{kJ mol}^{-1}$$

2.13.3 Hess's Law

Calculate ΔH for the reaction

$$FeO(s) + 2H^+(aq) \rightarrow H_2O(l) + Fe^{2+}(aq) \tag{1}$$

given that

$$2Fe(s) + 1\tfrac{1}{2}O_2(g) \rightarrow Fe_2O_3(s) \qquad \Delta H = -822.2 \text{ kJ mol}^{-1} \tag{2}$$

$$2FeO(s) + \tfrac{1}{2}O_2(g) \rightarrow Fe_2O_3(s) \qquad \Delta H = -284.2 \text{ kJ mol}^{-1} \tag{3}$$

$$H_2(g) + \tfrac{1}{2}O_2(g) \rightarrow H_2O(l) \qquad \Delta H = -285.8 \text{ kJ mol}^{-1} \tag{4}$$

$$Fe(s) + 2H^+(aq) \rightarrow Fe^{2+}(aq) + H_2(g) \qquad \Delta H = -\ \ 86.2 \text{ kJ mol}^{-1} \tag{5}$$

Answer

This question asks for the value of ΔH for reaction (1). To this end, equations (2) to (5) will be manipulated in an appropriate algebraic fashion to yield equation (1).

Inspection of equation (1) shows that $FeO(s)$ is required on the LHS, and therefore, $\tfrac{1}{2} \times$ (3) will achieve this end. Likewise, $1 \times$ (4) plus $1 \times$ (5) yields the necessary RHS of equation (1). Therefore, to start with, take $\tfrac{1}{2} \times$ (3) + (4) + (5), which gives

$$FeO(s) + \tfrac{3}{4}O_2(g) + Fe(s) + 2H^+(aq) \rightarrow \tfrac{1}{2}Fe_2O_3(s) + Fe^{2+}(aq) + H_2O(l)$$
$$\Delta H = \tfrac{1}{2} \times (-284.2) + (-285.8) + (-86.2) = -514.1 \text{ kJ mol}^{-1} \tag{6}$$

Equation (6) clearly contains unwanted $Fe(s)$ (LHS) and $\tfrac{1}{2}Fe_2O_3(s)$ (RHS). Subtraction of $\tfrac{1}{2} \times$ (2) from (6) eliminates these (and also the $\tfrac{3}{4}O_2$) and gives

$$FeO(s) + 2H^+(aq) \rightarrow Fe^{2+}(aq) + H_2O(l)$$

$$\Delta H = -514.1 - \tfrac{1}{2} \times (-822.2) = -103 \text{ kJ mol}^{-1}$$

which is the value of ΔH for reaction (1).

[Note: The thermochemistry of the one $H_2O(l)$ molecule required to balance this equation must be taken into account regardless of the fact that (aq) indicates a large quantity of water present in general, but not involved in the reaction as such.]

2.13.4 Enthalpy of Formation of Ions

Use the following data to calculate $\Delta_f H^{\ominus}(OH^-(aq))$ at 298 K:

$$\Delta H^{\ominus}_{298 \text{ K}} \text{ (ionisation of water)} = +56.8 \text{ kJ mol}^{-1}$$

$$\Delta H^{\ominus}_{298 \text{ K}} \text{ (formation of water)} = -285.8 \text{ kJ mol}^{-1}$$

Answer

The data are represented by the thermochemical equations

$$H_2O(l) + (aq) \rightarrow H^+(aq) + OH^-(aq) \qquad \Delta H^{\ominus}_{298 \text{ K}} = +56.8 \text{ kJ mol}^{-1} \tag{1}$$

$$H_2(g) + \tfrac{1}{2}O_2(g) \rightarrow H_2O(l) \qquad \Delta H^{\ominus}_{298 \text{ K}} = -285.8 \text{ kJ mol}^{-1} \tag{2}$$

Therefore, adding (1) and (2),

$$H_2(g) + \tfrac{1}{2}O_2(g) + (aq) \rightarrow H^+(aq) + OH^-(aq) \qquad \Delta H^{\ominus}_{298\,K} = -229.0 \text{ kJ mol}^{-1}$$

$$(3)$$

To proceed to the final result, the convention $\Delta_f H^{\ominus}(H^+(aq)) = 0$ must be taken into account, i.e.

$$\tfrac{1}{2}H_2(g) - e + (aq) \rightarrow H^+(aq) \qquad \Delta H^{\ominus}_{298\,K} = 0 \qquad\qquad (4)$$

Therefore, subtracting (4) from (3),

$$\tfrac{1}{2}H_2(g) + \tfrac{1}{2}O_2(g) + e + (aq) \rightarrow OH^-(aq) \qquad \Delta H^{\ominus}_{298\,K} = -229.0 \text{ kJ mol}^{-1}$$

or

$$\Delta_f H^{\ominus}_{298\,K}(OH^-(aq)) = -229.0 \text{ kJ mol}^{-1}$$

2.13.5 Kirchhoff Equation

The standard enthalpy of formation of HCl(g) at 298 K is equal to -92.3 kJ mol^{-1}. Calculate the value of this quantity at 1000 K. Molar heat capacities in this temperature range are given by the empirical equations

$$C_p(H_2)/\text{J K}^{-1}\text{ mol}^{-1} = 27.28 + 3.25 \times 10^{-3}T + 0.50 \times 10^5 T^{-2}$$

$$C_p(Cl_2)/\text{J K}^{-1}\text{ mol}^{-1} = 36.90 + 0.25 \times 10^{-3}T - 2.84 \times 10^5 T^{-2}$$

$$C_p(HCl)/\text{J K}^{-1}\text{ mol}^{-1} = 26.53 + 4.60 \times 10^{-3}T + 1.09 \times 10^5 T^{-2}$$

where T is the thermodynamic temperature.

Answer

$$\tfrac{1}{2}H_2(g) + \tfrac{1}{2}Cl_2(g) \rightarrow HCl(g) \qquad \Delta H^{\ominus}_{298\,K} = -92.3 \text{ kJ mol}^{-1}$$

and

$$\Delta C_p = C_p(HCl) - \tfrac{1}{2}C_p(H_2) - \tfrac{1}{2}C_p(Cl_2)$$

$$= (-5.56 + 2.85 \times 10^{-3}T + 2.26 \times 10^5 T^{-2}) \text{ J K}^{-1}\text{ mol}^{-1}$$

According to the Kirchhoff equation

$$\Delta H^{\ominus}_{1000\,K} - \Delta H^{\ominus}_{298\,K} = \int_{298\,K}^{1000\,K} \Delta C_p\, dT$$

$$= \int_{298\,K}^{1000\,K} (-5.56 + 2.85 \times 10^{-3}T + 2.26 \times 10^5 T^{-2})\, dT$$

$$= \left[-5.56T + 2.85 \times 10^{-3} T^2/2 - 2.26 \times 10^5 T^{-1} \right]_{298\,K}^{1000\,K}$$

$$= -5.56(1000 - 298) + \frac{2.85 \times 10^{-3}}{2}(1000^2 - 298^2)$$

$$\qquad - 2.26 \times 10^5 \left(\frac{1}{1000} - \frac{1}{298} \right)$$

$$= -3903 + 1298 + 532 = -2073 \text{ J mol}^{-1}$$

$$= -2.1 \text{ kJ mol}^{-1}$$

Therefore,

$$\Delta H^{\ominus}_{1000\,K} = -92.3 - 2.1 = -94.4 \text{ kJ mol}^{-1}$$

2.13.6 Enthalpy of Sublimation

From the following data, calculate the standard enthalpy of sublimation of ice at $-50°C$.

Mean heat capacity of ice = 1.975 J K^{-1} g^{-1}
Mean heat capacity of liquid water = 4.185 J K^{-1} g^{-1}
Mean heat capacity of water vapour = 1.860 J K^{-1} g^{-1}
Enthalpy of fusion of ice at $0°C$ = 333.5 J g^{-1}
Enthalpy of vaporisation of water at $100°C$ = 2255.2 J g^{-1}

(GRSC, Part I)

Answer

$$\Delta_s^g H_{223\,K}^{\ominus} = \Delta_s^l H_{223\,K}^{\ominus} + \Delta_l^g H_{223\,K}^{\ominus}$$

Applying Hess's law,

$$\Delta_s^l H_{223\,K}^{\ominus} = (H_{273\,K}^{\ominus} - H_{223\,K}^{\ominus})(s) + \Delta_s^l H_{273\,K}^{\ominus} + (H_{223\,K}^{\ominus} - H_{273\,K}^{\ominus})(l)$$

$$= (1.975 \times 50) + 333.5 - (4.185 \times 50) \text{ J g}^{-1}$$

$$= 223 \text{ J g}^{-1}$$

Similarly,

$$\Delta_l^g H_{223\,K}^{\ominus} = (H_{373\,K}^{\ominus} - H_{223\,K}^{\ominus})(l) + \Delta_l^g H_{373\,K}^{\ominus} + (H_{223\,K}^{\ominus} - H_{373\,K}^{\ominus})(g)$$

$$= (4.185 \times 150) + 2255.2 - (1.860 \times 150) \text{ J g}^{-1}$$

$$= 2604 \text{ J g}^{-1}$$

Therefore,

$$\Delta_s^g H_{223\,K}^{\ominus}(H_2O) = 223 + 2604 = 2827 \text{ J g}^{-1}$$

2.13.7 Average Bond Enthalpy

Calculate the average O—H bond enthalpy in water from the following data:

$H_2O(l) \rightarrow H_2O(g)$	$\Delta H = +40.6$ kJ mol^{-1}	(1)
$2H(g) \rightarrow H_2(g)$	$\Delta H = -435.0$ kJ mol^{-1}	(2)
$O_2(g) \rightarrow 2O(g)$	$\Delta H = +489.6$ kJ mol^{-1}	(3)
$2H_2(g) + O_2(g) \rightarrow 2H_2O(l)$	$\Delta H = -571.6$ kJ mol^{-1}	(4)

(University of Sheffield, BSc, 1st year)

Answer

The average O—H bond enthalpy is half of ΔH for the process

$$H_2O(g) \rightarrow 2H(g) + O(g)$$

Taking $\frac{1}{2} \times (3) - (1) - (2) - \frac{1}{2} \times (4)$ gives

$$H_2O(g) \rightarrow 2H(g) + O(g)$$

$$\Delta H = (\tfrac{1}{2} \times 489.6) - 40.6 - (-435.0) - [\tfrac{1}{2} \times (-571.6)] \text{ kJ mol}^{-1}$$

$$= +925 \text{ kJ mol}^{-1}$$

The average O—H bond enthalpy in water is, therefore, equal to 462.5 kJ mol^{-1}.

2.13.8 Strain Energy

Calculate the strain energy of (a) cyclopropane, C_3H_6, and (b) cyclohexane, C_6H_{12}, using the following data. Comment on the values obtained.

$\Delta_f H(C_3H_6(g)) = +53 \text{ kJ mol}^{-1}$

$\Delta_f H(C_6H_{12}(g)) = -123 \text{ kJ mol}^{-1}$

$\Delta_f H(C(g)) = +715 \text{ kJ mol}^{-1}$

$\Delta_f H(H(g)) = +218 \text{ kJ mol}^{-1}$

$E(C—C) = +355 \text{ kJ mol}^{-1}$

$E(C—H) = +408 \text{ kJ mol}^{-1}$

Answer

(a) From the enthalpy of formation data,

$$C_3H_6(g) \rightarrow 3C(g) + 6H(g)$$

$$\Delta H = (3 \times 715) + (6 \times 218) - 53$$

$$= 3400 \text{ kJ mol}^{-1}$$

From the bond enthalpies,

$$C_3H_6(g) \rightarrow 3C(g) + 6H(g)$$

$$\Delta H = (3 \times 355) + (6 \times 408)$$

$$= 3513 \text{ kJ mol}^{-1}$$

The difference between these values (113 kJ mol^{-1}) is the strain energy of cyclopropane.

(b) By a similar pair of calculations (7029 and 7026 kJ mol^{-1}, respectively) the strain energy of cyclohexane works out to be only 3 kJ mol^{-1}.

   This reflects the fact that the bond angles in cyclohexane are close to the natural tetrahedral angle ($109°$), whereas in cyclopropane, the bond angles are $60°$ and, consequently, the system is strained and of a higher energy than would otherwise be the case.

2.13.9 Enthalpy and Entropy Changes

Use the following data for lead to evaluate

(a) $H^{\ominus}_{1000 \text{ K}} - H^{\ominus}_{298 \text{ K}}$

(b) $S^{\ominus}_{1000 \text{ K}} - S^{\ominus}_{298 \text{ K}}$

$C_p^{\ominus}(Pb(s))/\text{J K}^{-1} \text{ mol}^{-1} = 23.6 + 9.6 \times 10^{-3} T$

$C_p^{\ominus}(Pb(l))/\text{J K}^{-1} \text{ mol}^{-1} = 32.2 - 2.75 \times 10^{-3} T$

where T is the thermodynamic temperature.

$T^{\ominus}_{\text{fusion}} = 601 \text{ K}$ $\qquad \Delta_s^l H^{\ominus} = 4.77 \text{ kJ mol}^{-1}$

Answer

(a) $H^{\ominus}_{1000\ K} - H^{\ominus}_{298\ K} = (H^{\ominus}_{601\ K} - H^{\ominus}_{298\ K})(s) + \Delta^l_s H^{\ominus} + (H^{\ominus}_{1000\ K} - H^{\ominus}_{601\ K})\ (l)$

$$= \int_{298\ K}^{601\ K} C^{\ominus}_p(s)\ dT + \Delta^l_s H^{\ominus} + \int_{601\ K}^{1000\ K} C^{\ominus}_p(l)\ dT$$

$$= \int_{298\ K}^{601\ K} (23.6 + 9.6 \times 10^{-3}\ T)\ dT + 4770 + \int_{601\ K}^{1000\ K} (32.2 - 2.75 \times 10^{-3}\ T)\ dT$$

$$= \left[23.6\ (601 - 298) + \frac{9.6 \times 10^{-3}}{2}\ (601^2 - 298^2) \right] + 4770$$

$$+ \left[32.2\ (1000 - 601) - \frac{2.75 \times 10^{-3}}{2}\ (1000^2 - 601^2) \right]\ J\ mol^{-1}$$

$$= [(7151 + 1308) + 4770 + (12\ 848 - 878)]\ J\ mol^{-1}$$

$$= 25\ 199\ J\ mol^{-1} = 25.2\ kJ\ mol^{-1}$$

(b) $S^{\ominus}_{1000\ K} - S^{\ominus}_{298\ K} = (S^{\ominus}_{601\ K} - S^{\ominus}_{298\ K})(s) + \Delta^l_s S^{\ominus} + (S^{\ominus}_{1000\ K} - S^{\ominus}_{601\ K})(l)$

$$= \int_{298\ K}^{601\ K} \frac{C^{\ominus}_p(s)}{T}\ dT + \frac{\Delta^l_s H^{\ominus}}{T^{\ominus}} + \int_{601\ K}^{1000\ K} \frac{C^{\ominus}_p(l)}{T}\ dT$$

$$= \int_{298\ K}^{601\ K} \left(\frac{23.6}{T} + 9.6 \times 10^{-3} \right)\ dT + \frac{4770}{601} + \int_{601\ K}^{1000\ K} \left(\frac{32.2}{T} - 2.75 \times 10^{-3} \right) dT$$

$$= \left[23.6 \ln\left(\frac{601}{298}\right) + 9.6 \times 10^{-3}(601 - 298) \right] + \frac{4770}{601}$$

$$+ \left[32.2 \ln\left(\frac{1000}{601}\right) - 2.75 \times 10^{-3}\ (1000 - 601) \right]$$

$$= 16.56 + 2.91 + 7.94 + 16.39 - 1.10$$

$$= 42.7\ J\ K^{-1}\ mol^{-1}$$

2.13.10 Isothermal Expansion

A monatomic gas (assumed ideal) at 298 K and a pressure of 2 atm is expanded to a final pressure of 1 atm:

(a) isothermally and reversibly,
(b) isothermally against a constant pressure of 1 atm,
(c) adiabatically and reversibly.

Calculate for each of these expansions

(i) ΔS, the increase in the entropy of the gas,
(ii) ΔA, the increase in the Helmholtz free energy of the gas,
(iii) ΔG, the increase in the Gibbs free energy of the gas.

Answer

This is a continuation of Worked Example 2.13.1. Again we write p_1 = 2 atm, p_2 = 1 atm, $T_1 = T_2$ = 298 K.

(a) *Reversible isothermal expansion*

(i) $\Delta S = R \ln (p_1/p_2) = 8.314 \ln 2 = 5.76 \text{ J K}^{-1} \text{ mol}^{-1}$
(ii) $\Delta A = \Delta U - T\Delta S = 0 - (298 \times 5.76) = -1720 \text{ J mol}^{-1}$
(iii) $\Delta G = \Delta H - T\Delta S = 0 - (298 \times 5.76) = -1720 \text{ J mol}^{-1}$
     i.e. $\Delta A = \Delta G = w_{\text{reversible}} = w_{\text{maximum}}$.

(b) *Rapid isothermal expansion*

Since S, A and G are state functions, ΔS, ΔA and ΔG depend only on initial and final states. T_1, T_2, p_1 and p_2 are the same for the reversible and the irreversible expansions; therefore, ΔS, ΔA and ΔG must also be the same, i.e.

$$\Delta S = 5.76 \text{ J K}^{-1} \text{ mol}^{-1} \qquad \Delta A = \Delta G = -1720 \text{ J mol}^{-1}$$

and $\Delta A = \Delta G < w_{\text{irreversible}}$.

(c) *Reversible adiabatic expansion*

(i)   For a reversible process, $\Delta S = \int dq/T$ (second law), but if the process is adiabatic, $q = 0$, therefore, $\Delta S = 0$.
(ii) $\Delta A = \Delta U = -900 \text{ J mol}^{-1}$
(iii) $\Delta G = \Delta H = -1500 \text{ J mol}^{-1}$ (see part (c) of answer to Worked Example 2.13.1).

2.13.11 Degree of Dissociation

For the thermal decomposition of cyclobutane at 500 K,

$$C_4H_8 (g) \rightleftharpoons 2C_2H_4 (g) \qquad \Delta G^{\ominus}_{500 \text{ K}} = -9.0 \text{ kJ mol}^{-1}$$

Estimate the mole fractions of C_4H_8 and C_2H_4 in an equilibrium mixture at 500 K and at a total pressure of 5 atm. State any assumptions made.

Answer

It is assumed that no other reaction takes place and that ideal gas behaviour applies. The dissociation of cyclobutane and the equilibrium pressures can then be represented as follows, where p is the total pressure and α the degree of dissociation:

$$C_4H_8 (g) \rightleftharpoons 2C_2H_4 (g)$$

$$\frac{(1-\alpha)p}{1+\alpha} \qquad \frac{2\alpha p}{1+\alpha}$$

$$K_p = \frac{(p_{C_2H_4})^2}{p_{C_4H_8}} = \frac{[2\alpha p/(1+\alpha)]^2}{(1-\alpha)p/(1+\alpha)}$$

$$= \frac{4\alpha^2\, p}{1-\alpha^2}$$

$$\ln(K_p/\text{atm}) = -\frac{\Delta G^{\ominus}}{RT} = \frac{-(-9000)}{8.314 \times 500} = 2.165$$

giving

$$K_p = 8.715 \text{ atm}$$

Therefore, for $p = 5$ atm,

$$K_p = 8.715 \text{ atm} = \frac{4\alpha^2 \times 5 \text{ atm}}{1 - \alpha^2}$$

giving

$$\alpha = 0.551$$

The mole fractions at equilibrium are therefore,

$$x(C_4H_8) = \frac{1 - \alpha}{1 + \alpha} = \frac{1 - 0.551}{1 + 0.551} = 0.29$$

$$x(C_2H_4) = \frac{2\alpha}{1 + \alpha} = \frac{2 \times 0.551}{1 + 0.551} = 0.71$$

2.13.12 Equilibrium Constant from Thermochemical Data

For the reaction

$$CO(g) + H_2O(g) \rightleftharpoons CO_2(g) + H_2(g)$$

use the following data to estimate the temperature at which the equilibrium constant will be equal to unity. Discuss, qualitatively, the validity of any approximations that are made.

Substance	$CO(g)$	$H_2O(g)$	$CO_2(g)$	$H_2(g)$
$\Delta_f H^{\ominus}_{298 \text{ K}}/\text{kJ mol}^{-1}$	-110.5	-242.5	-393.5	0
$S^{\ominus}_{298 \text{ K}}/\text{J K}^{-1}\text{mol}^{-1}$	197.5	188.7	213.7	130.6

If the initial gas mixture contains 30.9% CO, 18.1% H_2O, 13.0% CO_2, 8.0% H_2 and 30% N_2, calculate the composition of the equilibrium mixture when $K_p = 1$.

Answer

$$\ln K^{\ominus}_p = \frac{\Delta S^{\ominus}}{R} - \frac{\Delta H^{\ominus}}{RT}$$

Ideally, values of $\Delta H^{\ominus}$ and $\Delta S^{\ominus}$ at the temperature T in question are required. In practice, T is, as yet, unknown, and only data at 298 K are available in any case. As an approximation, both $\Delta H^{\ominus}$ and $\Delta S^{\ominus}$ may be considered temperature-independent. In both of these approximations, the error incurred depends on the magnitude of ΔC_p for the reaction and that of $(T - 298 \text{ K})$. Since reactants and products each consist of one diatomic and one triatomic gas molecule, ΔC_p is likely to be small and even though $(T - 298 \text{ K})$ turns out to be several hundred kelvins, the errors in these approximations should still be small. Moreover, since the enthalpy and entropy terms in the above equation have opposite signs, there will be some cancelling of errors.

$$\Delta H^{\ominus} = \sum \Delta_f H^{\ominus}(\text{products}) - \sum \Delta_f H^{\ominus}(\text{reactants})$$

$$= (-393.5 + 0) - (-110.5 - 242.5)$$

$$= -40.5 \text{ kJ mol}^{-1} = -40\,500 \text{ J mol}^{-1}$$

$$\Delta S^{\ominus} = \sum S^{\ominus}(\text{products}) - \sum S^{\ominus}(\text{reactants})$$

$$= (213.7 + 130.6) - (197.5 + 188.7)$$

$$= -41.9 \text{ J K}^{-1} \text{ mol}^{-1}$$

Therefore,

$$\ln K_p^{\ominus} = \ln 1 = 0 = \frac{-41.9}{8.314} - \frac{-40\,500}{8.314\,T}$$

i.e.

$$T = \Delta H / \Delta S$$

giving

$$T = 965 \text{ K}$$

Ideal gas behaviour is assumed. This is justified at such a high temperature provided that the pressure (unstated) is not too high. Since $\Delta n = 0$, the composition of the equilibrium mixture will be pressure-independent.

Let the equilibrium composition at 965 K be $(30.9 - x)\%$ CO, $(18.1 - x)\%$ H_2O, $(13.0 + x)\%$ CO_2, $(8.0 + x)\%$ H_2 and 30% N_2. Therefore,

$$K_p^{\ominus} = 1 = \frac{p_{CO_2} \times p_{H_2}}{p_{CO} \times p_{H_2O}} = \frac{(13.0 + x)\,(8.0 + x)}{(30.9 - x)\,(18.1 - x)}$$

giving $x = 6.5$ and an equilibrium composition of 24.4% CO, 11.6% H_2O, 19.5% CO_2, 14.5% H_2 and 30% N_2.

2.13.13 Van't Hoff Isobar

Equilibrium constants for the isomerisation reaction,

1-butene $\rightleftharpoons$ *trans*-2-butene

at selected temperatures are as follows:

T/K	883	826	779	733	702	686
$K^{\ominus}$	1.10	1.20	1.36	1.49	1.63	1.72

Estimate average values of $\Delta H^{\ominus}$ and $\Delta S^{\ominus}$ in this temperature range.

Answer

$$\ln K^{\ominus} = \frac{\Delta S^{\ominus}}{R} - \frac{\Delta H^{\ominus}}{RT}$$

If the temperature dependence of $\Delta S^{\ominus}$ and $\Delta H^{\ominus}$ is small, a plot of $\ln K^{\ominus}$ against $1/T$ should be a straight line of slope $- \Delta H^{\ominus}/R$ and intercept $\Delta S^{\ominus}/R$.

T/K	883	826	779	733	702	686
$10^3\,K/T$	1.133	1.211	1.284	1.364	1.425	1.458
$\ln K^{\ominus}$	0.095	0.182	0.307	0.399	0.489	0.542

From the graph (Fig. 2.6)

$$\Delta H^{\ominus} = -8.314 \times 1.38 \times 10^3 = -11.5 \times 10^3 \text{ J mol}^{-1}$$

$$= -11.5 \text{ kJ mol}^{-1}$$

$$\Delta S^{\ominus} = -1.48 \times 8.314 = -12.3 \text{ J K}^{-1} \text{ mol}^{-1}$$

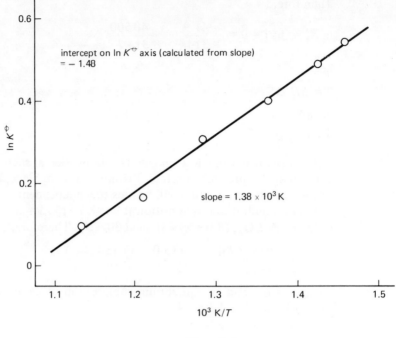

Figure 2.6

2.13.14 Dissociation Equilibrium and Bond Enthalpy

Hydrogen is 0.142% dissociated at 2200 K and 0.632% dissociated at 2500 K, the total pressure being 1 atm in each case. Calculate K_p for the dissociation at each of these temperatures and determine the mean enthalpy of dissociation over this temperature range. Approximate $1 - \alpha^2$ to unity.

The enthalpy of dissociation of hydrogen (i.e. the H—H bond enthalpy) at 298 K is equal to 436 kJ mol^{-1}. Compare the high-temperature value with this and discuss any difference.

Answer

$$H_2(g) \quad \rightleftharpoons \quad 2H(g)$$

$$\frac{(1 - \alpha)\,p}{1 + \alpha} \qquad \frac{2\,\alpha\,p}{1 + \alpha}$$

$$K_p = 4\alpha^2 p/(1 - \alpha^2) \approx 4\alpha^2 \qquad \text{(for small } \alpha \text{ and } p = 1 \text{ atm)}$$

Therefore

$$K_p(2200 \text{ K}) = 4 \times (0.001\,42)^2 = 8.0656 \times 10^{-6}$$

and

$$K_p(2500 \text{ K}) = 4 \times (0.006\,32)^2 = 1.5977 \times 10^{-4}$$

Since,

$$\ln K_p = \frac{\Delta S}{R} - \frac{\Delta H}{RT}$$

then

$$\ln K_p(2500 \text{ K}) - \ln K_p(2200 \text{ K}) = -\frac{\Delta H}{R}\left(\frac{1}{2500} - \frac{1}{2200}\right)$$

or

$$\ln\left(\frac{K_p(2500 \text{ K})}{K_p(2200 \text{ K})}\right) = \ln\left(\frac{1.5977 \times 10^{-4}}{8.0656 \times 10^{-6}}\right) = \frac{+\Delta H}{8.314}\left(\frac{2500 - 2200}{2500 \times 2200}\right)$$

which gives $\Delta H = 455\,000$ J mol^{-1} = 455 kJ mol^{-1}.

This is 19 kJ mol^{-1} higher than the 298 K value of 436 kJ mol^{-1}. Two factors will contribute to this difference.

(a) Dissociation involves enhancement of the occupancy of vibrational energy levels as far as the dissociation limit (see Sections 8.12.2, 8.12.3). It also involves the translational energy of $1.5RT$ for H_2 being replaced by a translational energy of $2 \times 1.5RT$ for 2H, i.e. an increase of $1.5RT$. This increase at 2350 K will exceed that at 298 K by $1.5 \times R \times (2350 - 298) = 25\,600$ J mol^{-1} = 25.6 kJ mol^{-1}.

(b) At 2350 K, some of the hydrogen molecules will already be in excited vibrational energy states and so require less input of energy to achieve dissociation. A rough estimate of this can be made as follows. The vibrational frequency of the hydrogen molecule is approximately 1.2×10^{14} s^{-1} and, therefore, the energy of the first excited vibrational state is $N_A h\nu = 6.0 \times 10^{23} \times 6.6 \times 10^{-34} \times 1.2 \times 10^{14} = 47.5 \times 10^3$ J mol^{-1} above that of the ground state. The ratio of populations in the first excited and ground vibrational states is given by the Boltzmann distribution as $\exp(-47.5 \times 10^3/8.314 \times 2350) = 0.088$. Allowing for even smaller fractions in second and higher vibrational energy states, the average vibrational energy of the hydrogen molecules at 2350 K will be between 4.5 and 5 kJ mol^{-1} above the ground-state energy.

Taking (a) and (b) into account, the dissociation energy of hydrogen in the 2200 to 2500 K range would be expected to be about $436 + 25.6 - 4.75 = 457$ kJ mol^{-1}, which conforms with the value calculated from degrees of dissociation.

2.13.15 Relative Stability of Oxidation States

For the reaction

$$2CuO(s) \rightleftharpoons Cu_2O(s) + \tfrac{1}{2}O_2(g)$$

$\Delta H^{\ominus}(298 \text{ K}) = 145.6$ kJ mol^{-1} and $\Delta S^{\ominus}(298 \text{ K}) = 116.3$ J K^{-1} mol^{-1}. Calculate the free-energy change $\Delta G^{\ominus}(298 \text{ K})$ and estimate $\Delta G^{\ominus}(1250 \text{ K})$. Comment, briefly, on the significance of the $\Delta G^{\ominus}$ values regarding the stability of copper oxides.

Answer

$$\Delta G^{\ominus}(298 \text{ K}) = \Delta H^{\ominus}(298 \text{ K}) - 298 \times \Delta S^{\ominus}(298 \text{ K})$$

$$= 145.6 - \frac{298 \times 116.3}{1000}$$

$$= +111.0 \text{ kJ mol}^{-1}$$

Assuming ΔH and ΔS to be temperature-independent,

$$\Delta G^{\ominus}(1250 \text{ K}) = \Delta H^{\ominus}(298 \text{ K}) - 1250 \times \Delta S^{\ominus}(298 \text{ K})$$

$$= 145.6 - \frac{1250 \times 116.3}{1000}$$

$$= + 0.2 \text{ kJ mol}^{-1}$$

At 298 K, the large positive $\Delta G^{\ominus}$ reflects the fact that copper(II) oxide is by far the more stable of the two oxides. At 1250 K, $\Delta G^{\ominus} \approx 0$ and the oxides have approximately equal stability. Above 1250 K, $\Delta G^{\ominus}$ will be negative and copper(I) oxide will be the more stable.

2.13.16 Dissociation Pressure

Estimate the temperature at which the equilibrium pressure due to the dissociation of solid ammonium chloride in a closed vessel is equal to one atmosphere.

Substance	$NH_4Cl(s)$	$NH_3(g)$	$HCl(g)$
$\Delta_f H^{\ominus}_{298 \text{ K}}/\text{kJ mol}^{-1}$	-314.5	-46.0	-92.3
$S^{\ominus}_{298 \text{ K}}/\text{J K}^{-1}\text{ mol}^{-1}$	95.0	192.3	186.8

Answer

$$NH_4Cl(s) \rightleftharpoons HCl(g) + NH_3(g)$$

$$\Delta H^{\ominus}_{298 \text{ K}} = -46.0 - 92.3 - (-314.5)$$
$$= +176.2 \text{ kJ mol}^{-1}$$

$$\Delta S^{\ominus}_{298 \text{ K}} = 192.3 + 186.8 - 95.0$$
$$= +284.1 \text{ J K}^{-1}\text{ mol}^{-1}$$

$$K^{\ominus} = \frac{a(\text{HCl}) \times a(\text{NH}_3)}{a(\text{NH}_4\text{Cl})}$$

The ammonium chloride is in its standard state of unit activity (pure solid); therefore, assuming ideal gas behaviour, the equilibrium constant can be expressed as

$$K_p = p(\text{HCl}) \times p(\text{NH}_3)$$

For a total pressure of 1 atm, $p(\text{HCl}) = p(\text{NH}_3) = 0.5$ atm and $K_p = 0.25$ atm^2.

$$\ln K^{\ominus} = \frac{\Delta S^{\ominus}}{R} - \frac{\Delta H^{\ominus}}{RT}$$

Therefore, assuming $\Delta H^{\ominus}$ and $\Delta S^{\ominus}$ to be temperature-independent,

$$\ln 0.25 = \frac{284.1}{8.314} - \frac{176\,200}{8.314T}$$

giving

$$T = 596 \text{ K}$$

2.13.17 Optimisation of Reaction Conditions

Investigate the feasibility of synthesising ethanol by the gas-phase reaction

$$C_2H_4(g) + H_2O(g) \rightleftharpoons C_2H_5OH(g)$$

Using a suitable catalyst, this reaction is fast enough for practical purposes only at temperatures in excess of about $250°C$.

Substance	$C_2H_4(g)$	$H_2O(g)$	$C_2H_5OH(g)$
$\Delta_f H^{\ominus}_{298\,K}$ /kJ mol^{-1}	52.3	-242.5	-234.8
$S^{\ominus}_{298\,K}$ /J K^{-1} mol^{-1}	219.5	188.7	282.6

Answer

$$\Delta H^{\ominus}_{298\,K} = -234.8 - (52.3 - 242.5) = -44.6 \text{ kJ mol}^{-1}$$

$$\Delta S^{\ominus}_{298\,K} = 282.6 - (219.5 + 188.7) = -125.6 \text{ J K}^{-1} \text{ mol}^{-1}$$

The reaction is exothermic and, therefore, favoured thermodynamically by low temperature. To start, consider the thermodynamics of the process at the lowest temperature practicable from the kinetic point of view, i.e. 523 K. Assuming ΔH and ΔS to be temperature-independent,

$$\ln K^{\ominus}_p = \frac{\Delta S^{\ominus}}{R} - \frac{\Delta H^{\ominus}}{RT} = \frac{-125.6}{8.314} - \frac{-44\,600}{8.314 \times 523} = -4.85$$

and

$$K^{\ominus}_p = 7.8 \times 10^{-3} \text{ atm}^{-1}$$

This value for K_p may appear discouragingly small. However, there are two potentially helpful features of this reaction.

(a) Separation of product from reaction mixture (fractional distillation) is relatively easy. It is, therefore, unnecessary to aim at a very high yield.

(b) $\Delta n = -1$, so the reaction will be favoured by high pressure.

Let a and b be the initial amounts of C_2H_4 and H_2O, respectively (where $b > a$, reflecting the cost of these reactants). For an extent of reaction ξ, equilibrium partial pressures will, therefore, be as follows:

$$C_2H_4(g) \quad + \quad H_2O(g) \quad \rightleftharpoons C_2H_5OH(g)$$

$$\frac{(a-\xi)p}{(a+b-\xi)} \qquad \frac{(b-\xi)p}{(a+b-\xi)} \qquad \frac{\xi p}{(a+b-\xi)}$$

Therefore

$$K_p = \frac{p_{C_2H_5OH}}{p_{C_2H_4}\,p_{H_2O}} = \frac{(a+b-\xi)}{(a-\xi)(b-\xi)p}$$

Suppose $b = 5$ mol, $a = 1$ mol and $\xi = 0.2$ mol (i.e. 20% yield with respect to ethene), then

$$7.8 \times 10^{-3} \text{ atm}^{-1} = \frac{0.2\,(5+1-0.2)}{(1-0.2)(5-0.2)\,p}$$

giving

$$p = 39 \text{ atm}$$

Industrial practice broadly reflects this answer.

2.13.18 Graphical Determination of Fugacity

The compressibility factor pV_m/RT for nitrogen at $0°C$ and various pressures is as follows:

p/atm	50	100	200	300	400	500
pV_m/RT	0.985	0.985	1.036	1.134	1.256	1.389

Use a graphical procedure to evaluate the fugacities of nitrogen at pressures of 100, 300 and 500 atm at $0°C$.

Answer

The fugacity f of a gas is defined by the isothermal expressions

$$dG_m = RT \, d \ln f \qquad \text{and} \qquad \lim_{p \to 0} (f/p) = 1$$

Since, for any gas at constant temperature, $dG = V \, dp$, then

$$d \ln f = V_m \, dp/RT$$

Let α represent the difference between the ideal molar volume RT/p and the actual molar volume V_m of the gas, i.e.

$$\alpha = RT/p - V_m$$

Therefore, substituting for V_m,

$$d \ln f - d \ln p = -\alpha \, dp/RT$$

which integrates to

$$\ln (f/p) = - \int_0^p (\alpha/RT) \, dp$$

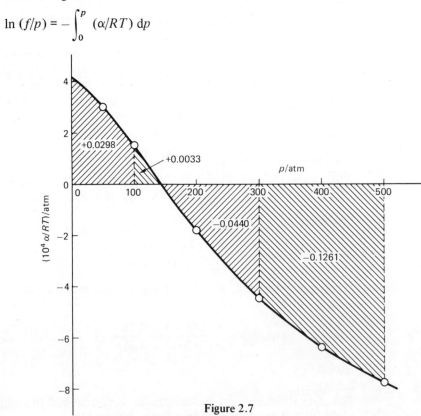

Figure 2.7

This integral can be evaluated graphically from a plot of α/RT against p (Fig. 2.7). The expression for α rearranges to the more convenient form

$$\frac{\alpha}{RT} = \frac{1}{p}\left(1 - \frac{pV_m}{RT}\right)$$

p/atm	$\displaystyle\int_0^p (\alpha/RT)\,\mathrm{d}p$	$\ln (f/p)$	f/p	f/atm
100	+ 0.0298	− 0.0298	0.971	97
300	− 0.0109	+ 0.0109	1.011	303
500	− 0.1370	+ 0.1370	1.147	573

[Note: f/p is the activity coefficient of the gas.]

2.13.19 Calculation of Fugacity from an Equation of State

At high temperatures and pressures, a possible equation of state for gases is

$$pV_m = RT + bp$$

where b is a constant. Calculate the fugacity of carbon monoxide at 1000 K and 1000 atm according to this equation if $b = 40\ \text{cm}^3\ \text{mol}^{-1}$.

Answer

$\mathrm{d}\ln f = V_m\ \mathrm{d}p/RT$ \qquad (see previous example)

Therefore, substituting $(RT/p) + b$ for V_m,

$$\mathrm{d}\ln f = \frac{\mathrm{d}p}{p} + \frac{b}{RT}\ \mathrm{d}p = \mathrm{d}\ln p + \frac{b}{RT}\ \mathrm{d}p$$

Integrating between zero pressure (where $f/p \to 1$) and a given pressure p,

$\ln f = \ln p + bp/RT$

For 1000 K and 1000 atm,

$$\ln\left(\frac{f}{1000\ \text{atm}}\right) = \frac{(40 \times 10^{-6}\ \text{m}^3\ \text{mol}^{-1}) \times (1000 \times 1.013 \times 10^5\ \text{N m}^{-2})}{8.314\ \text{J K}^{-1}\ \text{mol}^{-1} \times 1000\ \text{K}}$$

which gives

$f = 1630\ \text{atm}$

2.14 Unworked Examples

2.14.1
CaC_2 (15 g) is reacted with excess water at 298 K and atmospheric pressure. Calculate w, the work done on the system, by the evolved ethyne.

2.14.2
Calculate the minimum and maximum work required to compress 1 mol of ideal gas from 1 atm to 2 atm isothermally at 298 K.

2.14.3

To what pressure must nitrogen at 300 K and 1 atm be adiabatically and reversibly compressed in order to raise its temperature to 400 K? The mean value of C_p for nitrogen over this temperature range is 29.4 J K^{-1} mol^{-1}.

2.14.4

Nitrogen gas, originally at 298 K and 1 atm, is compressed adiabatically to 10 atm. Taking C_V to be 21 J K^{-1} mol^{-1} and temperature-independent, calculate the maximum temperature that is attainable as a result of this compression.

2.14.5

(a) Are the terms 'adiabatic' and 'isoentropic' synonymous?

(b) Calculate ΔH and ΔG when one mole of nitrogen (C_p = 29.1 J K^{-1} mol^{-1}, γ = 1.4), initially at 298 K and 1 atm, is compressed adiabatically and reversibly to 10 atm.

2.14.6

(a) The enthalpy of combustion of glucose is -2800 kJ mol^{-1} at 298 K. Approximately how many grams of glucose would a mountaineer of body mass 75 kg need to consume for a climb of 1000 m, assuming 25% conversion to vertical ascent?

(b) During this ascent, the woollen clothing of this ill-clad mountaineer absorbed 1 kg of rainwater, and its subsequent evaporation was 50% at the expense of body heat. $\Delta_l^g H$ (H$_2$O) = 43 kJ mol^{-1}. Estimate (i) the resulting fall in body temperature (assumed uniform, and taking C_p = 5 J K^{-1} g^{-1}), and (ii) how much additional glucose (at 50% efficiency) would have to be consumed to compensate for this loss of body heat.

2.14.7

The increase in temperature (at around 25°C) arising from the combustion of 1.47 g of tungsten carbide

$$WC(s) + 2\tfrac{1}{2}O_2(g) \rightarrow WO_3(s) + CO_2(g)$$

in a bomb calorimeter can be duplicated by an input of 8.94 kJ of electrical energy. Calculate ΔU and ΔH for this reaction.

2.14.8

Given the following thermochemical data at 298 K,

$$C_2H_2(g) + 2\tfrac{1}{2}O_2(g) \rightarrow 2CO_2(g) + H_2O(l) \qquad \Delta H = -1299 \text{ kJ mol}^{-1}$$

$$\Delta_f H(CO_2(g)) = -393.5 \text{ kJ mol}^{-1} \qquad \Delta_f H(H_2O(l)) = -286 \text{ kJ mol}^{-1}$$

calculate ΔH for the spontaneous detonation of ethyne to give carbon and hydrogen.

C_p for C(s) and H$_2$(g) at 298 K are 8.5 and 28.8 J K^{-1} mol^{-1}, respectively. Estimate the maximum temperature that ethyne originally at 298 K would reach on detonation. Discuss the assumptions upon which this estimate is based.

2.14.9

Methanol (5.27 g) was combusted in excess oxygen in a bomb calorimeter at 25°C. 119.5 kJ of heat was evolved. Calculate ΔU and ΔH.

2.14.10

From the following thermochemical information, calculate the standard enthalpy of formation of $N_2O(g)$ at 298 K.

$$C(s) + 2N_2O(g) \rightarrow CO_2(g) + 2N_2(g) \qquad \Delta H^{\ominus}_{298\,K} = 557.5 \text{ kJ mol}^{-1}$$

$$C(s) + O_2(g) \rightarrow CO_2(g) \qquad \Delta H^{\ominus}_{298\,K} = -393.5 \text{ kJ mol}^{-1}$$

2.14.11

From the following enthalpies of combustion, calculate the enthalpy of formation of liquid benzene at 298 K.

$$C_6H_6(l) + 7\tfrac{1}{2}O_2(g) \rightarrow 6CO_2(g) + 3H_2O(l) \qquad \Delta H^{\ominus}_{298\,K} = -3267.4 \text{ kJ mol}^{-1}$$

$$C(s) + O_2(g) \rightarrow CO_2(g) \qquad \Delta H^{\ominus}_{298\,K} = -393.5 \text{ kJ mol}^{-1}$$

$$H_2(g) + \tfrac{1}{2}O_2(g) \rightarrow H_2O(l) \qquad \Delta H^{\ominus}_{298\,K} = -285.8 \text{ kJ mol}^{-1}$$

2.14.12

Calculate the enthalpy of formation of aqueous hydrogen peroxide, given that

	$-\Delta H/\text{kJ mol}^{-1}$
$SnCl_2(aq) + 2HCl(aq) + H_2O_2(aq) \rightarrow SnCl_4(aq) + 2H_2O$	371.6
$SnCl_2(aq) + HCl(aq) + HOCl(aq) \rightarrow SnCl_4(aq) + H_2O$	314.0
$2HI(aq) + HOCl(aq) \rightarrow I_2(s) + HCl(aq) + H_2O$	215.2
$\tfrac{1}{2}H_2(g) + \tfrac{1}{2}I_2(g) + aq \rightarrow HI(aq)$	55.1
$H_2(g) + \tfrac{1}{2}O_2(g) \rightarrow H_2O(l)$	286.1

(University of Durham, BSc, 1st year)

2.14.13

The enthalpy change accompanying the reaction

$$C_2F_4(g) + Cl_2(g) \rightarrow C_2F_4Cl_2(g)$$

was studied at 363 K in a constant-flow calorimeter. Tetrafluoroethene, flowing at a rate of 1.155 mol s^{-1}, and chlorine, flowing at a rate of $1.018 \times 10^{-5} \text{ mol s}^{-1}$, were mixed and passed over catalyst in the calorimeter at 1 atm. Reaction occurred quantitatively in accordance with the above equation and went to complete exhaustion of one reactant. The rate of energy release was 2.442 J s^{-1}. Calculate the molar quantities ΔH and ΔU for the reaction at this temperature.

(GRSC, Part I)

2.14.14

The enthalpies of formation of $NaOH(s)$, $Na^+(aq)$ and $OH^-(aq)$ at 298 K are -428, -240 and -230 kJ mol^{-1}, respectively. Calculate the enthalpy of solution of NaOH to infinite dilution in water at this temperature.

2.14.15

The standard enthalpies of formation at 298 K of $CH_4(g)$, $HCl(g)$ and $CH_3Cl(g)$ are -74.8, -92.3 and $-86.3 \text{ kJ mol}^{-1}$, respectively. Calculate $\Delta H^{\ominus}$ (523 K) for the reaction

$$CH_3Cl(g) + H_2(g) \rightarrow CH_4(g) + HCl(g)$$

given that the mean values of heat capacity in the temperature range 298 to 523 K for $CH_4(g)$, $HCl(g)$, $CH_3Cl(g)$ and $H_2(g)$ are 42.8, 29.2, 49.0 and $29.0 \text{ J K}^{-1} \text{ mol}^{-1}$, respectively.

2.14.16

The standard enthalpies of formation of $CO(g)$ and $CO_2(g)$ at 300 K are -110.5 and -393.5 kJ mol^{-1}, respectively, and the mean C_p values in the temperature range 300 to 1300 K for $CO(g)$, $CO_2(g)$ and $O_2(g)$ are 31.4, 46.4 and 32.4 J K^{-1} mol^{-1}, respectively. Calculate $\Delta H^{\ominus}(1300$ K) for the combustion of carbon monoxide.

2.14.17

Given the following data:

$$CO(g) + H_2O(g) \rightarrow CO_2(g) + H_2(g) \qquad \Delta H^{\ominus}_{298\,K} = -40.5 \text{ kJ mol}^{-1}$$

$C_p(CO(g))/\text{J K}^{-1}\text{ mol}^{-1} = 27.5 + 5 \times 10^{-3} T$

$C_p(H_2O(g))/\text{J K}^{-1}\text{ mol}^{-1} = 30.5 + 10 \times 10^{-3} T$

$C_p(CO_2(g))/\text{J K}^{-1}\text{ mol}^{-1} = 31.0 + 21 \times 10^{-3} T$

$C_p(H_2(g))/\text{J K}^{-1}\text{ mol}^{-1} = 28.1 + 2.5 \times 10^{-3} T$

where T is the thermodynamic temperature, calculate $\Delta H^{\ominus}$ for the above reaction at 1000 K.

2.14.18

Calculate the C—Cl bond enthalpy in chloromethane, given that the enthalpies of formation of $CH_3Cl(g)$, $CH_4(g)$, $C(g)$, $H(g)$ and $Cl(g)$ are -86, -75, $+713$, $+218$ and $+121$ kJ mol^{-1}, respectively.

2.14.19

Calculate the individual bond enthalpies for CH_3—H, CH_2—H, CH—H and C—H in the methane molecule. The enthalpies of formation of $CH_4(g)$, $CH_3(g)$, $CH_2(g)$, CH(g), C(g) and H(g) are -75, 134, 397, 596, 713 and 218 kJ mol^{-1}, respectively.

2.14.20

The bond dissociation energy of the first hydrogen–sulphur bond in hydrogen sulphide, $D(\text{H—SH})$, is 376.6 kJ mol^{-1}. Calculate the enthalpy of formation and the bond dissociation enthalpy of the free radical, HS$^{\bullet}$, given that

$H_2S(g) \qquad \Delta_f H^{\ominus} = -20.1 \text{ kJ mol}^{-1}$

$S(g) \qquad \Delta_f H^{\ominus} = +277.0 \text{ kJ mol}^{-1}$

$D(\text{H—H}) = +436.0 \text{ kJ mol}^{-1}$

(University of Nottingham, BSc, Part I)

2.14.21

From the following thermochemical data, calculate the resonance energy of methylbenzene:

	$\Delta H^{\ominus}_{298\,K}$ /kJ mol^{-1}
$C_7H_8(l) + 9O_2(g) \rightarrow 7CO_2(g) + 4H_2O(l)$	-3910
$C_7H_8(l) \rightarrow C_7H_8(g)$	$+38.1$
$H_2(g) \rightarrow 2H(g)$	$+436.0$
$C(s) \rightarrow C(g)$	$+715.0$
$H_2(g) + \frac{1}{2}O_2(g) \rightarrow H_2O(l)$	-285.8
$C(s) + O_2(g) \rightarrow CO_2(g)$	-393.5

Bond enthalpies/kJ mol^{-1}:

E (C—H) = 413.0 E (C—C) = 345.6 E (C=C) = 610.0

(University of Nottingham, BSc, 1st year)

2.14.22

Calculate the lattice energy of caesium fluoride given the following ΔH/kJ mol^{-1} values:

Formation of CsF(s)	− 550.2
Sublimation of Cs	78.2
Removal of one electron from Cs(g)	375.4
Dissociation of F_2(g)	157.8
Addition of one electron to F (g)	− 332.6

(GRSC, Part I)

2.14.23

Calculate the electron affinity of bromine atoms from the following data:

Lattice energy of NaBr = + 736 kJ mol^{-1}
$\Delta_f H$(NaBr(s)) = − 361 kJ mol^{-1}
$\Delta_s^g H$(Na) = + 109 kJ mol^{-1}
$\Delta_f H$(Br(g)) = + 112 kJ mol^{-1}
$\Delta_i H$(Na) = + 490 kJ mol^{-1}

2.14.24

The heat capacity at constant (atmospheric) pressure of carbon dioxide is given by the expression

$$C_p/\text{J K}^{-1}\text{ mol}^{-1} = 26.8 + 42 \times 10^{-3}T - 15 \times 10^{-6}T^2$$

where T is the thermodynamic temperature.
(a) Calculate C_p at 300 K, 600 K and 1000 K and compare with the experimental values of 37.4, 47.2 and 52.3 J K^{-1} mol^{-1}, respectively.
(b) Calculate (i) the increase in enthalpy ΔH and (ii) the increase in entropy ΔS when one mole of carbon dioxide is heated from 300 K to 1000 K at constant pressure.

2.14.25

Calculate the increase in entropy ΔS when one mole of argon is (a) heated from 300 K to 500 K at constant pressure, and (b) compressed from 1 atm to 10 atm at constant temperature.

2.14.26

The heat capacity of liquid methylbenzene at ordinary temperatures is 156 J K^{-1} mol^{-1}. Calculate the increase in entropy when one mole of methylbenzene is heated from 20°C to 60°C.

(Liverpool Polytechnic, HNC)

2.14.27

Calculate the net entropy change when 20 g ice at 0°C is added to 100 g water at 40°C in an isolated system. The enthalpy of fusion of ice is 334.4 J g^{-1} and the heat capacity of water is 4.18 J K^{-1} g^{-1}.

2.14.28

Determine an approximate value for the entropy of liquid sodium at 500 K from the following data:

T/K	20	40	60	100	170	300	400	500
$C_p^{\ominus}/J\ K^{-1}\ mol^{-1}$	3.6	12.6	18.2	22.5	25.2	28.1	31.6	30.5

$T_{\text{fusion}}^{\ominus} = 370\ K \qquad \Delta_s^l H^{\ominus} = 2.55\ kJ\ mol^{-1}$

2.14.29

From the following data, evaluate the standard molar entropy of hydrogen chloride gas at 298 K.

$S^{\ominus}$ for solid HCl at its normal melting point of 159 K is 64.1 J K^{-1} mol^{-1} and the enthalpy of fusion at this temperature is 1.99 kJ mol^{-1}. From this melting point to the normal boiling point of 188 K the increase in entropy is 9.87 J K^{-1} mol^{-1}. The enthalpy of vaporisation at this temperature is 16.15 kJ mol^{-1}. The mean heat capacity C_p between this boiling point and 298 K and at one atmosphere pressure is 29.2 J K^{-1} mol^{-1}.

2.14.30

The latent heat of vaporisation of water at 373 K and 1 atm is 40.6 kJ mol^{-1}. For the vaporisation of one mole of water under these conditions, calculate w, ΔU, ΔH, ΔS, ΔA and ΔG.

2.14.31

When 0.75 mol of ethanoic acid is mixed with 0.75 mol of ethanol at 298 K, 0.59 mol of ethyl ethanoate is formed at equilibrium. When 0.9 mol of ethanoic acid is mixed with 0.6 mol of ethanol at 298 K, 0.54 mol of ethyl ethanoate is formed at equilibrium. Calculate K_c in each case and show that the law of mass action is obeyed. Calculate the standard Gibbs free-energy change for this esterification reaction.

2.14.32

At 298 K and 1 atm, dinitrogen tetroxide is 20% dissociated into nitrogen dioxide. Calculate the equilibrium constant and the standard free-energy change at this temperature for this reaction.

2.14.33

Calculate the equilibrium constant at 298 K and the composition of the equilibrium mixture for the isomerisation

$CH_3(CH_2)_2CH_3(g) \rightleftharpoons CH_3CH(CH_3)_2(g)$

$\Delta_f G_{298\ K}^{\ominus}(CH_3(CH_2)_2CH_3(g)) = -17.2\ kJ\ mol^{-1}$

$\Delta_f G_{298\ K}^{\ominus}(CH_3CH(CH_3)_2(g)) = -20.8\ kJ\ mol^{-1}$

(Liverpool Polytechnic, BSc, 1st year)

2.14.34

Iodine(ɪ) chloride is formed by the reaction

$\frac{1}{2}I_2(g) + \frac{1}{2}Cl_2(g) \rightleftharpoons ICl(g)$

In an equilibrium mixture at 498 K the total pressure is 1 atm and $p(I_2) = p(Cl_2)$. $\Delta G_{498\ K}^{\ominus} = -8.15\ kJ\ mol^{-1}$. Calculate the partial pressure of ICl.

(Liverpool Polytechnic, HNC)

2.14.35

Over a wide temperature range, the standard free energy of formation of water vapour at thermodynamic temperature T is given by the equation

$$\Delta_f G^\ominus = (-240\,000 + 6.95T + 12.9T \log_{10} T)\ \text{J mol}^{-1}$$

Use this datum to calculate the standard enthalpy and standard entropy of formation of water vapour at 1000 K.

2.14.36

For the reaction

$$N_2(g) + 3H_2(g) \rightleftharpoons 2NH_3(g)$$

at 300 K, $\Delta G^\ominus = -32$ kJ mol^{-1} and $\Delta H^\ominus = -92$ kJ mol^{-1}. Estimate $\Delta G^\ominus$ and $K_p^\ominus$ at 800 K.

2.14.37

The equilibrium constant for the reaction

$$I_2(g) \rightleftharpoons 2I(g)$$

is 1.14×10^{-2} atm at 1100 K and 4.74×10^{-2} atm at 1200 K. Calculate the mean enthalpy of dissociation over this temperature range.

(Liverpool Polytechnic, HNC)

2.14.38

For the reaction

$$PbS(s) + 1\tfrac{1}{2}O_2(g) \rightleftharpoons PbO(s) + SO_2(g)$$

$\Delta H^\ominus_{298\ K} = -415.7$ kJ mol^{-1} and $\Delta G^\ominus_{298\ K} = -390.1$ kJ mol^{-1}. Estimate the equilibrium constant at 800 K.

2.14.39

Mercury(II) oxide dissociates according to the reaction

$$2HgO(s) \rightleftharpoons 2Hg(g) + O_2(g)$$

At 693 K, the dissociation pressure is 0.51 atm and at 723 K it is 1.07 atm. Calculate (a) the equilibrium constant at each temperature and (b) the molar enthalpy of dissociation of mercury(II) oxide.

(University of Liverpool, BSc, Part I)

2.14.40

The dissociation pressure of calcium carbonate is 0.310 kPa at 600°C and 23.0 kPa at 800°C. Determine the mean enthalpy of dissociation of calcium carbonate in this temperature range.

2.14.41

The equilibrium constant K_p for the reaction

$$2NO(g) + O_2(g) \rightleftharpoons 2NO_2(g)$$

varies with temperature, as follows:

T/K	600	700	800	900	1000
K_p/atm^{-1}	140	5.14	0.437	0.0625	0.0131

Calculate the mean value of $\Delta H^\ominus$ for the reaction in this temperature range.

2.14.42
For the reaction

$$C_2H_5Cl(g) \rightleftharpoons C_2H_4(g) + HCl(g)$$

$\Delta H^{\ominus}_{298\,K} = 71.7$ kJ mol^{-1} and $\Delta S^{\ominus}_{298\,K} = 130.5$ J K^{-1} mol^{-1}. Estimate the temperature required to achieve 90% equilibrium conversion of reactant to products at a total pressure of 1 atm.

2.14.43
Investigate the feasibility of synthesising methanol by the gas-phase reaction

$$CO(g) + 2H_2(g) \rightleftharpoons CH_3OH(g)$$

for which $\Delta H^{\ominus}_{298\,K} = -90.7$ kJ mol^{-1} and $\Delta S^{\ominus}_{298\,K} = -219.0$ J K^{-1} mol^{-1}.

Assume that, in the presence of a suitable catalyst, a temperature of at least 550 K is needed to make the reaction go fast enough for practical purposes.

2.14.44
The following reaction has been suggested as a source of gaseous fuel from coal:

$$C(s) + H_2O(g) \rightleftharpoons CO(g) + H_2(g)$$

$$\Delta H^{\ominus}_{298\,K} = 132 \text{ kJ mol}^{-1} \qquad \Delta S^{\ominus}_{298\,K} = 134 \text{ J K}^{-1} \text{ mol}^{-1}$$

Is this a feasible proposition?

2.14.45
Compressibility factors for chloromethane vapour at 150°C are as follows:

p/atm	1	10	20	30	45	60
pV_m/RT	0.9950	0.9481	0.8914	0.8284	0.7208	0.5821

Determine the fugacity at 10 atm and 50 atm.

2.14.46
Compressibility factors for 2-propanol vapour at 200°C are as follows:

p/atm	0	2	6	10	14	18	22
pV_m/RT	1	0.9794	0.9368	0.8897	0.8373	0.7768	0.7051

Determine the fugacity at 10 atm and 20 atm.

2.14.47
Calculate the fugacity of hydrogen at 0°C and (a) 100 atm, (b) 1000 atm, according to the virial equation

$$pV_m/RT = 1.000 + 0.66 \times 10^{-3}(p/\text{atm}) + 0.06 \times 10^{-6}(p/\text{atm})^2$$

3 Phase Equilibria, Solutions and Mixtures

3.1 Introduction

Chapter 2 was concerned with the basic framework of thermodynamics and, in particular, with its application to energy changes and equilibrium in chemical reactions. In this chapter, thermodynamic principles are applied to the equilibria that can exist within a single material or between the components of a solution or mixture.

Solutions and mixtures are taken to be systems of two or more components that are homogeneous throughout on a molecular scale. A convenient distinction can be made between solutions (e.g. sucrose in water), where it is appropriate to distinguish between solute(s) and solvent, and mixtures (e.g. benzene and methylbenzene), where such a distinction is inappropriate.

The composition of a solution is often expressed in terms of its concentration (the amount of solute divided by the volume of solution). Sometimes, e.g. with solutions of electrolytes and when dealing with colligative properties, it is convenient to express composition in terms of molality (the amount of solute divided by the mass of solvent). For mixtures, it is usually most convenient to express composition in terms of mole fractions.

For a solution, it is usual to identify the solvent by subscript A and the solute(s) by subscripts B, C, etc., and in mixtures to identify the components by subscripts B, C, etc. For a two-component mixture of B and C the mole fractions are given by

$$x_B = \frac{n_B}{n_B + n_C} \qquad x_C = \frac{n_C}{n_B + n_C} \tag{3.1}$$

giving

$$x_B + x_C = 1 \tag{3.2}$$

3.2 Phase Equilibria

A system may comprise one or more phase(s). Different phases are characterised by the definite boundaries that exist between them. A system will not have more than one vapour phase, since all gases/vapours are miscible on a molecular scale; however, there may be one or more liquid phase(s) depending on miscibility and one or more solid phase(s) depending on the existence or otherwise of macroscopic boundaries within the solid part of the system.

3.2.1 The Phase Rule

If equilibrium in a system is influenced only by temperature, pressure and composition, then,

$$P + F = C + 2 \qquad (3.3)$$

where P is the number of phases, as described above; C is the number of components, which is the smallest number of independent chemical constituents needed to fix the composition of every phase in the system; and F is the number of degrees of freedom, which is the number of intensive variables (temperature, pressure, composition) that can independently be varied without changing the number of phases.

Example 3.1

The most difficult quantity to comprehend of those involved in the phase rule is C, the number of components. We shall deduce the value of C for the following systems: (a) $CaCO_3(s) \rightleftharpoons CaO(s) + CO_2(g)$ and (b) an aqueous solution of ethanoic acid.

(a) Three distinct chemical species ($CaCO_3$, CaO and CO_2) can be recognised, but since they are in equilibrium, it is only necessary to know the amounts of two of them in order to determine the amount of the third, i.e. $C = 2$. For the special case of starting with pure $CaCO_3$, then $n(CaO) = n(CO_2)$ and this additional relationship reduces the number of components further to $C = 1$.

(b) Four species, H_2O, CH_3COOH, H^+ and CH_3COO^-, can be recognised, but (i) there is material balance between CH_3COOH and $H^+ + CH_3COO^-$, and (ii) there is equality between H^+ and CH_3COO^- to give electroneutrality, and therefore $C = 4 - 2 = 2$. ■

For a one-component system the maximum number of degrees of freedom (in the simple context of this discussion) is 2, i.e. temperature and pressure. For a two-component system, there is also freedom to fix the composition of one of the components, but, having done this, the composition of the other component follows automatically; the maximum number of degrees of freedom is, therefore, equal to 3.

3.2.2 Phase Diagrams

These express the phase equilibrium situation in terms of the intensive properties that make up the degrees of freedom. Thus, for a one-component system, the axes of the phase diagram will simply represent temperature and pressure. For a two-component system, the maximum number of degrees of freedom is 3. The choice lies between a three-dimensional phase diagram, or one or more two-dimensional plots for constant value(s) of one of the intensive variables involved. Compositions of three-component systems are best represented on triangular graph paper.

3.2.3 One-Component Systems

Figures 3.1, 3.2 and 3.3 show phase diagrams for water, carbon dioxide and sulphur. None of these is drawn to scale.

Consider, first, the phase diagram for water (Fig. 3.1). The three areas illustrated each represent a single phase (solid, liquid or vapour). In each case, for any

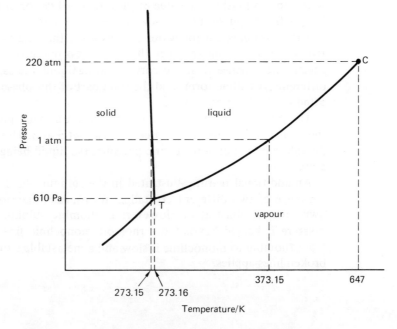

Figure 3.1 Phase diagram of water (schematic).

selected temperature there is a range of possible pressures, i.e. $F = 2$. The phase rule, $P + F = C + 2$, therefore, holds with $P = 1$, $F = 2$ and $C = 1$.

Along any of the three lines of the phase diagram there are two phases in equilibrium. Now, if the temperature is selected, there is no further freedom to select the pressure (or vice versa), i.e. $F = 1$. Now the phase rule holds with $P = 2$, $F = 1$ and $C = 1$.

Finally, the intersection of the three lines (the triple point, T) represents the only situation where solid, liquid and vapour phases are in equilibrium. There

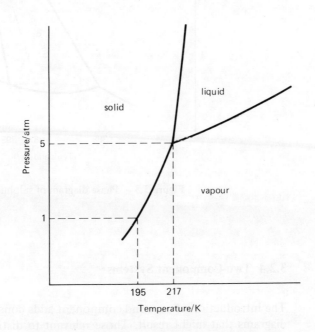

Figure 3.2 Phase diagram of carbon dioxide (schematic).

is no choice of either the value of pressure (610 Pa) or of temperature (273.16 K), i.e. $F = 0$. The phase rule holds with $P = 3$, $F = 0$ and $C = 1$.

The phase diagram for water is unusual in that the solid/liquid line has a negative slope, reflecting the fact that ice is less dense than liquid water. Solids are usually more dense than the corresponding liquid. Ice can, in fact, exist in several different crystalline forms and the solid part of this phase diagram is quite complicated — which is not shown in Fig. 3.1.

The most significant feature of the carbon dioxide phase diagram (Fig. 3.2) is the fact that the triple point pressure is about 5 atm. This means that solid carbon dioxide sublimes at atmospheric pressure, the liquid being stable only above about 5 atm.

An additional feature illustrated in the sulphur phase diagram (Fig. 3.3) is the existence of two different crystalline forms, each thermodynamically stable in its own area, as illustrated. However, if rhombic sulphur at normal atmospheric pressure is heated beyond the rhombic/monoclinic line, the rate of conversion from rhombic to monoclinic is slow and a metastable situation represented by the broken lines applies.

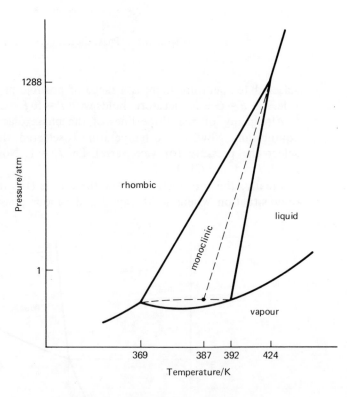

Figure 3.3   Phase diagram of sulphur (schematic).

3.2.4 Two-Component Systems

The introduction of a second component adds considerably to the variety of phase diagrams that might result. Those relevant to distillation are discussed in Section 3.7.

70

3.2.5 Solid–Liquid Equilibrium

Figure 3.4 shows a simple eutectic phase diagram for the benzene–naphthalene system. The form of such a phase diagram can be established by investigating what happens when mixtures of various compositions are cooled or heated (thermal analysis). This is illustrated in Fig. 3.5 for the benzene–naphthalene system.

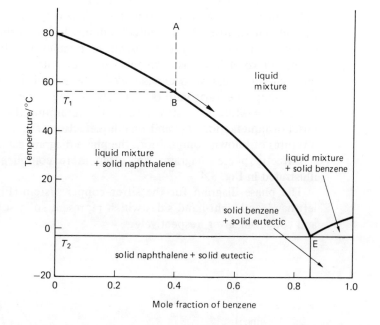

Figure 3.4   Simple eutectic phase diagram of the benzene–naphthalene system.

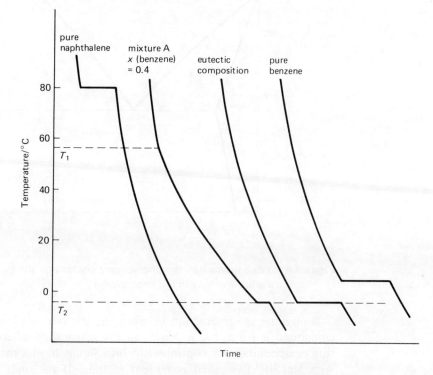

Figure 3.5   Cooling curves for the benzene–naphthalene system.

For pure liquid benzene or pure liquid naphthalene, a steady cooling rate will be observed until the melting point is reached (Fig. 3.5), at which point the temperature will remain constant whilst the latent heat is dissipated, after which the temperature of the solid will fall steadily towards that of its surroundings. The mixture of eutectic composition will behave similarly.

For a liquid mixture of composition A, the temperature will fall steadily until point B on the liquidus curve is reached (Fig. 3.4). At this point, pure solid naphthalene begins to form, the remaining liquid becomes correspondingly enriched in benzene and the temperature falls very slowly following the path of the liquidus curve towards the eutectic point, E. When the liquid phase reaches the eutectic composition, the temperature remains steady whilst solid eutectic is formed. Two characteristic temperatures are, therefore, observed: T_1, where the onset of solidification occurs, and T_2, where solidification is completed. An alternative/supplementary method for establishing these two temperatures is to heat the solid mixture at a steady rate and determine the temperature at which the onset of liquefaction, T_2, and final liquefaction, T_1, occur. By studying a series of mixtures of known composition, the phase diagram can be constructed.

Eutectic phase diagrams are often more complicated than the simple one illustrated in Fig. 3.4.

The phase diagram for the silver–copper system (Fig. 3.6) shows areas at the left-hand and right-hand sides which represent solid solutions of silver in copper and copper in silver, respectively.

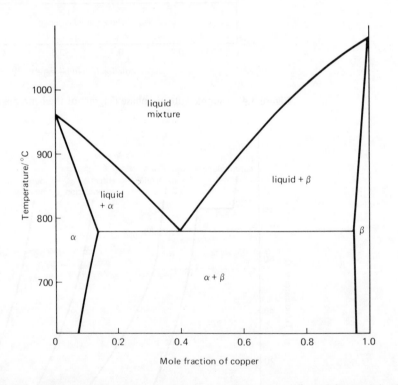

Figure 3.6   Phase diagram of the silver–copper system at 1 atm (α and β are solid solutions of Cu in Ag and Ag in Cu, respectively).

Sometimes the interaction between the components is so strong that an actual compound is formed, e.g. Mg_2Si in the magnesium–silicon system (Fig. 3.7). If this compound melts continuously into liquid having the same composition (as with Mg_2Si), it is called congruent melting. If the melt does not continuously have the same composition as the compound, it is called incongruent melting.

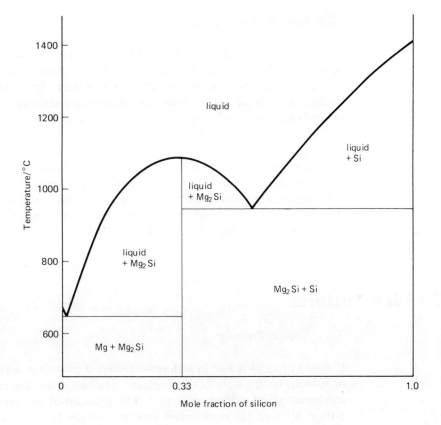

Figure 3.7   Phase diagram of the magnesium–silicon system at 1 atm.

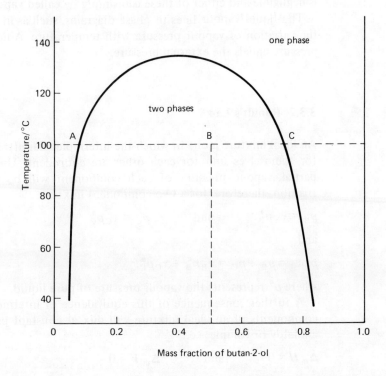

Figure 3.8   Phase diagram of the butan-2-ol–water system.

3.2.6 Partially Miscible Liquids

Figure 3.8 shows the phase diagram for the butan-2-ol–water system. Above the curve there is complete miscibility ($P = 1$), but below the curve there exist two immiscible, saturated solutions ($P = 2$). Consider, for example, a 0.5:0.5 mass fraction mixture at 100°C. The two phases will constitute a saturated solution of butan-2-ol in water of composition A, and a saturated solution of water in butan-2-ol of composition C. The masses of these solutions will be in the ratio BC:AB. The line ABC is called a tie line. The temperature (134°C) corresponding to the maximum of the curve is called the critical solution temperature. Above this temperature, the liquids are miscible in all proportions.

Examples are known where there is a minimum critical solution temperature (triethylamine–water) and where there is both a maximum and a minimum critical solution temperature (nicotine–water).

3.3 Ideal Mixtures

3.3.1 Vapour Pressure

If liquid or solid is put in a closed, evacuated container, some of it will evaporate or sublime until a state of equilibrium is reached, when the rates of formation and condensation of vapour are equal. The pressure of the vapour under these conditions is called the **equilibrium vapour pressure**. If the above process is repeated, but this time with air in the container, the resulting partial pressure of the substance in question is called the **saturation vapour pressure**. At normal pressures the difference between equilibrium vapour pressure and saturation vapour pressure is negligible and either of these can simply be called **vapour pressure**.

The liquid/vapour lines in phase diagrams, such as in Figs 3.1, 3.2 and 3.3, give the variation of vapour pressure with temperature. A liquid boils when its vapour pressure equals the external pressure.

3.3.2 Raoult's Law

An ideal mixture is one in which the intermolecular attractions of the components for themselves and for each other are equivalent. Under these conditions, the partial vapour pressure of each component will be proportional to its mole fraction; therefore, for a two-component mixture,

$$p_B = x_B p_B^{\bullet} \qquad \text{and} \qquad p_C = x_C p_C^{\bullet} \tag{3.4}$$

and

$$p_{total} = p_B + p_C = x_B p_B^{\bullet} + x_C p_C^{\bullet} \tag{3.5}$$

where $p^{\bullet}$ represents the vapour pressure of pure liquid.

A further consequence of this equivalence of intermolecular forces is that the components of an ideal mixture will mix at constant pressure without change in enthalpy or volume, i.e.

$$\Delta_m H = 0 \qquad \text{and} \qquad \Delta_m V = 0 \tag{3.6}$$

It follows that the closest approach to ideality is to be found in mixtures of chemically similar components, e.g. benzene and methylbenzene (Fig. 3.9).

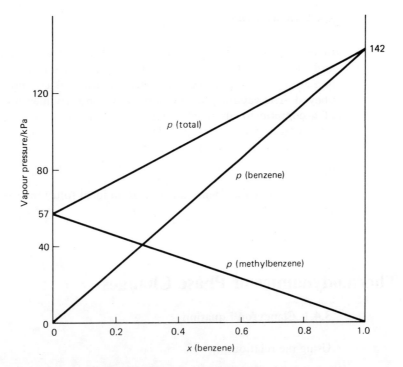

Vapour pressure of benzene–methylbenzene mixtures at 365 K. Approximately ideal behaviour is observed.

3.3.3 Real Mixtures – Deviations from Raoult's Law

In real mixtures, deviation from ideality can be positive, $p_B > x_B p_B^{\bullet}$ (where the components have less than the 'ideal' level of attraction for one another), or negative, $p_B < x_B p_B^{\bullet}$ (where the components have more than the 'ideal' level of attraction for one another).

Figure 3.10 shows the general forms of vapour pressure–composition plots for non-ideal mixtures.

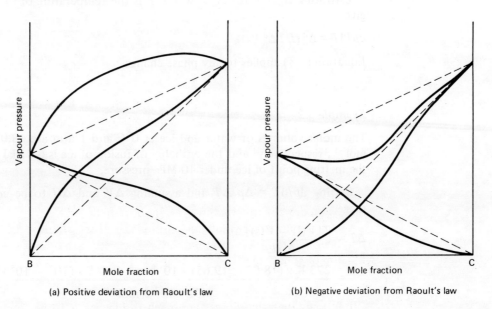

(a) Positive deviation from Raoult's law   (b) Negative deviation from Raoult's law

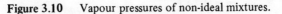

Figure 3.10   Vapour pressures of non-ideal mixtures.

3.3.4 Henry's Law

In Fig. 3.10, the broken lines represent what would be ideal behaviour. As the mole fraction of a component in a real mixture approaches unity, its vapour pressure curve approaches the ideal line for that component, i.e. Raoult's law is obeyed. The vapour pressure curve also tends to linearity when the mole fraction of a component approaches zero; however, the limiting slope for a real mixture differs from the ideal slope. The vapour pressure of a given component at low mole fraction is, therefore, given by

$$p_B = kx_B \qquad (3.7)$$

which is known as Henry's law. For an ideal solution, $k = p_B^\bullet$, and for a non-ideal solution, $k \neq p_B^\bullet$.

3.4   Thermodynamics of Phase Changes

3.4.1 Clapeyron Equation

Using the relationship

$$dG = V\,dp - S\,dT$$

(equation (2.55)), the free-energy change dG resulting from an infinitesimal change from phase α to phase β in a single substance is given by

$$dG = (V_\beta\,dp - S_\beta\,dT) - (V_\alpha\,dp - S_\alpha\,dT)$$

If the phases are in equilibrium, $dG = 0$, and this equation rearranges to

$$(V_\beta - V_\alpha)\,dp - (S_\beta - S_\alpha)\,dT = 0$$

or

$$\Delta_\alpha^\beta V\,dp = \Delta_\alpha^\beta S\,dT$$

Substituting $\Delta_\alpha^\beta H/T$ for $\Delta_\alpha^\beta S$, where T is the temperature of the phase transition, gives

$$dp/dT = \Delta_\alpha^\beta H/T\Delta_\alpha^\beta V \qquad (3.8)$$

Equation (3.8) applies to any phase change.

Example 3.2

The molar volumes of water and ice at 0°C and 1 atm are 18.02 and 19.65 cm³ mol⁻¹, respectively, and the enthalpy of fusion of ice is 6.01 kJ mol⁻¹. Calculate the melting point of ice under 10 MPa pressure.

Setting $dp/dT = \Delta p/\Delta T$ and assuming ΔV and ΔH to be constant over this range,

$$\Delta T = \frac{T[V(l) - V(s)]\Delta p}{\Delta_s^l H}$$

$$= \frac{273\ \text{K} \times (18.02 - 19.65) \times 10^{-6}\ \text{m}^3\ \text{mol}^{-1} \times (10^7 - 10^5)\ \text{Pa}}{6.01 \times 10^3\ \text{J}\ \text{mol}^{-1}}$$

$$= -0.73\ \text{K}$$

i.e. the melting point under a pressure of 10 MPa (nearly 100 atm) is $-0.73°C$ (or 272.42 K). ∎

3.4.2 Clausius–Clapeyron Equation

A more convenient expression than equation (3.8) can be developed which is applicable to vaporisation and sublimation.

Consider a liquid in equilibrium with its vapour. The molar volume of the vapour will be very much greater than the molar volume of the liquid and, as a good approximation, $V(l) - V(g)$ can be replaced by $V(g)$, and equation (3.8) written as

$$dp/dT = \Delta_l^g H/TV(g)$$

If, in addition, ideal gas behaviour is assumed, $V(g)$ can be replaced by RT/p, giving

$$\frac{1}{p}\frac{dp}{dT} = \frac{d \ln p}{dT} = \frac{\Delta_l^g H}{RT^2} \tag{3.9}$$

which, on integration, takes the form

$$\ln p = \text{constant} - \Delta_l^g H/RT \tag{3.10}$$

Example 3.3

The vapour pressure of ethanol is 24.1 mmHg at 10°C and 44.0 mmHg at 20°C. Calculate the mean enthalpy of vaporisation of ethanol over this temperature range.

$$\ln\left(\frac{p_2}{p_1}\right) = -\frac{\Delta_l^g H}{R}\left(\frac{1}{T_2} - \frac{1}{T_1}\right) = +\frac{\Delta_l^g H}{R}\left(\frac{T_2 - T_1}{T_1 T_2}\right)$$

Therefore

$$\ln\left(\frac{44.0}{24.1}\right) = \frac{\Delta_l^g H}{8.314}\left(\frac{293 - 283}{283 \times 293}\right)$$

giving

$$\Delta_l^g H = 41\,500 \text{ J mol}^{-1} = 41.5 \text{ kJ mol}^{-1}$$ ∎

3.4.3 Trouton's Rule

The entropy of vaporisation at normal boiling temperature has a value of about 85 to 90 J K^{-1} mol^{-1} for most liquids. This reflects similar increases in degree of disorder when liquids vaporise at their respective boiling points. Exceptions are noted in the case of hydrogen-bonded liquids, e.g. water ($\Delta_l^g S_{373\,K}^{\ominus} = 109$ J K^{-1} mol^{-1}), where the extra order in the liquid due to hydrogen bonding corresponds to a lower entropy than would otherwise be the case, and so a higher entropy of vaporisation. Liquids such as ethanoic acid ($\Delta_l^g S_{391\,K}^{\ominus} = 62$ J K^{-1} mol^{-1}) have low entropies of vaporisation as a result of dimerisation (the amount is viewed in terms of CH_3COOH, but much of the entropy of vaporisation relates to $(CH_3COOH)_2$).

3.5 Partial Molar Quantities

Partial molar volumes are considered first in this section in order to obtain a clear understanding of the basic concept of partial molar quantities. A set of equivalent partial molar quantities, known as the chemical potential, is then considered. The meaning of chemical potential may be more difficult to visualise than that of partial molar volume, but it is of central importance to the thermodynamics covered in this chapter, and, therefore, an essential study topic.

3.5.1 Partial Molar Volumes

If volume V_1 of a liquid is added to volume V_2 of the same liquid at a given temperature and pressure, the intermolecular interactions and hence the intermolecular spacing will be unchanged and the resulting volume will, quite simply, be $V_1 + V_2$ (i.e. $\Delta_m V = 0$). However, if volume V_1 of a liquid is added to volume V_2 of a different liquid (in which it is miscible) the intermolecular interaction and, consequently, the intermolecular spacing will be specific to the particular mixture and the volume of the liquid mixture will generally differ from $V_1 + V_2$ (i.e. $\Delta_m V \neq 0$). Only for an ideal mixture will $\Delta_m V = 0$ (equation (3.6)).

The value of $\Delta_m V$ for a non-ideal mixture depends not only on the nature of the components of the mixture but also on their relative proportions. It is convenient to express this in terms of a **partial molar volume**

$$V_B = \left(\frac{\partial V}{\partial n_B} \right)_{T,p,n_{C,\ldots}} \tag{3.11}$$

V_B represents the volume increase per mole when component B is added to the mixture in question at constant temperature, pressure and composition. Maintenance of constant composition dictates that the volume of the mixture must be much greater than the volume of added B.

The infinitesimal increase dV in the volume of a two-component system due to the addition of dn_B moles of B and dn_C moles of C at constant temperature and pressure is, therefore, given by

$$dV = \left(\frac{\partial V}{\partial n_B} \right)_{T,p,n_C} dn_B + \left(\frac{\partial V}{\partial n_C} \right)_{T,p,n_B} dn_C$$

$$= V_B \, dn_B + V_C \, dn_C \tag{3.12}$$

and the total volume of the mixture is given by

$$V = n_B V_B + n_C V_C \tag{3.13}$$

Direct measurement of partial molar volumes involving either extremely small amounts of added component and/or an extremely large volume of mixture is somewhat impracticable.

A possible method for determining partial molar volumes is to measure the volumes of mixtures containing variable amounts of one component mixed with fixed amount(s) of the other component(s), as illustrated in Fig. 3.11.

A better method involves measurement of intercepts, and is illustrated in Worked Example 3.8.3.

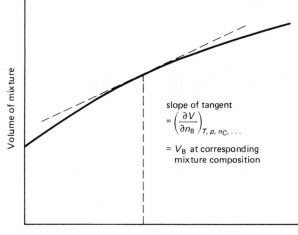

slope of tangent
$$= \left(\frac{\partial V}{\partial n_B} \right)_{T, p, n_C, \ldots}$$

$= V_B$ at corresponding mixture composition

Amount, n_B, of component B added to fixed amount(s) of other component(s) in mixture

Figure 3.11 Partial molar volume.

3.5.2 Gibbs–Duhem Equation

Complete differentiation of equation (3.13) gives

$$dV = n_B \, dV_B + V_B \, dn_B + n_C \, dV_C + V_C \, dn_C \qquad (3.14)$$

But from equation (3.12)

$$dV = V_B \, dn_B + V_C \, dn_C$$

Therefore, from (3.12) and (3.14)

$$n_B \, dV_B + n_C \, dV_C = 0 \qquad (3.15)$$

Corresponding expressions can be written for other partial molar quantities.

3.5.3 Partial Molar Enthalpies

Partial molar enthalpies can be considered in a similar way, and these are important when considering the thermochemistry of solutions and mixtures.

3.5.4 The Chemical Potential

For a closed system (equation (2.55))

$$dG = \left(\frac{\partial G}{\partial p} \right)_{T, n_B, \ldots} dp + \left(\frac{\partial G}{\partial T} \right)_{p, n_B, \ldots} dT$$

$$= V \, dp - S \, dT$$

i.e. changes in pressure and temperature effect a change in Gibbs free energy, as indicated. Consider now an open system, i.e. a system that may exchange matter with its surroundings. This exchange of matter will also result in a free-energy change and, to take this into account, equation (2.55) is extended to

$$dG = V \, dp - S \, dT + \sum \left(\frac{\partial G}{\partial n_B} \right)_{T, p, n_C, \ldots} dn_B \qquad (3.16)$$

The partial differential

$$\left(\frac{\partial G}{\partial n_B} \right)_{T,p,n_C,\ldots}$$

is the partial molar Gibbs free energy of component B. It is given the name **chemical potential** and the symbol μ, i.e.

$$dG = V\,dp - S\,dT + \sum \mu_B\,dn_B \tag{3.17}$$

This is a fundamental equation of considerable importance in thermodynamics.

In a similar manner, the chemical potential can be expressed in terms of other thermodynamic functions, as follows:

$$\mu = \left(\frac{\partial G}{\partial n_B} \right)_{T,p,n_C,\ldots} = \left(\frac{\partial U}{\partial n_B} \right)_{S,V,n_C,\ldots} = \left(\frac{\partial H}{\partial n_B} \right)_{S,p,n_C,\ldots}$$

$$= \left(\frac{\partial A}{\partial n_B} \right)_{T,V,n_C,\ldots} = -T\left(\frac{\partial S}{\partial n_B} \right)_{U,V,n_C,\ldots} \tag{3.18}$$

For a single substance, the chemical potential is the same as the molar Gibbs free energy; therefore, for a perfect gas,

$$\mu = \mu^{\ominus} + RT \ln p \tag{3.19}$$

and, for a real gas,

$$\mu = \mu^{\ominus} + RT \ln f \tag{3.20}$$

3.5.5 Equilibrium in Multiphase Systems

A most important use of chemical potential concerns the criterion of equilibrium for a component distributed between two or more phases. Consider component B distributed between phases α and β at constant temperature and pressure. If an amount dn_B of B is transferred from phase α to phase β, then the free-energy change for the whole system is given by

$$dG = \mu_B^{\beta}\,dn_B - \mu_B^{\alpha}\,dn_B$$

But, at equilibrium, $dG = 0$, and therefore

$$\mu_B^{\alpha} = \mu_B^{\beta} \tag{3.21}$$

i.e. **the chemical potential of a given component is the same in every phase of a system at equilibrium at constant temperature and pressure.**

3.5.6 Solutions and Mixtures

Chemical potential has a central role in the study of the thermodynamics of solutions and mixtures. Consider, first, an ideal mixture in equilibrium with its vapour. For component B in the vapour phase, equation (3.19) takes the form

$$\mu_B(g) = \mu_B^{\ominus}(g) + RT \ln p_B \tag{3.22}$$

However, the chemical potential of B is the same in the liquid mixture (equation (3.21)); therefore

$$\mu_B(\text{mixture}) = \mu_B^{\ominus}(g) + RT \ln p_B \tag{3.23}$$

But, for an ideal mixture, Raoult's law ($p_B = p_B^\bullet x_B$) applies, and therefore (3.23) becomes

$$\mu_B(\text{mixture}) = [\mu_B^\ominus(g) + RT \ln p_B^\bullet] + RT \ln x_B \tag{3.24}$$

The term in square brackets is constant at a given temperature and is the chemical potential of pure liquid B (since, $\mu_B^\bullet(l) = \mu_B(g) = \mu_B^\ominus(g) + RT \ln p_B^\bullet$). Since pure liquid represents the standard state of unit activity, then for component B of an ideal mixture,

$$\mu_B = \mu_B^\ominus + RT \ln x_B \tag{3.25}$$

For a real mixture, this equation becomes

$$\mu_B = \mu_B^\ominus + RT \ln a_B \tag{3.26}$$

where a_B is the activity of component B, and $a_B/x_B = f_B$ is the activity coefficient of B.

The Gibbs–Duhem equation (3.15) can be expressed in terms of chemical potentials for a two-component mixture of B and C as

$$n_B \, d\mu_B + n_C \, d\mu_C = 0 \tag{3.27}$$

The application of the above theory of solutions and mixtures to the determination of activities and activity coefficients is explained by way of Worked Example 3.8.4.

3.6 Colligative Properties

Colligative properties include depression of freezing point, elevation of boiling point and osmotic pressure. They are properties of dilute solutions of non-volatile solutes that depend on the number of solute molecules and not on their nature. All are related to a lowering of vapour pressure. They provide a useful means of determining relative molecular masses and activity coefficients.

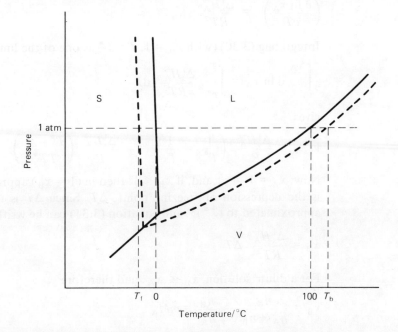

Figure 3.12 Effects of vapour pressure lowering on freezing point and boiling point.

3.6.1 Lowering of Vapour Pressure

Consider a dilute solution of an involatile solute B in solvent A. If Raoult's law holds, then

$$p_A = p_A^{\bullet} x_A = p_A^{\bullet}(1 - x_B) \tag{3.28}$$

The consequence of this lowering of vapour pressure is illustrated in Fig. 3.12 (not to scale) for the case of an involatile solute in aqueous solution.

Addition of involatile solute gives a lowering of vapour pressure and the solid/liquid and liquid/vapour curves are displaced from the full curves for pure solvent to the broken curves for the solution. The normal boiling point is, therefore, elevated from 100°C to T_b, and the normal freezing point is depressed from 0°C to T_f.

3.6.2 Depression of Freezing Point

Assume that pure solvent (rather than solid solution) separates out on freezing, and that ideal solution behaviour is observed. The chemical potentials of the solvent in the solid and liquid phases can, therefore, be equated, as follows:

$$\mu_A^{\ominus}(s) = \mu_A(\text{solution}) = \mu_A^{\ominus}(l) + RT \ln x_A$$

i.e.

$$RT \ln x_A = -[\mu_A^{\ominus}(l) - \mu_A^{\ominus}(s)] = -\Delta_s^l G_A^{\ominus}$$

or

$$\ln x_A = -\Delta_s^l G_A^{\ominus}/RT \tag{3.29}$$

Differentiating equation (3.29) with respect to temperature (and using the Gibbs–Helmholtz relation in the form $[\partial(\Delta G/T)/\partial T]_p = -\Delta H/T^2$ (Section 2.11.5)) gives

$$\left(\frac{\partial \ln x_A}{\partial T}\right)_p = \frac{\Delta_s^l H_A^{\ominus}}{RT^2} \tag{3.30}$$

Integrating (3.30) (with $x_A = 1$, $T = T^{\bullet}$ as one of the limits), i.e.

$$\int_1^{x_A} d \ln x_A = \int_{T^{\bullet}}^T \frac{\Delta_s^l H_A^{\ominus}}{RT^2} \, dT$$

gives

$$\ln x_A = \frac{\Delta_s^l H_A^{\ominus}}{R} \left(\frac{1}{T^{\bullet}} - \frac{1}{T}\right) = -\frac{\Delta_s^l H_A^{\ominus}}{R} \left(\frac{T^{\bullet} - T}{TT^{\bullet}}\right) \tag{3.31}$$

Now, $x_A = 1 - x_B$ and, if $x_B \ll 1$, then $\ln(1 - x_B)$ approximates to $-x_B$. $T^{\bullet} - T$ is the depression of freezing point, ΔT. Since ΔT is usually small, $TT^{\bullet}$ can be approximated to $(T^{\bullet})^2$, and equation (3.31) can be written as

$$x_B = \frac{\Delta_s^l H_A^{\ominus}}{RT^2} \Delta T \tag{3.32}$$

For a dilute solution, $x_B \ll x_A$, and therefore

$$x_B = \frac{n_B}{n_A + n_B} \approx \frac{n_B}{n_A} = m M_A$$

where m is the molality of the solution (i.e. the amount of solute divided by the mass of solvent) and M_A is the molar mass of the solvent. Therefore, substituting in (3.32) and rearranging the resulting expression, gives

$$\Delta T = \frac{RT^2 M_A}{\Delta_s^l H_A^{\ominus}} \, m = K_f m \tag{3.33}$$

K_f is called the cryoscopic constant of the solvent. Within the limitations of the assumptions involved in this derivation (formation of pure solid solvent and dilute ideal solution), the depression of freezing point is proportional to the molality of the solution.

Example 3.4

Calculate the cryoscopic constant of water given that the enthalpy of fusion is 6.01 kJ mol^{-1}.

$$K_f = \frac{RT^2 M_A}{\Delta_s^l H_A^{\ominus}} = \frac{8.314 \times (273.15)^2 \times 18.01 \times 10^{-3}}{6.01 \times 10^3}$$

$$= 1.86 \text{ K (mol kg}^{-1})^{-1} \qquad \blacksquare$$

Example 3.5

The freezing point of an aqueous solution of glucose (3.00 g) in water (50.0 g) is $-0.62°C$. Calculate the relative molecular mass of glucose.

$$m = \frac{3 \times 1000}{50 \times M_r} \text{ mol kg}^{-1} = \frac{\Delta T}{K_f} = \frac{0.62 \text{ K}}{1.86 \text{ K (mol kg}^{-1})^{-1}}$$

giving

$$M_r = \frac{3 \times 1000 \times 1.86}{50 \times 0.62} = 180$$

For this particular example, an error of 0.01 K in the value of ΔT would produce an error of 3 in the value of M_r. $\qquad \blacksquare$

3.6.3 Elevation of Boiling Point

Again, consider a dilute, ideal solution of an involatile solute B dissolved in solvent A. $T^{\bullet}$ is the normal boiling temperature of pure solvent, i.e. at this temperature, $p_A^{\bullet} = 1$ atm. The vapour pressure of the solution at temperature $T^{\bullet}$ is equal to $p_A^{\bullet} x_A$ (i.e. it is less than $p_A^{\bullet}$). The solution boils at a higher temperature T, at which its vapour pressure is equal to $p_A^{\bullet}$ (at $T^{\bullet}$) (i.e. 1 atm). For the solution, therefore, there are the following two pairs of temperature and pressure:

$$T^{\bullet}, p_A^{\bullet} x_A \qquad \text{and} \qquad T, p_A^{\bullet}$$

Substituting these into the integrated form of the Clausius–Clapeyron equation (3.9), we obtain

$$\ln \left(\frac{p_A^{\bullet} x_A}{p_A^{\bullet}} \right) = - \frac{\Delta_l^g H_A^{\ominus}}{R} \left(\frac{1}{T^{\bullet}} - \frac{1}{T} \right)$$

i.e.

$$\ln x_A = - \frac{\Delta_l^g H_A^{\ominus}}{R} \left(\frac{T - T^{\bullet}}{TT^{\bullet}} \right) \tag{3.34}$$

where $T - T^{\bullet} = \Delta T$ is the elevation of boiling point.

Equation (3.34) is analogous to equation (3.31) for the depression of freezing point and can be developed in a corresponding fashion to give

$$\Delta T = \frac{RT^2 M_A}{\Delta_l^g H_A^{\ominus}}\, m = K_b m \tag{3.35}$$

where K_b is called the ebullioscopic constant of the solvent.

3.6.4 Osmotic Pressure

Osmosis takes place when a solution and its solvent are separated from each other by a semipermeable membrane, i.e. a membrane that is permeable to the solvent, but not to the solute. The tendency to equalise chemical potentials (and, hence, concentrations) on either side of the membrane results in a net diffusion of solvent across the membrane to the solution side. The counter-pressure necessary to balance this osmotic flow is called the **osmotic pressure**.

The success of osmotic pressure measurement depends very much on the performance of the membrane. In practice, a membrane that is completely impermeable to solute might not allow a sufficient rate of solvent transport and the most suitable membrane in practice is one that is at the point of being very slightly 'leaky' to the solute. It is advantageous to use an osmometer in which the ratio of membrane area to liquid volume is as large as possible, in order to make the approach to equilibrium as rapid as possible. To this end, as well, the liquid level is pre-set in turn slightly above and slightly below the anticipated equilibrium level and the osmotic pressure is determined by extrapolating the half-sum to infinite time.

The equilibrium requirement is that the chemical potential of the solvent must be the same on either side of the semipermeable membrane. Assume ideal solution behaviour. If the chemical potential of the solvent on the solution side is compared with that on the solvent side of the membrane, it is (a) lower by $RT \ln x_A$ due to the presence of solute (see equation (3.25)), and (b) higher by

$$\int_0^{\pi} V_A \; \mathrm{d}p = \Pi V_A$$

due to the osmotic pressure Π (see equation (2.56)). Therefore

$$\Pi V_A = -RT \ln x_A = -RT \ln(1 - x_B) \tag{3.36}$$

For a dilute solution, V_A (partial molar volume) $\approx V_m$ (molar volume) and $\ln(1 - x_B) \approx -x_B$. Also, $x_B \approx n_B/n_A$. Therefore, on the basis of these approximations,

$$\Pi V_m n_A = RT n_B$$

i.e.

$$\Pi V = RT n_B \tag{3.37}$$

where V is the volume of solvent in which an amount n_B of solute is dissolved. This is known as the Morse equation.

If, as a further approximation, V is assumed to be equal to the volume of the solution, equation (3.37) becomes

$$\Pi = cRT \tag{3.38}$$

This is known as the van't Hoff osmotic pressure equation.

Osmotic pressure is particularly useful in the study of macromolecules, as illustrated in the following example.

Example 3.6

Calculate (a) the freezing-point depression and (b) the osmotic pressure at 298 K of a solution containing 1 g of a macromolecular material ($M_r = 20\,000$) dissolved in 100 cm^3 of water. Assume ideal behaviour.

(a) $\Delta T = K_f m = 1.86$ K (mol kg^{-1})$^{-1}$ $\times$ $\dfrac{10}{20\,000}$ mol kg^{-1}

$= 0.000\,93$ K

(b) $\Pi = cRT = \dfrac{10^4}{20\,000}$ mol m^{-3} $\times 8.314 \times 298$ J mol^{-1}

$= 1240$ N m^{-2} = 12.6 cm water ∎

The above freezing-point depression is far too small to be measured with sufficient accuracy, and, even more importantly, it would be far too sensitive to small amounts of impurity of low relative molecular mass. Osmotic pressure provides a measurable quantity (up to $M_r \approx 10^6$) and the effect of any material of low relative molecular mass to which the membrane is permeable can almost be eliminated.

Deviations from ideality can be quite significant, especially when studying solutions of linear polymers, and it is usual to make osmotic pressure measurements over a range of small concentrations and extrapolate the results to zero concentration, i.e. equation (3.38) is used in the form

$$M = RT/\lim_{\rho \to 0} (\Pi/\rho) \qquad (3.39)$$

where ρ is the solution concentration expressed as the mass of solute divided by the volume of solution and M is the molar mass of the solute.

3.7 Distillation

3.7.1 Liquid–Vapour Phase Diagrams

A pure liquid at a given pressure boils at a fixed temperature. A liquid mixture, however, boils over a range of temperature, and the vapour produced generally has a composition different from that of the liquid mixture.

Consider a two-component system of miscible liquids. There will be a maximum of three degrees of freedom (temperature, pressure and one of the mole fractions) to be represented. In practice, distillation is carried out at constant pressure; but first, consider the dependence of vapour pressure on composition at constant temperature.

Figure 3.9 showed the vapour pressure of a mixture of benzene and methylbenzene (which approximates to ideality) as a function of composition and at 365 K. The total vapour pressure for any liquid composition is given by

$p = p_B + p_M$

$= x_B(l)p_B^\bullet + x_M(l)p_M^\bullet \qquad (3.40)$

where B and M represent benzene and methylbenzene, respectively.

The mole fractions of benzene and methylbenzene in the vapour phase will be proportional to their respective vapour pressures, i.e.

$$x_B(g) = \frac{p_B}{p_B + p_M} = \frac{x_B(l)p_B^\bullet}{x_B(l)p_B^\bullet + x_M(l)p_M^\bullet} \qquad (3.41)$$

and

$$x_M(g) = \frac{p_M}{p_B + p_M} = \frac{x_M(l)p_M^\bullet}{x_B(l)p_B^\bullet + x_M(l)p_M^\bullet} \tag{3.42}$$

Example 3.7

At 365 K, the vapour pressures of benzene and methylbenzene are 142 and 57 kPa, respectively. Calculate the composition of the vapour in equilibrium with a benzene–methylbenzene mixture in which the mole fraction of the methyl-benzene is 0.60.

$x_M(l) = 0.60$, and therefore $x_B(l) = 0.40$. Using equations (3.41) and (3.42)

$$x_B(g) = \frac{0.40 \times 142}{(0.40 \times 142) + (0.60 \times 57)} = 0.624$$

$$x_M(g) = \frac{0.60 \times 57}{(0.40 \times 142) + (0.60 \times 57)} = 0.376$$

and, of course, $x_B(g) + x_M(g) = 1$. ∎

Example 3.7 demonstrates that the composition of the vapour phase differs from that of the liquid phase and that the vapour phase is enriched with the more volatile component. If this calculation is repeated for other compositions, the results can be used to construct a pressure–composition diagram (Fig. 3.13a).

Similar pressure–composition phase diagrams can be constructed for other constant temperatures. A constant pressure can then be selected for all of these and the resulting points on the liquid and vapour lines transferred onto a temperature–composition phase diagram. Figure 3.13b gives the temperature–composition diagram of the benzene–methylbenzene system at 1 atm, which has been produced in this way. Points A and B in Fig. 3.13a correspond to points A and B in Fig. 3.13b.

In Fig. 3.13b, the lower curve represents the boiling temperature of the mixture plotted against the mole fraction of benzene in the liquid phase, and the upper

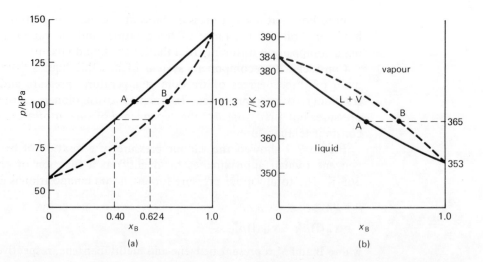

Figure 3.13 (a) Total vapour pressure above a mixture of benzene and methylbenzene at 365 K as a function of both liquid (full line) and gas-phase (broken curve) compositions. (b) Temperature-composition plot at constant total pressure of 1 atm (101.3 kPa) for the benzene–methylbenzene system.

curve represents the boiling temperature of the mixture plotted against the mole fraction of benzene in the vapour phase.

At any point above the upper curve in Fig. 3.13b, the mixture will be entirely in the vapour phase, and at any point below the lower curve it will be entirely in the liquid state. Liquid and vapour coexist at equilibrium between these curves.

At a given temperature, it is conventional to express the compositions of the liquid and vapour phases as x and y, respectively.

3.7.2 Simple Distillation

Phase diagrams such as Fig. 3.13b can now be used to help understand the process of distillation. For clarity, this diagram has been redrawn as Fig. 3.14.

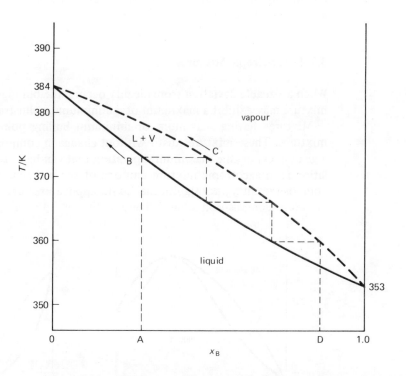

Figure 3.14   Distillation of benzene–methylbenzene mixtures.

Suppose that liquid mixture of composition A is heated. At its boiling point B the composition of the vapour initially formed will be C (i.e. it is enriched in benzene, the more volatile component). This can be led off and condensed to liquid of composition C. As more and more of the liquid is vaporised, however, the composition of the remaining liquid becomes enriched in methylbenzene and the composition and boiling point follow the liquidus line, as indicated. The composition of the vapour will change correspondingly.

3.7.3 Fractional Distillation

Much better separation of components can be effected by fractionation. A fractionating column may be a tube packed with glass beads (as frequently used in the laboratory), or a bubble-cap arrangement (as frequently used for large-scale distillation). Vapour travels up the column, where it condenses. The condensed liquid then flows back until it is revaporised. This process of successive vaporisation and condensation continues, thus permitting a high level of separation to be achieved.

The efficiency of a fractionating column is expressed in terms of theoretical plates. The number of theoretical plates is equal to the number of successive infinitesimal vaporisations at equilibrium to give the separation actually achieved. For example, inspection of Fig. 3.14 shows that enrichment of benzene from composition A to composition D by fractional distillation would require a system operating at three theoretical plates. The distillation flask itself will contribute one of these.

The number of theoretical plates depends on the reflux ratio, which is the ratio of the rate at which liquid is returned to the distillation column at the top of the column to the rate at which distilled liquid is collected. Maximum separation is achieved under a condition of total reflux.

3.7.4 Azeotropic Mixtures

When a sizeable deviation from ideality occurs, the boiling-point curve for a binary mixture may exhibit a maximum or a minimum, as illustrated in Fig. 3.15.

Mixtures having maximum or minimum boiling points are called azeotropic mixtures. These mixtures distil without change in composition. It follows that, at a given pressure, the maximum separation that can be achieved by fractional distillation is to azeotropic mixture and one of the pure components. The azeotropic composition may vary significantly with applied pressure.

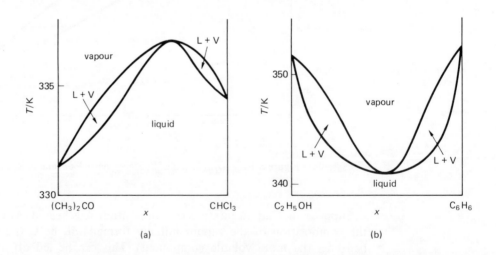

Figure 3.15 Maximum and minimum boiling-point mixtures as exhibited by (a) propanone-trichloromethane and (b) ethanol–benzene systems.

3.7.5 Immiscible Liquids – Steam Distillation

A two-phase mixture boils when the sum of the vapour pressures of the components equals the external pressure, i.e. at a temperature below the boiling point of either component.

Steam is blown through a liquid that is immiscible with water and the vapour condensed. In this way it is possible to distil high-boiling liquids at below 100°C.

This is particularly useful if the substance in question is unstable at higher temperatures.

3.8 Worked Examples

3.8.1 Clausius–Clapeyron Equation

The vapour pressure of trichloromethane varies with temperature, as follows:

$\theta_C/°C$	40	50	60	70	80
$p/10^5$ Pa	0.485	0.700	0.975	1.325	1.790

Calculate the enthalpy of vaporisation and entropy of vaporisation of trichloromethane at its normal boiling point.

Answer

The integrated form of the Clausius–Clapeyron equation is

$$\ln p = \text{constant} - \Delta_l^g H/RT$$

according to which, a plot of $\ln p$ versus $1/T$ (Fig. 3.16) should approximate to a straight line of slope $-\Delta_l^g H/R$.

T/K	313	323	333	343	353
10^3 K$/T$	3.193	3.095	3.002	2.914	2.832
$\ln(p/\text{Pa})$	10.79	11.16	11.49	11.79	12.09

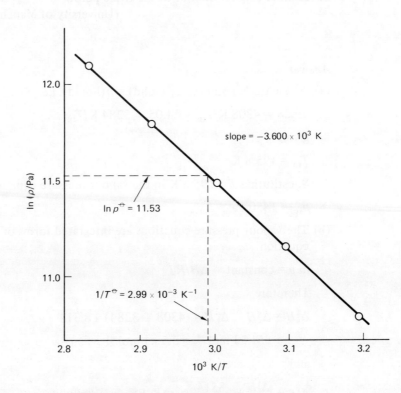

Figure 3.16 $\ln p$ versus $1/T$ for trichloromethane.

The normal boiling point corresponds to a pressure of 1 atm (i.e. 1.013×10^5 Pa). Interpolation at $\ln(1.013 \times 10^5)$ (i.e. at 11.53) gives 10^3 K/T = 2.990 and T = 334.4 K.

$$\Delta_l^g H(334.4 \text{ K}) = -R \times (\text{slope of graph at 334.4 K})$$
$$= -8.314 \times (-3.600 \times 10^3)$$
$$= 29\,930 \text{ J mol}^{-1} = 29.9 \text{ kJ mol}^{-1}$$

$$\Delta_l^g S(334.4 \text{ K}) = \frac{\Delta_l^g H(334.4 \text{ K})}{334.4 \text{ K}} = \frac{29\,930}{334.4}$$
$$= 89.5 \text{ J K}^{-1} \text{ mol}^{-1}$$

This is in accordance with Trouton's rule (see Section 3.4.3).

3.8.2 Triple Point

The vapour pressures of sulphur dioxide in the solid and liquid states are given by the equations

$$\ln(p(\text{solid})/\text{Pa}) = 29.28 - 4308 \text{ K}/T$$

$$\ln(p(\text{liquid})/\text{Pa}) = 24.05 - 3284 \text{ K}/T$$

where T is the thermodynamic temperature. Calculate (a) the temperature and pressure of the triple point of sulphur dioxide, and (b) the enthalpy and entropy of fusion of sulphur dioxide at the triple point.

(University of Manchester, BSc (Ord), Final)

Answer

(a) At the triple point (tp), $p(\text{solid}) = p(\text{liquid})$, i.e.

$$29.28 - 4308 \text{ K}/T_{tp} = 24.05 - 3284 \text{ K}/T_{tp}$$

giving

$$T_{tp} = 195.8 \text{ K}$$

Substituting $T = 195.8$ K in the vapour pressure equations then gives

$$p_{tp} = 1450 \text{ Pa}$$

(b) The vapour pressure equations are integrated forms of the Clausius–Clapeyron equation

$$\ln p = \text{constant} - \Delta H/RT$$

Therefore

$$\Delta_s^l H = \Delta_s^g H - \Delta_l^g H = (4308 - 3284) \times 8.314$$
$$= 8514 \text{ J mol}^{-1} = 8.5 \text{ kJ mol}^{-1}$$

and

$$\Delta_s^l S = \frac{\Delta_s^l H}{T_{tp}} = \frac{8514}{195.8} = 43.5 \text{ J K}^{-1} \text{ mol}^{-1}$$

3.8.3 Partial Molar Volumes

The following data were obtained for a series of ethanol–water mixtures at 25°C:

Mass fraction of ethanol	0	0.1	0.2	0.3	0.4	0.5
Specific volume/cm³ g⁻¹	1.003	1.019	1.033	1.049	1.071	1.095

Mass fraction of ethanol	0.6	0.7	0.8	0.9	1.0
Specific volume/cm³ g⁻¹	1.121	1.154	1.188	1.224	1.270

Determine the partial molar volumes of ethanol and water in a mixture containing 0.5 mass fraction of each component.

Answer

The volume V of a mixture of components B and C is given by

$$V = v\,(m_B + m_C)$$

where v is the specific volume of the mixture and m_B and m_C are the masses of B and C. Differentiating this expression with respect to m_B at constant T, p and m_C, one obtains

$$\left(\frac{\partial V}{\partial m_B}\right)_{T,p,m_C} = v_B = v + (m_B + m_C)\left(\frac{\partial v}{\partial m_B}\right)_{T,p,m_C}$$

where v_B is the partial specific volume of component B. But

$$\left(\frac{\partial v}{\partial m_B}\right)_{T,p,m_C} = \frac{dv}{dw_C}\left(\frac{\partial w_C}{\partial m_B}\right)_{T,p,m_C}$$

where w_C is the mass fraction of component C. Since

$$w_C = m_B/(m_B + m_C)$$

then

$$\left(\frac{\partial w_C}{\partial m_B}\right)_{T,p,m_C} = \frac{-m_C}{(m_B + m_C)^2}$$

and

$$v_B = v - \left(\frac{m_C}{m_B + m_C}\right)\frac{dv}{dw_C} = v - w_C\frac{dv}{dw_C}$$

$$= \text{intercept of tangent on } w_B = 1 \text{ axis}$$

Similarly, v_C = intercept of tangent on $w_C = 1$ axis.

Therefore, from Fig. 3.17, the partial specific volumes at $w(\text{ethanol}) = w(\text{water}) = 0.5$ are

$$v\,(\text{ethanol}) = 1.220 \text{ cm}^3 \text{ g}^{-1}$$

$$v\,(\text{water}) = 0.967 \text{ cm}^3 \text{ g}^{-1}$$

These can be converted to partial molar volumes by multiplying by the respective molar masses, i.e.

$$V\,(\text{ethanol}) = 1.220 \times 46 = 56.1 \text{ cm}^3 \text{ mol}^{-1}$$

$$V\,(\text{water}) = 0.967 \times 18 = 17.4 \text{ cm}^3 \text{ mol}^{-1}$$

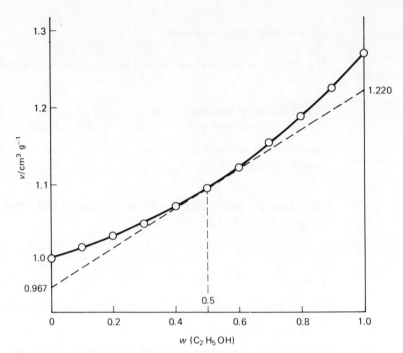

Figure 3.17 Specific volume versus mass fraction for ethanol-water mixtures.

3.8.4 Activity, Activity Coefficient, Chemical Potential and the Gibbs–Duhem Relationship

The following vapour pressures refer to aqueous sucrose solutions at 25°C:

m/mol kg^{-1}	0	0.2	0.5	1.0	2.0
p/Pa	3167	3155	3136	3104	3033

Determine the following quantities for the 2.0 mol kg^{-1} solution:
(a) the activity of the water,
(b) the activity coefficient of the water,
(c) the difference between the chemical potential of the water in the solution and that in pure water,
(d) the activity of the sucrose,
(e) the activity coefficient of the sucrose.

Answer

(a) The standard state of unit solvent activity is taken to be pure solvent. The solvent activity a_A in the solution is given by

$$a_A = p/p^\bullet$$

where p is the pressure of solvent vapour in equilibrium with the solution and $p^\bullet$ is the pressure of the vapour in equilibrium with pure solvent. Strictly, this should be the ratio of the corresponding fugacities, but any deviations from ideality will virtually cancel. The activity of the water in the 2.0 mol kg^{-1} solution is, therefore, given by

$$a(\text{water}) = 3033/3137 = 0.9577$$

(b) The activity coefficient f of the solvent can be defined in terms of the mole fraction of the solvent x_A, and is given by

$$f_A = a_A/x_A$$

Now

$$x(\text{water}) = \frac{n(\text{water})}{n(\text{water}) + n(\text{sucrose})}$$

$$= \frac{1000/18}{1000/18 + 2.0} = 0.9653$$

Therefore

$$f(\text{water}) = 0.9577/0.9653 = 0.9921$$

(c) The chemical potential of the water in the solution, μ, is related to the chemical potential of pure water, $\mu^{\ominus}$, by

$$\mu - \mu^{\ominus} = RT \ln a = 8.314 \times 298 \times \ln 0.9577$$

$$= -107 \text{ J mol}^{-1}$$

(d) To obtain information concerning solute activities and activity coefficients, use is made of the Gibbs–Duhem relationship,

$$x_A \, d\mu_A + x_B \, d\mu_B = 0$$

Since $\mu = \mu^{\ominus} + RT \ln a$, i.e. $d\mu = RT \, d(\ln a)$, this can be rewritten as

$$x_A \, d(\ln a_A) + x_B \, d(\ln a_B) = 0$$

or

$$d(\ln a_B) = -(x_A/x_B) \, d(\ln a_A)$$

A graph of x_A/x_B versus $\ln a_A$ is plotted in Fig. 3.18.

$m/\text{mol kg}^{-1}$	0.2	0.5	1.0	2.0
x_A/x_B	278	111	55.6	27.8
a_A	0.9962	0.9902	0.9801	0.9577
$\ln a_A$	-0.0038	-0.0098	-0.0201	-0.0432

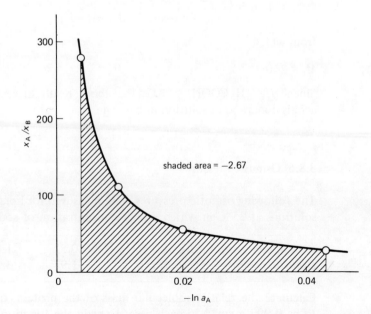

Figure 3.18

From the graph,

$$\ln a_B (\text{in } 2.0 \text{ mol kg}^{-1} \text{ solution}) - \ln a_B (\text{in } 0.2 \text{ mol kg}^{-1} \text{ solution}) = 2.67$$

As an approximation, it will be assumed that the 0.2 mol kg^{-1} solution is sufficiently dilute for the sucrose activity to be taken as equal to its mole fraction. Therefore, for the 2.0 mol kg^{-1} solution.

$$\ln a(\text{sucrose}) = 2.67 + \ln \left(\frac{0.2}{1000/18 + 0.2} \right)$$

giving

$$a(\text{sucrose}) = 0.052$$

(e) $f(\text{sucrose}) = \dfrac{a(\text{sucrose})}{x(\text{sucrose})} = \dfrac{0.052 \times (1000/18 + 2.0)}{2.0}$

$$= 1.50$$

3.8.5 Relative Molecular Mass from Freezing-Point Depression

1.00 g of benzenecarboxylic acid dissolved in 20.0 g benzene has a freezing point of 4.36°C, compared with the freezing point of pure benzene of 5.40°C. The enthalpy of fusion of benzene is 9.89 kJ mol^{-1}. Calculate the apparent relative molecular mass of benzenecarboxylic acid and comment on the result.

Answer

The freezing-point depression is given by

$$\Delta T = \frac{R T_f T_f^{\bullet} n_B}{\Delta_s^l H_A (n_A + n_B)}$$

Therefore

$$5.40 - 4.36 = \frac{8.314 \times (278.55 \times 277.51) \times (1/M_r)}{9890 \times (20/78.1 + 1/M_r)}$$

from which

$$M_r = 240$$

Since $M_r(C_6H_5COOH) = 122$, the above result suggests that benzenecarboxylic acid is dimerised in solution in benzene.

3.8.6 Osmotic Pressure

The following osmotic pressures were measured for horse haemoglobin in aqueous solutions at 25°C in which a high concentration of sodium chloride was present:

Protein concentration/(g/100 cm^3)	0.5	1.0	1.5	2.0
Osmotic pressure/(cm solution)	1.91	3.90	5.94	8.08

Calculate the relative molecular mass of the protein, taking the solution density to be 0.997 g cm^{-3} in each case. Explain the function of the high concentration of sodium chloride.

Answer

Osmotic pressure data are extrapolated to zero concentration to allow for deviations from ideality and the molar mass of the protein is calculated using equation (3.39),

$$M = RT/ \lim_{\rho \to 0} (\Pi/\rho)$$

where ρ is the mass concentration. The data are plotted in Fig. 3.19, from which

$$\lim_{\rho \to 0} (\Pi/\rho) = 3.76 \text{ (cm solution)}/(g/100 \text{ cm}^3)$$

$$= \frac{3.76 \times 10^{-2} \text{ m} \times 0.997 \times 10^3 \text{ kg m}^{-3} \times 9.81 \text{ m s}^{-2}}{10 \text{ kg m}^{-3}}$$

$$= 36.77 \text{ J kg}^{-1}$$

Therefore

$$M = \frac{8.314 \times 298}{36.77} = 67.4 \text{ kg mol}^{-1}$$

i.e.

$$M_r = 67\,400$$

The role of the excess sodium chloride is to minimise the inequality of small-ion concentrations either side of the membrane (Donnan equilibrium).

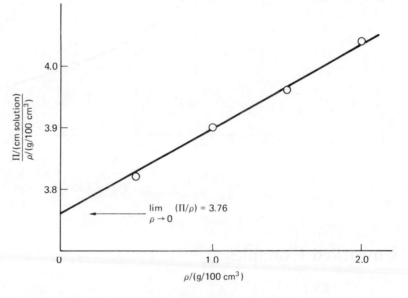

Figure 3.19

3.8.7 Distillation

Use the following data to construct a graph of liquid and vapour composition versus boiling point for the tetrachloromethane–tetrachloroethane system:

$x(CCl_4)$	0	0.1	0.2	0.3	0.4	0.6	0.8	1.0
$y(CCl_4)$	0	0.469	0.670	0.800	0.861	0.918	0.958	1.0
$\theta_C/^\circ C$	120.8	108.5	100.8	93.0	89.3	83.3	79.9	76.0

A mixture with $x(l)(CCl_4) = 0.4$ is distilled under equilibrium conditions until 40 mole per cent of this liquid has been vaporised. Calculate (a) the final mole fractions of CCl_4 in the liquid and in the vapour, and (b) the final temperature.

Answer

The phase diagram is shown in Fig. 3.20. To obtain the required final compositions and final temperature, a tie line ABC is drawn such that B is at $x(l)$ $(CCl_4) = 0.4$ and AB:BC = (mole fraction vaporised):(mole fraction still liquid) = 0.4:0.6. A and C give the final compositions of liquid and vapour phases, i.e. $x(l)$ $(CCl_4) = 0.21$ and $x(g)$ $(CCl_4) = 0.69$. Tie line ABC is at the final temperature of 99.5°C.

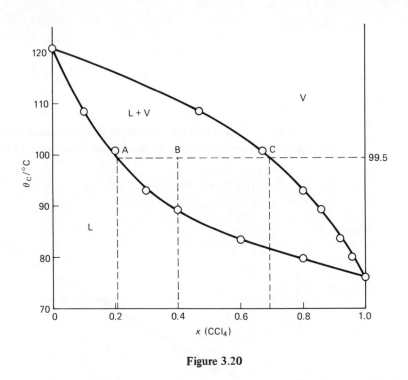

Figure 3.20

3.9   Unworked Examples

3.9.1
A substance is known to exist in two solid forms, X and Y, as well as in the liquid and vapour phases. Three stable triple points have been observed.

$\theta_C/°C$	p/atm	*Phases*
10	1	X, Y, vapour
80	10	Y, liquid, vapour
50	1000	X, Y, liquid

Sketch the pressure–temperature phase diagram for this one-component system and indicate the stable phase for each region.

3.9.2

Anhydrous iron(II) chloride is oxidised on heating in steam:

$$3FeCl_2(s) + 4H_2O(g) \rightleftharpoons Fe_3O_4(s) + 6HCl(g) + H_2(g)$$

Write down a set of components for this phase equilibrium. Calculate the number of degrees of freedom and identify suitable variables to represent the degrees of freedom.

3.9.3

Bismuth and cadmium form no compound or solid solution with each other, but form a eutectic of 0.4 mass fraction cadmium which solidifies at 140°C. The melting points of bismuth and cadmium are 270°C and 320°C, respectively. Assuming that the liquidus lines are straight, obtain the following information for an alloy which is 0.7 mass fraction cadmium:
(a) the temperature at which the alloy begins to crystallise from the melt,
(b) the mass fraction of solid cadmium in the alloy at 170°C,
(c) the mass fraction of eutectic in the alloy at 100°C.

3.9.4

An equimolar mixture of nitrobenzene and hexane forms two conjugate solutions at 10°C, one of which contains 0.17 mole fraction nitrobenzene and constitutes 0.41 mole fraction of the system. Calculate the composition of the other solution.

3.9.5

The melting points of mixtures of p-aminoazobenzene (A) and 3,5-dihydroxy-methylbenzene (B) are as follows:

$x(A)$	0	10	23	35	45	55	65	80	100
$\theta_C/°C$	108	101	90	98	103.5	104.5	101.5	112	127

Plot the phase diagram for this system, labelling all the areas. Neglect possible solid solution formation. What type of system does this phase diagram represent? Sketch, qualitatively, a possible cooling curve of the melt where $x(A) = 0.35$.

3.9.6

The melting points of mixtures of N-methylurea and phenol are as follows:

$\theta_C/°C$	41.0	13.0	−7.0	2.0	7.7	16.0	43.0	77.0	98.0
$x(C_2H_6N_2O)$	0.055	0.185	0.275	0.373	0.447	0.473	0.553	0.767	1.0

Plot the phase diagram for the system (neglecting possible solid solution formation). What type of system does this phase diagram represent?

3.9.7

Lithium chloride (m.p. 615°C) and calcium chloride (m.p. 760°C) form a eutectic at 490°C which contains 0.62 mole fraction calcium chloride. At the eutectic temperature, the system contains two solid solutions, α and β, with 0.31 and 0.94 mole fraction calcium chloride, respectively. Assuming that liquidus and solidus lines are straight, draw a temperature–composition phase diagram for this system.

Liquid mixture with $x(CaCl_2) = 0.80$ is slowly cooled; determine
(a) the temperature at which solid first appears,
(b) the composition of the solid which first appears,
(c) the composition of the mixture at 550°C,
(d) the composition of the solid formed at 490°C.

3.9.8

The melting point of sodium is 370.6 K at one atmosphere pressure. Under these conditions, the densities of solid and liquid sodium are 0.951 and 0.928 g cm^{-3}, respectively. The standard enthalpy of fusion of sodium at 370.6 K is 3.05 kJ mol^{-1}. Estimate the pressure increase required to raise this melting point by 1 K.

(GRSC, Part I)

3.9.9

At 127°C, HgI$_2$ undergoes a polymorphic change from the red to the yellow form. The enthalpy of transition is 1250 J mol^{-1} and the change in molar volume on transition is 5.4 cm^3 mol^{-1}, the red form being the less dense. Calculate the rate of change of transition temperature with pressure at 127°C.

(University of Sheffield, BSc, 1st year)

3.9.10

From the following data obtain an appropriate equation relating the vapour pressure of water and thermodynamic temperature.

Celsius temperature	20	40	60	80	100
Vapour pressure/Pa	2335	7375	19 190	47 300	101 300

3.9.11

The vapour pressure of propanone is 0.152 atm at 10°C and 0.806 atm at 50°C. Calculate the enthalpy of vaporisation, assumed to be constant over this temperature range. At what temperature will propanone boil at 1 atm pressure?

3.9.12

The mean enthalpy of vaporisation of water between 90°C and 100°C is 2270 J g^{-1}. Calculate the vapour pressure of water at 90°C.

3.9.13

The vapour pressure of chloromethane is represented by the equation

$$\log_{10}(p/\text{mmHg}) = 7.48 - 1149 \text{ K}/T$$

Calculate (a) the molar enthalpy of vaporisation, (b) the normal boiling point, and (c) the entropy of vaporisation at the normal boiling point.

3.9.14

The vapour pressure of mercury varies with temperature, as follows:

$\theta_C/°C$	50	100	150	200	300
p/Pa	1.69	36.4	374	2300	32 900

Calculate the mean enthalpy of vaporisation over this temperature range and use this value to calculate the entropy of vaporisation at the normal boiling point of mercury.

3.9.15

Nitrogen containing ethoxyethane vapour (1.00 × 10^{-3} mol dm^{-3} at 25°C) was passed slowly at 1 atm through a cold trap at −80°C. The enthalpy of vaporisation of ethoxyethane is 28.5 kJ mol^{-1} at its normal boiling point of 35°C. Making reasonable assumptions, estimate the maximum percentage recovery of ethoxyethane in the cold trap.

3.9.16

Small amounts of trichloroethanoic acid were added to a fixed amount of water at 25°C and the total volume of the mixture was measured.

$n(CCl_3COOH)$/mol	0.0316	0.0455	0.0626	0.0785	0.0975
V(mixture)/cm^3	54.3	55.6	57.2	58.6	60.4

Determine (a) the average value of the partial molar volume of trichloroethanoic acid over this concentration range, and (b) the initial volume of water.

3.9.17

The following data refer to sulphuric acid–water mixtures at 25°C:

Mass fraction of H_2SO_4	0	0.1	0.2	0.3	0.4	0.5
Density/g cm^{-3}	0.997	1.064	1.137	1.215	1.299	1.391

Mass fraction of H_2SO_4	0.6	0.7	0.8	0.9	1.0
Density/g cm^{-3}	1.494	1.606	1.722	1.809	1.826

Determine the partial molar volumes of sulphuric acid and water for solutions containing 0.25, 0.5 and 0.75 mass fraction sulphuric acid.

3.9.18

At 35°C, $p^{\bullet}(CH_3COCH_3) = 346$ mmHg and $p^{\bullet}(CHCl_3) = 291$ mmHg, and for a mixture of composition $x(CH_3COCH_3) = 0.4$ and $x(CHCl_3) = 0.6$ the partial pressures are $p(CH_3COCH_3) = 100$ mmHg and $p(CHCl_3) = 154$ mmHg. Calculate the activities and activity coefficients of the components of this mixture.

3.9.19

The activity coefficients of lead in various lead–bismuth alloys are as follows:

x(Pb)	1.0	0.9	0.8	0.6	0.4	0.2	0.0
f(Pb)	1.000	0.993	0.978	0.880	0.728	0.580	0.480

Calculate the activity coefficient of the bismuth in alloys containing 0.40 and 0.80 mole fraction of lead.

3.9.20

The vapour pressures of benzene in the solid and liquid states are given by the equations

$\ln(p(\text{solid})/\text{Pa}) = 27.57 - 5319\ \text{K}/T$ \quad (250 K < T < 280 K)

$\ln(p(\text{liquid})/\text{Pa}) = 23.23 - 4108\ \text{K}/T$ \quad (275 K < T < 315 K)

$\ln(p(\text{liquid})/\text{Pa}) = 22.52 - 3875\ \text{K}/T$ \quad (315 K < T < 370 K)

Calculate (a) the temperature and pressure of the triple point, (b) the cryoscopic constant of benzene, and (c) the entropy of vaporisation of benzene at its normal boiling point.

3.9.21

Pure benzene freezes at 5.40°C and a solution of 0.223 g of phenylethanoic acid ($C_6H_5CH_2COOH$) in 4.4 g of benzene freezes at 4.47°C. The enthalpy of fusion of benzene is 9.89 kJ mol^{-1}. Calculate the apparent relative molecular mass of phenylethanoic acid and comment on the result.

(University of Nottingham, BSc, Part I)

99

3.9.22

The normal boiling point of ethanol is $78.0°C$ and the enthalpies of formation of liquid ethanol and ethanol vapour at $78.0°C$ are -277.6 and -235.3 kJ mol^{-1}, respectively. Calculate the ebullioscopic constant for ethanol.

(GRSC, Part I)

3.9.23

A 0.2 mol kg^{-1} aqueous solution of a monobasic acid has a boiling point 0.150 K higher than that of pure water. The enthalpy of vaporisation of water is 2250 J g^{-1}. Calculate the dissociation constant of the acid consistent with these data.

(University of Nottingham, BSc, Part I)

3.9.24

The osmotic pressure of an aqueous solution of glucose (0.2 g dm^{-3}) at $25°C$ is equal to 54 mmHg. Calculate the relative molecular mass of glucose from this value.

3.9.25

The osmotic pressure of an aqueous solution of urea (2.31 g dm^{-3}) at $25°C$ is equal to 95.1 kPa. Calculate the relative molcular mass of urea.

3.9.26

Calculate for an aqueous solution of sucrose at $25°C$ with a molality equal to 0.20 mol kg^{-1}:
(a) the osmotic pressure according to equation (3.36),
(b) the osmotic pressure according to the Morse equation (3.37),
(c) the osmotic pressure according to the van't Hoff equation (3.38).
At $25°C$, a molality of 0.20 mol kg^{-1} is equivalent to a concentration of 0.192 mol dm^{-3} and the density of water is 0.997 g cm^{-3}. Compare these calculated values with an experimental value of 510 kPa.

3.9.27

The following osmotic pressures were measured for solutions of nitrocellulose in propanone at $25°C$:

Concentration/(g/100 cm³)	0.31	0.53	0.68	0.95	1.20
Osmotic pressure/(cm solution)	2.25	4.65	6.60	10.9	15.7

Calculate an average relative molecular mass, taking the solution density to be 0.79 g cm^{-3} in each case.

3.9.28

At 373 K, the saturated vapour pressures of heptane and methylbenzene are 106.0 kPa and 73.7 kPa, respectively. Assuming ideal behaviour, calculate
(a) the mole fraction of heptane (in the liquid phase) in a mixture boiling at 373 K under an external pressure of 101.3 kPa,
(b) the mole fraction of heptane in the initial condensate formed on distilling this mixture.

(Liverpool Polytechnic, BSc, 1st year)

3.9.29

The vapour pressures of 1,2-dibromoethane and 1,2-dibromopropane, both measured at 343 K, are, respectively, 12.90 kPa and 9.17 kPa. Assuming that these two liquids form an ideal mixture, calculate the mole fraction of 1,2-dibromopropane in the vapour phase which is in equilibrium at 343 K with a liquid containing 50 per cent by mass of each of these components.

(GRSC, Part I)

3.9.30

The vapour pressures of ethane and ethene over the temperature ranges indicated are given by

$$\ln(p(C_2H_6)/Pa) = 21.65 - 1881\ K/T \qquad (114\ K < T < 297\ K)$$
$$\ln(p(C_2H_4)/Pa) = 21.70 - 1738\ K/T \qquad (105\ K < T < 282\ K)$$

(a) Calculate the ratio of the vapour pressure of C_2H_4 to that of C_2H_6 at the normal boiling temperatures of each.
(b) Calculate the boiling points of C_2H_4 and C_2H_6 under 3.04 MPa (30 atm).
(c) Calculate the ratio of the vapour pressure of C_2H_4 to that of C_2H_6 at the boiling points calculated in (b).
(d) Does increased pressure enhance the separation of C_2H_4 from C_2H_6 by distillation?

3.9.31

The following data refer to the tetrachloromethane–ethanol system:

Boiling point/°C	77.9	72.8	68.0	65.0	63.6	64.3	75.9
$x(CCl_4)$(liquid)	0	0.064	0.176	0.336	0.63	0.728	1.0
$x(CCl_4)$(vapour)	0	0.25	0.45	0.55	0.63	0.67	1.0

Describe the result of (a) initially distilling, and (b) fractionally distilling an equimolar liquid mixture.

3.9.32

The vapour pressure of the system N,N-diethylphenylamine–water is 101.3 kPa at 99.4°C and the vapour pressure of water at this temperature is 99.2 kPa. Calculate the mass of steam necessary to distil over 100 g of N,N-diethylphenylamine.

4 Reaction Kinetics

4.1 Introduction

From our knowledge of thermodynamics, we have developed methods for determining the direction of chemical change. However, the rate at which a chemical change takes place and its variation with conditions is covered by our understanding of **chemical kinetics** or **reaction rates**.

It is conventional to write down a chemical reaction in the form of its **stoichiometric equation**. This gives the simplest ratio of the number of molecules of reactant to the number of molecules of product. An example is the decomposition of dinitrogen pentoxide.

$$2N_2O_5 \rightarrow 4NO_2 + O_2$$

However, the stoichiometric equation does not necessarily represent the **mechanism** of the reaction. Ogg suggested that the above proceeds via three steps, as follows:

(1) $N_2O_5 \rightarrow NO_2 + NO_3\bullet$ fast
(2) $NO_2 + NO_3\bullet \rightarrow NO_2 + O_2 + NO\bullet$ slow
(3) $NO\bullet + NO_3\bullet \rightarrow 2NO_2$ fast

in which intermediates like the free radical, $NO_3\bullet$, are involved. Kinetic studies show that step (2) is the slowest stage of the reaction, so that the overall rate depends on this step, which is said to be the **rate-determining step**. The study of reaction rates provides evidence for determining the path by which a chemical change takes place and forms the basis of the investigation of reaction mechanisms.

4.2 Rate Laws

4.2.1 Rate of Reaction

For a simple reaction

$$A \rightarrow B + C$$

the concentration of A decreases with time as illustrated by a simple concentration–time graph shown in Fig. 4.1. The rate J can be expressed in terms of the decrease of reactant concentration [A] with time, i.e.

$$J = - d[A]/dt$$

However, it is equally valid to express the rate in terms of the increase in concentration of one of the product molecules, B and C, with time. Therefore

$$J = - \frac{d[A]}{dt} = + \frac{d[B]}{dt} = + \frac{d[C]}{dt} \tag{4.1}$$

For the general reaction

$$aA + bB \rightarrow cC + dD$$

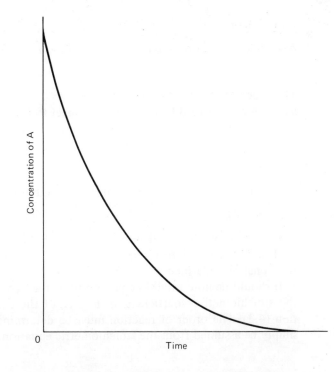

Figure 4.1   Typical concentration–time curve.

the rate is given by

$$J = -\frac{1}{a}\frac{d[A]}{dt} = -\frac{1}{b}\frac{d[B]}{dt} = +\frac{1}{c}\frac{d[C]}{dt} = +\frac{1}{d}\frac{d[D]}{dt} \qquad (4.2)$$

where $-a$, $-b$, c and d are the stoichiometric coefficients (see Section 2.12.4). Since the rate depends on these coefficients, the stoichiometric equation must be stated when such rates are quoted. For example, for the reaction

$$A + 2B \rightarrow AB_2$$

$$J = \frac{-d[A]}{dt} = -\frac{1}{2}\frac{d[B]}{dt} = +\frac{d[AB_2]}{dt}$$

4.2.2 Order of Reaction and Rate Constant

For the reaction $A \rightarrow B$, the rate, as measured by the slope of the concentration–time curve (see Fig. 4.1), is initially at a maximum, but decreases as the concentration of A decreases, so that

$$J \propto [A]^n$$

where n is a constant known as the **order of reaction**. The relationship between the rate and the concentration of reactant is called the **rate equation**, which for the above reaction takes the form

$$J = \frac{-d[A]}{dt} = k[A]^n \qquad (4.3)$$

where k is a constant for any reaction at one temperature and is called the **rate constant**.

103

In general,

A + B + C + ... → products

$$J = k[A]^{n_1} [B]^{n_2} [C]^{n_3} \ldots \tag{4.4}$$

The order of the reaction is $n_1 + n_2 + n_3 + \ldots$, the order with respect to A being n_1, with respect to B being n_2, with respect to C being n_3, etc.

As a consequence, the rate constant for the reaction has units that depend on the order. In a first-order reaction where

$$J = k[A]$$

k has dimensions $[\text{time}]^{-1}$ (e.g. unit of s^{-1}), but in a second-order reaction where

$$J = k[A][B]$$

k has dimensions $[\text{concentration}]^{-1}[\text{time}]^{-1}$ (e.g. units of $dm^3 \ mol^{-1} \ s^{-1}$).

However, not all reactions have simple rate equations, as the order can be fractional or undefined.

It should be noted that in equation (4.4) the exponents n_1, n_2, n_3, etc., are not the stoichiometric coefficients a, b, etc., of the chemical reaction used in equation (4.2). The order of reaction must be determined experimentally and cannot simply be assumed from the stoichiometric equation.

Example 4.1

The reaction

$$2NO(g) + O_2(g) \rightarrow 2NO_2(g)$$

has been investigated by measuring the initial rates of decrease of pressure in known mixtures of gases, with the following results:

Initial pressure of NO/atm	2.0	2.0	1.0
Initial pressure of O_2 /atm	2.0	1.0	2.0
Initial rate of decrease of pressure/atm min^{-1}	0.8	0.4	0.2

Determine the order of the reaction with respect to each reactant.

Applying equation (4.4) to this system gives

$$J = k(p_{NO})^x (p_{O_2})^y$$

Using the first two sets of data,

$$0.8 = k(2.0)^x(2.0)^y$$

and

$$0.4 = k(2.0)^x(1.0)^y$$

Dividing gives

$$2 = 2^y \qquad \text{i.e.} \qquad y = 1$$

Using the first and last sets of data,

$$0.8 = k(2.0)^x(2.0)^y$$

$$0.2 = k(1.0)^x(2.0)^y$$

Dividing gives

$$4 = 2^x \qquad \text{i.e.} \qquad x = 2$$

Hence the rate is given by

$$J = k(p_{NO})^2 (p_{O_2})$$

i.e. the reaction is second-order with respect to NO, first-order with respect to O_2 and overall third-order. ∎

4.3 Integrated Rate Equations

The normal method of determining the order of a reaction, and, subsequently, the rate constant of a chemical reaction, is to use an integrated form of the rate equation.

4.3.1 First-Order Reactions

For a first-order reaction, equation (4.3) becomes

$$-\frac{d[A]}{dt} = k[A] \tag{4.5}$$

If a represents the initial concentration of reactant A and x represents the concentration of product at time t, the concentration of A at time t is given by $a - x$. Therefore the rate J can be expressed as

$$J = \frac{dx}{dt} = -\frac{d(a-x)}{dt} \tag{4.6}$$

Combining equations (4.5) and (4.6) gives

$$dx/dt = k(a-x)$$

Rearranging,

$$\frac{dx}{a-x} = k \, dt \tag{4.7}$$

Integration of equation (4.7) gives

$$-\ln(a-x) = kt + \text{constant} \tag{4.8}$$

Since at $t = 0$, $x = 0$, the constant is equal to $-\ln a$, so that equation (4.8) becomes

$$kt = \ln\left(\frac{a}{a-x}\right) \tag{4.9}$$

This is the first-order integrated rate equation. It is sometimes expressed in alternative forms as

$$kt = \ln\left(\frac{[A]_0}{[A]}\right) \tag{4.10}$$

or

$$kt = \ln\left(\frac{c_0}{c}\right) \tag{4.11}$$

where $[A]_0$ or c_0 is the initial concentration and $[A]$ or c is the concentration at time t.

Example 4.2

The following data were obtained for the hydrolysis of glucose in aqueous solution at 298 K:

Time/min	0	60	130	180	240	300
Glucose concentration/mol dm^{-3}	1.000	0.807	0.630	0.531	0.427	0.345

Show that the reaction is first-order and determine the rate constant for the hydrolysis.

If the reaction is first-order, then equation (4.9) can be used in the form

$$\ln a - \ln(a - x) = kt$$

where a is the initial concentration of glucose and $a - x$ is the glucose concentration at any time t. A plot of $\ln(a - x)$ will be linear for a first-order reaction and the slope will be equal to $-k$.

From the data,

$(a - x)$/mol dm^{-3}	1.000	0.807	0.630	0.531	0.427	0.345
$\ln[(a - x)/\text{mol dm}^{-3}]$	0.000	−0.214	−0.462	−0.633	−0.851	−1.064
t/min	0	60	130	180	240	300

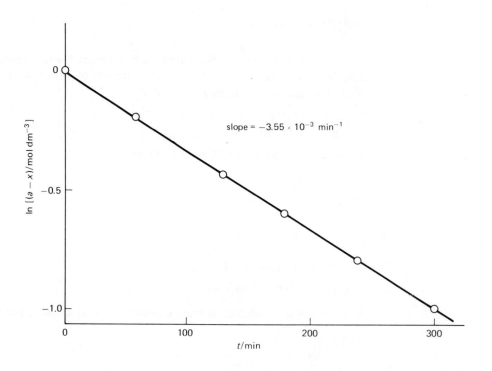

Figure 4.2 First-order plot for glucose hydrolysis.

A plot of $\ln(a - x)$ against t is shown in Fig. 4.2. Since the graph is a straight line, the reaction is first-order and

$$\text{slope} = -k = -3.55 \times 10^{-3} \text{ min}^{-1}$$

giving

$$k = 5.92 \times 10^{-5} \text{ s}^{-1}$$

4.3.2 Second-Order Reactions

Similar derivations, although mathematically more complex, can be carried out for a range of orders of reaction. They are outlined in most textbooks covering reaction kinetics. A commonly used one is that for second-order reactions where there is a single reactant or where two reactants have equal initial concentration, a.

For the reaction

$$2A \rightarrow \text{products}$$

(or $A + B \rightarrow$ products where $[A]_{t=0} = [B]_{t=0}$)

equation (4.3) becomes

$$dx/dt = k(a - x)^2$$

or

$$dx/(a - x)^2 = k \, dt$$

Integrating gives

$$kt = \frac{1}{a - x} + \text{constant}$$

Since $x = 0$ at $t = 0$, constant $= -1/a$, and

$$kt = \frac{1}{a - x} - \frac{1}{a} \tag{4.12}$$

or

$$k = \frac{1}{at} \left(\frac{x}{a - x} \right) \tag{4.13}$$

As with first-order reactions, equation (4.12) can be expressed in the alternative forms

$$kt = \frac{1}{[A]} - \frac{1}{[A]_0} \tag{4.14}$$

or

$$kt = \frac{1}{c} - \frac{1}{c_0}$$

4.3.3 Other Types of Reaction

(a) *Zero-Order Reactions*

These are not common but may occur in heterogeneous systems, particularly gas reactions on a surface. If the order n is zero, equation (4.3) becomes

$$-d[A]/dt = k[A]^0 = k$$

or

$$dx/dt = k$$

i.e. the rate is independent of concentration and the rate constant has the same units as the rate.

(b) *Third-Order Reactions*

If all the reactants have initial concentration a, the rate law becomes

$$dx/dt = k(a - x)^3$$

with the integrated rate equation being as given later in Table 4.1, which provides a summary of the elementary rate laws and integrated equations by order.

(c) *Fractional Order*

The reaction (and the reverse reaction)

$$H_2 + D_2 \rightarrow 2HD$$

follows three-halves order kinetics. This is often a feature of atomic and free-radical reactions (see Section 4.9).

(d) *Parallel Reactions*

For example,

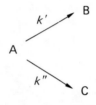

where, provided k' and k'' are rate constants of the same order,

$$\frac{\text{Amount of B formed after time } t}{\text{Amount of C formed after time } t} = \frac{k'}{k''}$$

(e) *Opposing Reactions*

For a reversible first-order reaction

$$A \underset{k_{-1}}{\overset{k_1}{\rightleftharpoons}} B$$

the concentration–time curves are as in Fig. 4.3. It is possible to show that the integrated rate equation is

$$\ln\left(\frac{x_e}{x_e - x}\right) = \frac{k_1 a t}{x_e} = (k_1 + k_{-1})t$$

where x_e is the equilibrium concentration of B.

(f) *Consecutive Reactions*

This type of reaction involves two steps, e.g.

$$A \xrightarrow{k_1} B \xrightarrow{k_2} C$$

A typical concentration–time graph is shown in Fig. 4.4. Readers are referred to specialist physical chemistry textbooks for treatment of these reactions.

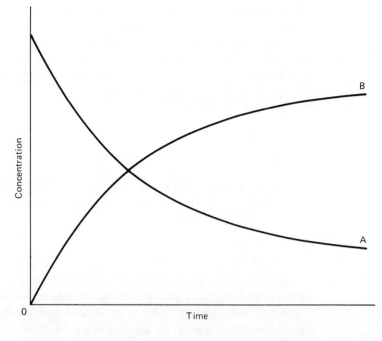

Figure 4.3   Concentration–time graph for an opposing reaction.

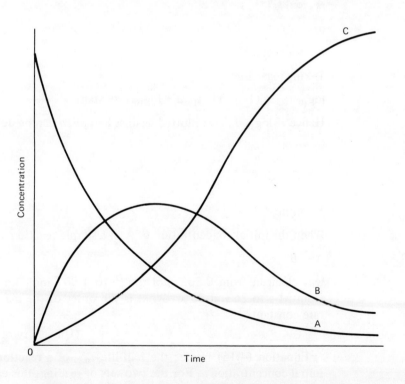

Figure 4.4   Concentration–time graph for a consecutive reaction.

4.3.4 Fractional Life of Reactions

From the integrated forms of the rate equations, it can be shown that there is a direct relationship between the order of a reaction and the time the reaction takes to proceed.

109

For instance, for a first-order reaction, the time taken for the concentration of reactant to decrease by a certain fraction is independent of the initial concentration a. Let $t_{0.5}$ be the time required for the initial concentration a to decrease to half its initial value, i.e. to $0.5a$. This is known as the **half-life** of the reaction. Therefore, for half-life conditions, equation (4.10) becomes

$$k = \frac{1}{t_{0.5}} \ln\left(\frac{a}{0.5a}\right) = \frac{\ln 2}{t_{0.5}} = \frac{0.693}{t_{0.5}}$$

In general, for fractional life $1/f$ of a first-order reaction,

$$t_{1/f} = (\ln f)/k$$

However, for a second-order reaction, with a single reactant or where the initial concentration of both reactants is equal to a, equation (4.12) applies, and for half-life conditions, this becomes

$$t_{0.5} = \frac{1}{k}\left(\frac{1}{0.5a} - \frac{1}{a}\right) = \frac{1}{ka}$$

Therefore, in this case, the half-life is inversely proportional to the initial concentration a, and the rate constant can be determined from the half-life.

The fractional-life approach is applicable to any order of reaction provided the initial concentrations of all the reactants are equal. In general, the half-life of a reaction of order n is related to the initial concentration a by

$$t_{0.5} \propto 1/a^{n-1}$$

or

$$t_{0.5} = \text{constant}/a^{n-1} \tag{4.15}$$

Taking logarithms,

$$\log_{10} t_{0.5} = (1 - n)\log_{10} a + \log_{10} (\text{constant})$$

Hence if $\log_{10} t_{0.5}$ is plotted against $\log_{10} a$, n can be determined from the slope.

Example 4.3

When the initial concentration of A in a simple reaction

A → B

was changed from 0.502 mol dm^{-3} to 1.007 mol dm^{-3}, the half-life dropped from 51 s to 26 s at 25°C. What is the order of the reaction and the value of the rate constant?

(University of Sheffield, BSc, 1st year)

Equation (4.15) relates the half-life $t_{0.5}$ of a reaction to the order n and the initial concentration a. For the two sets of readings this equation becomes

$$\log_{10}\left(\frac{(t_{0.5})_1}{(t_{0.5})_2}\right) = (n - 1)\log_{10}\left(\frac{a_2}{a_1}\right)$$

Substituting the two sets of data gives

$$\log_{10}\left(\frac{51}{26}\right) = (n - 1)\log_{10}\left(\frac{1.007}{0.502}\right)$$

from which $n = 2$. Hence the reaction is second-order.

For a second-order reaction, the half-life is related to the rate constant and the initial concentration by

$$t_{0.5} = \frac{1}{ka} \qquad \text{or} \qquad k = \frac{1}{at_{0.5}}$$

From the first set of data,

$$k = \frac{1}{0.502 \times 51} = 3.91 \times 10^{-2} \ \text{dm}^3 \ \text{mol}^{-1} \ \text{s}^{-1} \qquad\qquad \blacksquare$$

4.4 Determination of Order of Reaction and Rate Constant

The order of reaction and the rate constant can be determined using either of the forms of the rate laws listed in Table 4.1. If the differential form of the rate law is used, the rate is measured as a function of concentration as illustrated in Fig. 4.5 for concentrations c_1, c_2 and c_3. If the integrated form of the rate law is used, the variation of concentration with time is measured and a match is sought between the experimental data and one of the integrated rate equations given in Section 4.3.

Table 4.1 Summary of elementary rate laws

Order	Rate law in differential form	Rate law in integrated form	Typical units of k	Half-life proportional to
0	$\dfrac{dx}{dt} = k$	$kt = x$	$\text{mol dm}^{-3} \text{s}^{-1}$	a^1
1	$\dfrac{dx}{dt} = k(a-x)$	$kt = \ln\left(\dfrac{a}{a-x}\right)$	s^{-1}	$a^0 \ (=1)$
2	$\dfrac{dx}{dt} = k(a-x)^2$	$kt = \dfrac{x}{a(a-x)}$	$\text{dm}^3 \text{mol}^{-1} \text{s}^{-1}$	a^{-1}
2	$\dfrac{dx}{dt} = k(a-x)(b-x)$	$kt = \dfrac{1}{a-b} \ln\left(\dfrac{b(a-x)}{a(b-x)}\right)$	$\text{dm}^3 \text{mol}^{-1} \text{s}^{-1}$	-
3	$\dfrac{dx}{dt} = k(a-x)^3$	$kt = \dfrac{1}{2(a-x)^2} - \dfrac{1}{2a^2}$	$\text{dm}^6 \text{mol}^{-2} \text{s}^{-1}$	a^{-2}

The following two methods illustrate the general principles of this approach .

4.4.1 Van't Hoff Method

This is a differential method based on data obtained from graphs of the type illustrated in Fig. 4.5 If the rate of reaction J is measured at a number of concentrations, then, since from equation (4.3)

$$J = kc^n \tag{4.16}$$

$$\ln J = \ln k + n \ln c \tag{4.17}$$

Therefore, a plot of $\ln J$ versus $\ln c$ will be linear with slope equal to the order n. In theory, the rate constant can be obtained from the intercept, which is equal to $\ln k$ (and for illustrative purposes, this is done in Example 4.4), but extrapolation

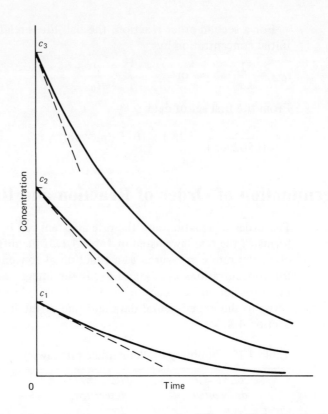

Figure 4.5 Concentration–time curves for different initial concentrations.

of data that have probably been obtained from the measurement of a tangent of the concentration versus time curve is unlikely to yield a reliable result. Therefore, in practice, this method would be used to determine the order and, once this has been established, k would be determined from the appropriate integrated equation.

Example 4.4

At 147°C, the initial rate of the gas-phase decomposition of 1,1-dimethylethyl peroxide (DMEP) depends on the initial concentration of DMEP thus:

[DMEP]/mol dm^{-3}	0.0200	0.0625	0.172
$(-d[DMEP]/dt)/10^{-4}$ mol dm^{-3} s^{-1}	0.0280	0.0875	0.240

From the data, establish that the reaction is first-order and calculate the rate constant at 147°C.

From equation (4.16),

$$J = k[DMEP]^n$$

where k is the rate constant and n is the order, and therefore

$$\ln J = \ln k + n \ln[DMEP]$$

$J/10^{-4}$ mol dm^{-3} s^{-1}	0.0280	0.0875	0.240
$\ln(J/\text{mol dm}^{-3}\text{ s}^{-1})$	−12.786	−11.646	−10.637
[DMEP]/mol dm^{-3}	0.0200	0.0625	0.172
$\ln([DMEP]/\text{mol dm}^{-3})$	−3.912	−2.773	−1.760

112

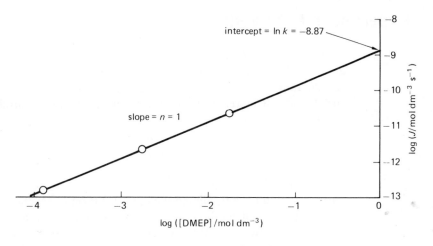

Figure 4.6 Van't Hoff method.

A plot of $\ln J$ versus $\ln[\text{DMEP}]$ is given in Fig. 4.6, from which the slope n is 1 and the intercept gives

$$\ln k = -8.874$$

giving

$$k = 1.4 \times 10^{-4} \text{ s}^{-1} \qquad \blacksquare$$

[Note: For reasons given above, k is best determined from a plot of $\ln c$ versus t or, since $n = 1$, k can be obtained from the average value of $J/[\text{DMEP}]$, which is $1.40 \times 10^{-4} \text{ s}^{-1}$.]

4.4.2 Ostwald Isolation Method

This technique requires that all the reactants except one are arranged to be in large excess, and the dependence of the reaction rate on the one reactant present in small concentration is studied. If necessary, this procedure can be repeated for each reactant in turn.

Consider the oxidation in aqueous solution of iodide ions by peroxydisulphate ions

$$2\text{I}^- + \text{S}_2\text{O}_8{}^{2-} \rightarrow \text{I}_2 + 2\text{SO}_4{}^{2-}$$

for which the rate equation is

$$J = k_2 [\text{S}_2\text{O}_8{}^{2-}][\text{I}^-]$$

i.e. the reaction is first-order with respect to $[\text{S}_2\text{O}_8{}^{2-}]$, first-order with respect to $[\text{I}^-]$ and overall second-order, with k_2 being the second-order rate constant.

If one of the reactants (in this case $[\text{I}^-]$) is in excess, its concentration remains essentially constant during the course of the reaction, and the reaction will appear to follow first-order kinetics and is said to be a **pseudo-first-order** reaction, i.e.

$$J = k'[\text{S}_2\text{O}_8{}^{2-}]$$

where the pseudo-first-order rate constant k' is equal to $k_2 [\text{I}^-]$.

This technique can be used as a differential or integral method and forms the basis of Worked Examples 4.11.4 and 4.11.9.

4.5   Experimental Methods

In order to determine the rate of a particular reaction by either a differential or an integral method, it is necessary to follow either

(a) the rate of decrease in concentration of a reactant, or

(b) the rate of increase in concentration of one of the products, by choosing an appropriate experimental method.

Clearly the basic requirements are

(i)   a good thermostat as rates change exponentially with temperature (see Section 4.6);

(ii) an accurate timing device;

(iii) a method of determining the concentration of reactant or product.

Normally the best methods for (iii) involve a measurement of a rapidly determinable physical property of the reaction mixture. (This avoids changing the reaction mixture during the experimental measurement and thereby changing the reaction conditions − e.g. chemical analysis requiring the withdrawal of a sample has this limitation.)

The following are some of the most commonly used techniques, and their application is illustrated by some of the worked examples included in Section 4.11.

4.5.1 Colorimetric and Spectrophotometric Methods

This usually involves selecting a suitable peak in the absorption spectrum of either a reactant or a product (the latter, if side-reactions involving a secondary reaction with the reactant are likely) and measuring absorbance as a function of time. (Absorbance is defined in Section 8.3 and its relationship to concentration outlined.) This method is illustrated in Worked Example 4.11.6.

4.5.2 Electrical Conductivity Method

Consider the reaction

$$CH_3COOC_2H_5 + OH^- \rightarrow CH_3COO^- + C_2H_5OH$$

It will be noted in Chapter 5 that the conductivity of hydroxyl (and hydrogen) ions greatly exceeds that of other ions such as ethanoate ions. Therefore a measurement of the conductivity is an appropriate method for following the rate of loss of hydroxyl ions in the above process.

4.5.3 Optical Rotation Method

Consider, for example,

$$C_{12}H_{22}O_{11} + H_2O \rightarrow C_6H_{12}O_6\,(glucose) + C_6H_{12}O_6\,(fructose)$$

A measurement of the optical rotation will be related to the change in concentration.

4.5.4 Refractive Index Method

This is useful for liquid-phase reactions.

4.5.5 Dilatometry Method

This follows the reaction by measuring the volume change during a liquid-phase reaction.

4.5.6 Gas Reactions from Change in Total Pressure

The total pressure at any time during a gas-phase reaction will be the sum of the partial pressures of all the gaseous reactant and product molecules. If the stoichiometry of the reaction is known, this can be used to enable the rate of decrease of reactant with time to be determined as a function of the measured total pressure. Side-reactions also cause a problem with this technique and the pressure must also be measured at constant volume. This method is illustrated in Worked Example 4.11.7.

4.5.7 Gas Evolution Method

If there is one gaseous product in a reaction, the gas evolved can be collected and its volume measured as a function of time. For example, the decomposition of benzenediazonium chloride proceeds via

$$C_6H_5N_2Cl \rightarrow C_6H_5Cl + N_2 \uparrow$$

and the rate constant can be determined from a measurement of the volume of nitrogen evolved during the reaction, as illustrated in Worked Example 4.11.8.

4.5.8 Chemical Analysis Method

If chemical analysis is to be employed (e.g. titration to estimate the acid liberated during the hydrolysis of an ester) precautions must be taken to ensure that no further reaction takes place between sampling and analysis. This is usually achieved by liberal dilution of the reaction mixture and/or a lowering of the temperature immediately after sampling. The other disadvantage of this technique is that normally one reaction mixture is needed for every sample (i.e. every reading) whereas this is not the case for all the previous techniques. The use of gas chromatography and other similar analytical tools means that very small samples can be withdrawn at set times without significant changes in reactant concentration occurring.

4.5.9 Fast Reactions

Reactions that take place in times as short as one second or less need special techniques involving flow methods or stopped-flow methods. Flash photolysis and shock-wave kinetic experiments are also relatively modern techniques for studying fast reactions where spectroscopic measurements are often used for analysis of the reaction mixture. The reader is referred to a specialist text for more information about these developments.

4.6 Arrhenius Equation and Activation Energy

The rate of a reaction, and therefore its rate constant, almost invariably increases as the temperature of the reaction is raised. Typically the rate doubles or triples for each 10 K rise in temperature (see Section 4.6.2).

The rate constant of a reaction is found to vary with the temperature in accordance with the Arrhenius equation, as follows

$$k = A \exp(- E^{\ddagger}/RT) \qquad (4.18)$$

where A is a constant known as the frequency factor or the pre-exponential factor and $E^{\ddagger}$ is the activation energy of the reaction. Taking logarithms, we have

$$\ln k = \ln A - E^{\ddagger}/RT \qquad (4.19)$$

4.6.1 Activation Energy

Consider a reaction

$$A + BC \rightarrow AB + C$$

The rate of the forward reaction is $k_1 [A] [BC]$ and the rate of the reverse reaction is $k_{-1} [AB] [C]$ where k_1 and k_{-1} are the rate constants of the forward and reverse reactions, respectively, and the equilibrium constant K is equal to k_1/k_{-1}. From the Arrhenius equation, it is seen that the rate of the forward reaction depends on the activation energy of the forward reaction, $E_1^{\ddagger}$, and the rate of the reverse reaction depends on the activation energy of the reverse reaction, $E_{-1}^{\ddagger}$. This implies that the reaction path from A + BC to AB + C involves an energy change $E_1^{\ddagger}$ while the reverse step involves an energy change $E_{-1}^{\ddagger}$. These conditions are satisfied if the reaction proceeds via an intermediate state that has energy $E_1^{\ddagger}$ greater than the initial state and energy $E_{-1}^{\ddagger}$ greater than the final state. This is illustrated in the energy diagram shown in Fig. 4.7 for an exothermic reaction. The intermediate state is known as the **transition state** (or **transition complex**). It is in equilibrium with A and BC and is represented by the superscript $\ddagger$.

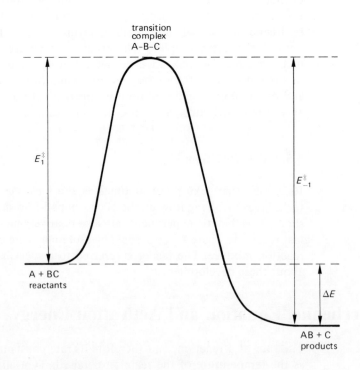

Figure 4.7   Potential-energy barrier for the exothermic reaction A + BC → AB + C.

Modern theories of chemical change (see Section 4.7) postulate that A and BC must acquire extra energy $E_1^{\ddagger}$ by collisions between the two molecules before they can form a transition complex A–B–C and hence AB + C. Only a small number of molecules acquire sufficient energy to react in the chemical sense to give products and those which do so can be thought of as having reached the top of the activation energy barrier to form the transition state and react to give products. It is easy to visualise that the lower the barrier (or the smaller the activation energy), the greater the number of activated molecules and the faster the reaction rate. Similarly, for the reverse reaction to take place, AB and C must acquire $E_{-1}^{\ddagger}$ before forming the transition complex A–B–C and hence A + BC, the activation energy for the reverse step being, therefore, $E_{-1}^{\ddagger}$.

A typical reaction pathway for

$$A + BC \rightarrow A\text{–}B\text{–}C \rightarrow AB + C$$

is illustrated in Fig. 4.8. The potential-energy curves for the diatomic molecules BC and AB have minima at points P and Q, respectively. One possible reaction pathway is PRQ representing

$$A + BC \rightarrow A + B + C \rightarrow AB + C$$

The energy for this pathway is at least the bond dissociation energy of BC. However, kinetic evidence shows that the actual reaction pathway is represented by PSQ, this can be likened to a contour diagram (see Fig. 4.9), in which the reaction pathway proceeds up a valley from P over a col at S, and down to a valley at Q.

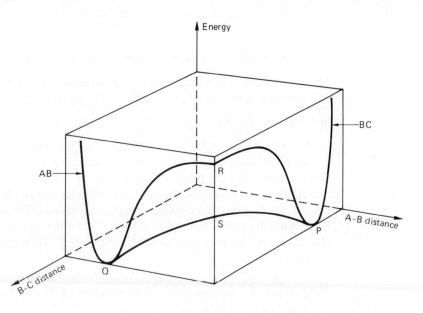

Figure 4.8   Potential-energy diagram for a linear A-B-C molecule.

4.6.2 Determination of Activation Energy

The Arrhenius equation predicts that the rate constant of a chemical reaction depends on the frequency of collisions between the reactant molecules and on the activation energy $E^{\ddagger}$, when expressed in the form

$$k = A \exp(-E^{\ddagger}/RT)$$

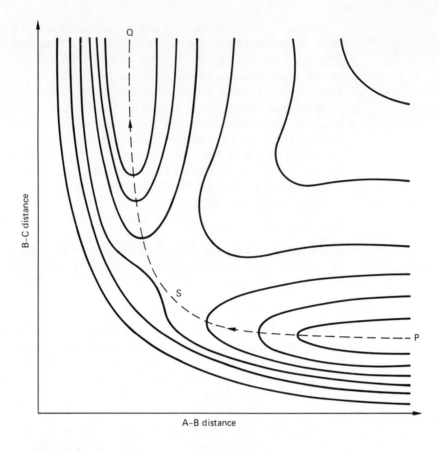

Figure 4.9   Potential-energy contour diagram for a linear A–B–C molecule.

The logarithmic form can be used to determine the activation energy when the rate constant is measured at a number of temperatures

$$\ln k = \ln A - E^{\ddagger}/RT$$

A plot of $\ln k$ against $1/T$ is linear with slope given by $-E^{\ddagger}/R$.

Figure 4.10 shows how the rate constant for the alkaline hydrolysis of iodo-ethane over the temperature range 20 to 80°C increases exponentially with temperature as predicted by the Arrhenius equation. It is noted that between 50 and 60°C, the rate constant doubles for this 10°C rise in temperature. Figure 4.11 confirms that a plot of $\ln k$ versus $1/T$ for these data is linear and provides the basis for the graphical determination of $E^{\ddagger}$ illustrated in Worked Example 4.11.10.

Alternatively, if rate constant k_1 at temperature T_1 and rate constant k_2 at temperature T_2 are measured, from equation (4.19) we have

$$\ln k_1 = \ln A - E^{\ddagger}/RT_1$$

and

$$\ln k_2 = \ln A - E^{\ddagger}/RT_2$$

Therefore

$$\ln\left(\frac{k_2}{k_1}\right) = -\frac{E^{\ddagger}}{R}\left(\frac{1}{T_2} - \frac{1}{T_1}\right)$$

or

$$\ln\left(\frac{k_2}{k_1}\right) = \frac{E^{\ddagger}}{R}\left(\frac{T_2 - T_1}{T_1 T_2}\right) \qquad (4.20)$$

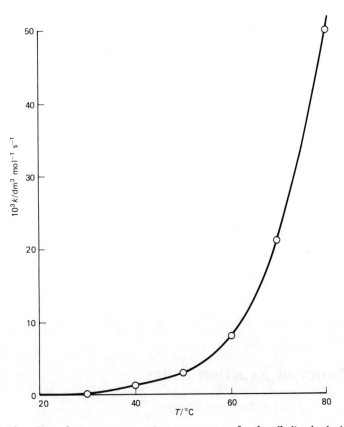

Figure 4.10 Plot of rate constant against temperature for the alkaline hydrolysis of iodoethane.

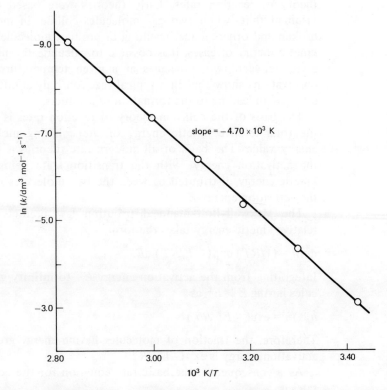

slope = -4.70×10^3 K

Figure 4.11 A plot of $\log_{10} k$ against $1/T$ for the alkaline hydrolysis of iodoethane giving $E^{\ddagger} = 8.314 \times 4.70 \times 10^3$ J mol^{-1} = 39.1 kJ mol^{-1}.

Example 4.5

If the rate constant for a reaction at 30°C is twice its value at 20°C, calculate the activation energy for the reaction.

(Liverpool Polytechnic, BSc, 1st year)

From equation (4.20)

$$\ln\left(\frac{k_2}{k_1}\right) = \frac{E^{\ddagger}}{R}\left(\frac{T_2 - T_1}{T_1 T_2}\right)$$

If k_2 is the rate constant at 30°C and k_1 is the rate constant at 20°C, $k_2/k_1 = 2$, and therefore

$$\ln 2 = \frac{E^{\ddagger}}{8.314}\left(\frac{303 - 293}{293 \times 303}\right)$$

giving

$$E^{\ddagger} = \frac{0.693 \times 8.314 \times 293 \times 303}{10} \text{ J mol}^{-1}$$

$$= 51.2 \text{ kJ mol}^{-1}$$

4.7 Theory of Reaction Rates

4.7.1 Collision Theory

The study of the kinetics of reactions in solution or in the gas phase has been undertaken for many years. Studies in the gas phase were the first to lead to a theory of reaction rates. Early theories were based on a collision model and assumed that, when two gas molecules collide, in most cases some bonds are broken and others made, resulting in product molecules being formed. From the kinetic theory of gases, it is possible to calculate the number of collisions taking place between two molecules at a given temperature and pressure. However, observations show that in a typical reaction only about one in 10^{14} collisions are effective in leading to the formation of products.

The basis of the collision theory of reaction rates is that reaction occurs when the total relative kinetic energy of the colliding molecules exceeds a critical energy value. The basis of all modern rate theories is that this critical energy is the activation energy, with the transition state being formed when the total kinetic energy distributed between the two molecules is greater than or equal to the activation energy $E^{\ddagger}$.

The Maxwell–Boltzmann distribution law predicts that the distribution of relative kinetic energy takes the form

$$dn/n = (1/RT)\exp(-E/RT)\,dE$$

Integrating from the activation energy $E^{\ddagger}$ to infinity gives the fraction of molecules having $E \geqslant E^{\ddagger}$ as

$$n_{E^{\ddagger}}/n = \exp(-E^{\ddagger}/RT) \tag{4.21}$$

Therefore, the fraction of molecules having energy greater than or equal to the activation energy is $\exp(-E^{\ddagger}/RT)$.

As a consequence, the basic rate equation for the collision theory of reaction rates is

$$\text{Rate} = \text{Collision rate} \times \exp(-E^{\ddagger}/RT)$$

120

Therefore, the higher the value of $E^{\ddagger}$ (i.e. the higher 'the activation energy barrier'), the smaller the number of molecules being activated and the slower the reaction rate. Consequently, reactions with high activation energies are slow unless carried out at high temperatures.

Example 4.6

The activation energy for the decomposition of hydrogen iodide is 184 kJ mol^{-1}. Calculate the fraction of activated molecules at (a) 500 K and (b) 700 K.

The fraction of activated molecules is given by $\exp(-E^{\ddagger}/RT)$. Therefore at 500 K

$$\exp(-E^{\ddagger}/RT) = \exp\left(-\frac{184\,000}{8.31 \times 500}\right) \approx 6 \times 10^{-20}$$

At 700 K

$$\exp(-E^{\ddagger}/RT) = \exp\left(-\frac{184\,000}{8.31 \times 700}\right) \approx 2 \times 10^{-14}$$

Hence increasing the temperature from 500 to 700 K increases the number of effective collisions (and hence the rate) by about a factor of 3×10^{5}. ∎

The rate of reaction J for the reaction

$$2A \rightarrow \text{products}$$

is therefore given by the collision rate multiplied by the fraction of molecules having energy greater than or equal to the activation energy $E^{\ddagger}$. Therefore,

$$J = 2Z_A \exp(-E^{\ddagger}/RT) \tag{4.22}$$

where the factor of 2 is introduced because two like molecules are involved in each collision and Z_A is the collision rate, i.e. the number of collisions per unit volume per unit time. Comparison with the Arrhenius equation (equation (4.18)) shows that collision theory predicts that the frequency factor A for the reaction can be determined from the collision rate. In reality, A factors calculated in this way show serious discrepancies with those obtained experimentally; indeed, differences of the order of 10^{-3} to 10^{-5} are quite common.

4.7.2 Absolute Rate Theory

This theory overcomes the inadequacies of simple collision theory by using statistical thermodynamics to provide a more exact method of deriving A factors. Its basis is to assume that the reaction path proceeds via a transition state (corresponding to the transition complex) $X^{\ddagger}$ and it is the rate of passage of $X^{\ddagger}$ through the transition state between the reactants and products that determines the rate of reaction.

Consider the reaction

$$\begin{array}{ccccc} A+B & \rightarrow & X^{\ddagger} & \rightarrow & C+D \\ \text{reactants} & & \text{transition} & & \text{products} \\ & & \text{state} & & \end{array}$$

Using statistical thermodynamics, it can be shown that the rate constant k is related to the equilibrium constant $K^\ddagger$ for the equilibrium between the reactant state and the transition state by

$$k = \frac{kT}{h} K^\ddagger \tag{4.23}$$

where k is the Boltzmann constant and h is Planck's constant. Since by analogy with conventional thermodynamics

$$K^\ddagger = \exp(-\Delta G^\ddagger / RT)$$

and

$$\Delta G^\ddagger = \Delta H^\ddagger - T\Delta S^\ddagger$$

the rate constant can be formulated in terms of the enthalpy of activation $\Delta H^\ddagger$ and the entropy of activation $\Delta S^\ddagger$ and was shown by Wynne-Jones and Eyring to be given by

$$k = \frac{kT}{h} \exp\left(\frac{\Delta S^\ddagger}{R}\right) \exp\left(-\frac{\Delta H^\ddagger}{RT}\right) \tag{4.24}$$

By taking logarithms in equations (4.19) (the Arrhenius equation) and (4.24) and differentiating with respect to $1/T$, it can be shown that for a unimolecular gas-phase reaction,

$$E^\ddagger = \Delta H^\ddagger + RT$$

and hence

$$k = \exp(1) \frac{kT}{h} \exp\left(\frac{\Delta S^\ddagger}{R}\right) \exp\left(-\frac{E^\ddagger}{RT}\right) \tag{4.25}$$

Comparison of equation (4.25) with equation (4.18) shows that, according to absolute rate theory, the frequency factor A can be determined from the entropy of activation and is given by

$$A = \exp(1) \frac{kT}{h} \exp\left(\frac{\Delta S^\ddagger}{R}\right)$$

4.8 Theory of Unimolecular Reactions

In a unimolecular reaction, a single reactant molecule isomerises or decomposes to give a product or products. In terms of absolute rate theory, the transition complex is considered to have a configuration similar to that of the reactant, so that for molecule A,

$$A \rightarrow A^\ddagger \rightarrow \text{products}$$

An example of a unimolecular reaction is the isomerisation of cyclopropane to propene:

4.8.1 Lindemann Theory

In this model, the molecules acquire their energy of activation by bimolecular collisions, but the reaction obeys first-order kinetics, except at low pressures.

Modern theories are merely refinements of Lindemann's approach. The theory assumes that the mechanism for reactant A can be represented as follows:

(1) activation $\qquad\qquad\qquad$ $A + A \xrightarrow{k_1} A^* + A$

(2) deactivation $\qquad\qquad\;\;$ $A^* + A \xrightarrow{k_{-1}} A + A$

(3) unimolecular decomposition $\qquad$ $A^* \xrightarrow{k_2}$ products

This mechanism assumes that there is a time lag between the activation and the reaction of the energised molecules A^* to give products. As a consequence, most of the A^* molecules collide with a normal reactant molecule (process (2)) and are deactivated before they can react to produce products (process (3)). This produces a **steady-state concentration** of energised molecules, i.e. their concentration remains steady and does not change during the course of the reaction. This so-called **steady-state hypothesis** is important in enabling the rates of free-radical reactions to be expressed simply, and this approach will be outlined in Section 4.9.

The rate of formation of A^* is given by

$$d[A^*]/dt = k_1[A]^2 - k_{-1}[A^*][A] - k_2[A^*]$$

But because a steady-state concentration of A^* is attained, $d[A^*]/dt = 0$, so that,

$$k_1[A]^2 - k_{-1}[A^*][A] - k_2[A^*] = 0$$

or

$$[A^*] = \frac{k_1[A]^2}{k_{-1}[A] + k_2}$$

The rate of reaction J expressed as the rate of formation of product is given by

$$J = k_2[A^*] = \frac{k_1 k_2[A]^2}{k_{-1}[A] + k_2} \qquad (4.26)$$

At high pressures, deactivation predominates, i.e.

$$k_{-1}[A][A^*] \gg k_2[A^*]$$

Therefore, equation (4.26) reduces to

$$J = \frac{k_1 k_2[A]}{k_{-1}} = k_\infty[A]$$

and the reaction is first-order with a rate constant k_∞ equal to $k_1 k_2/k_{-1}$. At low pressures, conversion to product predominates, with $k_{-1}[A][A^*] \ll k_2[A^*]$, so that equation (4.26) reduces to

$$J = k_1[A]^2 \qquad (4.27)$$

A comparison with experimental results is best illustrated by assuming that the rate J at any pressure is given by

$$J = k'[A] \qquad (4.28)$$

where k' is a rate coefficient that varies with pressure. From equation (4.26), it is seen that k' is given by

$$k' = \frac{k_1 k_2[A]}{k_{-1}[A] + k_2} = \frac{k_\infty}{1 + k_2[A]/k_{-1}} \qquad (4.29)$$

If k' is plotted against pressure, k' is seen to reach a limiting value k_∞ at high pressure and fall to zero at low pressure as predicted by Lindemann and illustrated in Fig. 4.12.

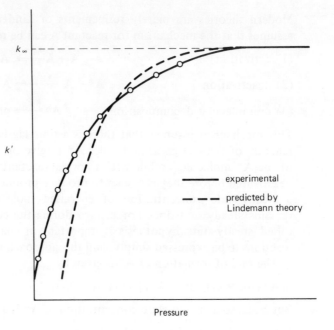

Figure 4.12   Plot of k' against pressure for a unimolecular reaction.

Inversion of equation (4.29) gives

$$\frac{1}{k'} = \frac{k_{-1}}{k_1 k_2} + \frac{1}{k_1 [A]} = \frac{1}{k_\infty} + \frac{1}{k_1 [A]} \tag{4.30}$$

Therefore, a plot of $1/k'$ versus $1/[A]$ will be linear with slope equal to $1/k_1$ and intercept $1/k_\infty$, as illustrated in Worked Example 4.11.14.

4.9   Atomic and Free-Radical Processes

In the early years of the study of the kinetics of chemical reactions, it was assumed that the process involved a single step in accordance with the stoichiometric equation. It is now recognised that the majority of chemical reactions are much more complex and proceed via a number of steps involving reactive intermediates such as atoms or free radicals.

For kinetic purposes, a free radical is an atomic or molecular species with one or more unpaired electrons. For example, a bromine atom has one unpaired electron and a ground-state oxygen atom has two unpaired electrons, but the definition also includes molecules such as nitrogen oxide (NO) and oxygen, which have unpaired electrons and can therefore be regarded as free radicals by this definition.

The kinetic data of these free-radical reactions has provided a fruitful method of elucidating reaction mechanisms. The aim of a kineticist is to postulate a reaction mechanism which is in qualitative and quantitative agreement with the experimental rate data. Some examples of this approach are considered in this section.

124

4.9.1 Types of Complex Reactions

(a) *Non-Chain Processes*

In this case, a free radical is formed which immediately reacts with itself or the reactant to give the product so that regeneration of the intermediate is not possible. For example, the iodination of acetone in acid solution proceeds via

$$CH_3COCH_3 \xrightarrow{\text{acid}} CH_3C{=}CH_2$$
$$\underset{OH}{|}$$

$$CH_3C{=}CH_2 + I_2 \longrightarrow CH_3CICH_2I$$
$$\underset{OH}{|} \qquad\qquad \underset{OH}{|}$$

$$CH_3CICH_2I \longrightarrow HI + CH_3COCH_2I$$
$$\underset{OH}{|}$$

(b) *Linear-Chain Reactions*

This is the most common type of free-radical reaction and proceeds via three types of steps, examples of which will be described later in this section.

(c) *Branched-Chain Reactions*

This situation arises when one radical reacts to produce two or more radicals, each of which in turn repeat the process. In the hydrogen–oxygen reaction, two such steps are

$$H\bullet + O_2 \rightarrow OH\bullet + O\colon$$
$$O\colon + H_2 \rightarrow OH\bullet + H\bullet$$

and the outcome of an ever-increasing build-up of radicals is inevitably an explosion.

4.9.2 Steady-State Approximation for Linear-Chain Reactions

It is found that in these processes, after a short induction time when the concentration of radicals is built up, steady-state conditions soon apply. This means the concentration of free radicals becomes more or less constant until the reactants are consumed, indicating that the rate at which free radicals are formed is equal to the rate at which they are consumed. In kinetic terms, therefore,

$$d[\text{radical}]/dt = 0$$

In order to assist in the solving of reaction mechanisms, it is assumed that this steady state is attained quickly and this approximation avoids the necessity of solving a large number of differential equations.

4.9.3 Examples of Linear-Chain Reactions

(a) *Decomposition of* N_2O_5

This reaction was introduced in Section 4.1 as a reaction that occurs in three steps (one being reversible), as follows:

(1) $N_2O_5 \underset{k_{-1}}{\overset{k_1}{\rightleftharpoons}} NO_2 + NO_3\bullet$

(2) $NO_2 + NO_3\bullet \overset{k_2}{\longrightarrow} NO + O_2 + NO_2$

(3) $NO + NO_3\bullet \overset{k_3}{\longrightarrow} 2NO_2$

The rate equations for the two intermediates $NO_3\bullet$ and NO are

$$d[NO_3\bullet]/dt = k_1[N_2O_5] - (k_{-1} + k_2)[NO_2][NO_3\bullet] - k_3[NO][NO_3\bullet]$$

$$d[NO]/dt = k_2[NO_2][NO_3\bullet] - k_3[NO][NO_3\bullet]$$

Using the steady-state approximation gives

$$d[NO_3\bullet]/dt = 0 \qquad \text{and} \qquad d[NO]/dt = 0$$

and, as a consequence,

$$[NO] = k_2[NO_2]/k_3 \tag{4.31}$$

and

$$[NO_3\bullet] = \frac{k_1[N_2O_5]}{(k_{-1} + 2k_2)[NO_2]} \tag{4.32}$$

The rate equation for the decomposition of N_2O_5 is

$$-d[N_2O_5]/dt = k_1[N_2O_5] - k_{-1}[NO_2][NO_3\bullet] \tag{4.33}$$

Substituting for $[NO_3\bullet]$ in equation (4.33) gives

$$-\frac{d[N_2O_5]}{dt} = \frac{2k_1k_2}{k_{-1} + 2k_2}[N_2O_5] \tag{4.34}$$

so that the above overall reaction mechanism predicts that the reaction shows first-order kinetics with a first-order rate constant given by $2k_1k_2/(k_{-1} + 2k_2)$. Experimental results confirm this.

(b) *Hydrogen–Bromine Gas Reaction*

This is the example most frequently quoted in textbooks. The experimental results show that

$$\frac{d[HBr]}{dt} = \frac{k[H_2][Br_2]^{1/2}}{1 + k'[HBr]/[Br_2]} \tag{4.35}$$

where k' is approximately equal to 10 and independent of temperature.

It can be shown that a linear-chain mechanism which has all the usual features (but, in addition, an inhibition step caused by the free radical attacking the product) will give a rate expression consistent with the experimental data. The mechanism is:

(1) chain initiation $\qquad\qquad Br_2 \overset{k_1}{\longrightarrow} Br\bullet + Br\bullet$

(2) chain propagation $\qquad Br\bullet + H_2 \overset{k_2}{\longrightarrow} HBr + H\bullet$

(3) chain propagation $\qquad$ H• + Br$_2$ $\xrightarrow{k_3}$ HBr + Br•

(4) chain inhibition by product $\qquad$ H• + HBr $\xrightarrow{k_4}$ H$_2$ + Br•

(5) chain termination $\qquad$ Br• + Br• $\xrightarrow{k_5}$ Br$_2$

Reference to a specialist textbook will show that, using the steady-state approximation, the following rate equation can be derived

$$\frac{d[HBr]}{dt} = \frac{2k_2\,(k_1/k_5)^{1/2}\,[H_2]\,[Br_2]^{1/2}}{1 + k_4[HBr]/k_3[Br_2]} \tag{4.36}$$

consistent with the experimental rate equation.

(c) Rice–Herzfeld Mechanisms

This is a general term used to describe the mechanism of the gas-phase decomposition of a number of simple organic compounds. One example is the thermal decomposition of ethanal, which is found experimentally to have three-halves order kinetics. It can be shown to follow the mechanism:

(1) $CH_3CHO \xrightarrow{k_1} CH_3\bullet + CHO\bullet$

(2) $CH_3\bullet + CH_3CHO \xrightarrow{k_2} CH_4 + CH_3CO\bullet$

(3) $CH_3CO\bullet \xrightarrow{k_3} CH_3\bullet + CO$

(4) $CH_3\bullet + CH_3\bullet \xrightarrow{k_4} C_2H_6$

(The above simplified mechanism neglects the subsequent reaction of CHO• and H• referred to in Section 4.9.4.)

Applying the steady-state approximation to $[CH_3\bullet]$ and $[CH_3CO\bullet]$, we have

$$d[CH_3\bullet]/dt = k_1[CH_3CHO] - k_2[CH_3\bullet][CH_3CHO] + k_3[CH_3CO\bullet]$$
$$-2k_4[CH_3\bullet]^2 = 0 \tag{4.37}$$

$$d[CH_3CO\bullet]/dt = k_2[CH_3][CH_3CHO] - k_3[CH_3CO\bullet] = 0 \tag{4.38}$$

Addition of equations (4.37) and (4.38) gives

$$k_1[CH_3CHO] - 2k_4[CH_3\bullet]^2 = 0$$

i.e.

$$[CH_3\bullet] = (k_1/2k_4)^{1/2}[CH_3CHO]^{1/2} \tag{4.39}$$

The rate of reaction, as measured by the rate of production of methane (this approximates to the rate of decomposition of CH_3CHO) is given by

$$J = k_2[CH_3\bullet][CH_3CHO]$$
$$= k_2(k_1/2k_4)^{1/2}[CH_3CHO]^{3/2} \tag{4.40}$$

This agrees with the experimental observation.

(d) Photochemical Reactions

All the above examples are thermal reactions, but a convenient method of initiating a free-radical reaction is by the absorption of electromagnetic radiation. As will be shown in Chapter 8, if the gas absorbs visible or ultraviolet light, there may be sufficient energy absorbed to excite the reactant molecule and this leads to free radicals being formed. For example, propanone vapour will absorb light and lead to chain initiation by the reaction

$$CH_3COCH_3 + h\nu \rightarrow CH_3COCH_3^* \rightarrow 2CH_3\bullet + CO$$

The ethanal decomposition described previously can also be initiated photochemically

$$CH_3CHO + h\nu \rightarrow CH_3CHO^* \rightarrow CH_3\bullet + CHO\bullet$$

4.9.4 Kinetic Data from Chain Reactions

The above example of the decomposition of ethanal can illustrate a number of the important features of the study of chain reactions. The mechanism predicts which are the major and minor products and experimentally it is observed that methane and carbon monoxide are the major products and ethane is a minor product. Hydrogen is also observed as a minor product and additional steps (which do not significantly influence the overall rate) can be suggested to explain this, e.g.

$$CHO\bullet \rightarrow H\bullet + CO$$

$$H\bullet + CH_3CHO \rightarrow H_2 + CH_3CO\bullet$$

(These steps were excluded from the kinetic derivation to simplify it.)

Equation (4.40) also gives a value for the overall rate constant in terms of the rate constants of the individual steps. A comparison with the experimental rate constants obtained from other examples of Rice–Herzfeld mechanisms enables the values of the rate constants such as k_1, k_2 and k_4 to be determined. Also, since from equation (4.40) the overall rate constant can be expressed as

$$k_2\left(\frac{k_1}{2k_4}\right)^{1/2} = A_2\left(\frac{A_1}{2A_4}\right)^{1/2} \exp\left(-\frac{E_2^{\ddagger} + \frac{1}{2}(E_1^{\ddagger} - E_4^{\ddagger})}{RT}\right)$$

it is seen that the overall activation energy is, therefore, given by

$$E^{\ddagger} = E_2^{\ddagger} + \tfrac{1}{2}(E_1^{\ddagger} - E_4^{\ddagger})$$

For the ethanal decomposition $E_1^{\ddagger}$ is known from the bond dissociation energy to be $332\,kJ\,mol^{-1}$ and kinetic studies have established that termination reactions such as

$$CH_3\bullet + CH_3\bullet = C_2H_6$$

have zero activation energy. The value of $E_2^{\ddagger}$ can be shown from the corresponding photochemical decomposition (where the bond is dissociated by radiation, not thermally) to be $32\,kJ\,mol^{-1}$, so that

$$E^{\ddagger} = 32 + \tfrac{1}{2}(332 - 0) = 198\,kJ\,mol^{-1}$$

This is in excellent agreement with the observed overall activation energy of $193\,kJ\,mol^{-1}$, and is seen to be much less than the energy needed to break the C—C bond in ethanal.

4.10 Reactions Between Ions in Solution

Reactions in solution are often so rapid that their rates are difficult to measure by conventional techniques. However, many reactions involving complex ions proceed at a measurable rate and have been studied extensively. It is found that, in such reactions, the rate depends on

(a) the nature of the solvent,

(b) the nature of the ions, and

(c) the ionic strength of the solution.

Of these, the influence of the ionic strength is of most interest. For the reaction between ions A and B,

$$A + B \rightarrow X^{\ddagger} \rightarrow products$$

The kinetic treatment is based on an assumption that the rate J depends only on the concentration of activated complex $X^{\ddagger}$, and is given by

$$J = - \frac{d[A]}{dt} = - \frac{d[B]}{dt} = k'[X^{\ddagger}]$$ (4.41)

For the equilibrium between the activated complex $X^{\ddagger}$ and the ions A and B,

$$K = \frac{a_{X^{\ddagger}}}{a_A a_B} = \frac{[X^{\ddagger}]}{[A][B]} \frac{\gamma_{X^{\ddagger}}}{\gamma_A \gamma_B}$$

where a denotes the activity and γ the activity coefficient. Rearranging gives

$$[X^{\ddagger}] = K[A][B] \gamma_A \gamma_B / \gamma_{X^{\ddagger}}$$

Therefore, from equation (4.41)

$$J = k'K[A][B] \gamma_A \gamma_B / \gamma_{X^{\ddagger}}$$ (4.42)

But the rate J is also given by

$$J = k[A][B]$$ (4.43)

where k is the rate constant. Combining equations (4.42) and (4.43),

$$k = k'K \gamma_A \gamma_B / \gamma_{X^{\ddagger}}$$

If k_0 is the rate constant at infinite dilution when the activity coefficients can be taken as unity, this becomes

$$k_0 = k'K$$

giving in general

$$k = k_0 \gamma_A \gamma_B / \gamma_{X^{\ddagger}}$$

Taking logarithms,

$$\log_{10} k = \log_{10} k_0 + \log_{10}(\gamma_A \gamma_B / \gamma_{X^{\ddagger}})$$ (4.44)

In solution, the Debye–Hückel limiting law (Section 5.6.2) relates γ_i to the ionic strength I and valency z_i by

$$\log_{10} \gamma_i = - A z_i^2 \sqrt{I}$$

or

$$\log_{10}(\gamma_A \gamma_B / \gamma_{X^{\ddagger}}) = - A[(z_A^2 + z_B^2) - (z_A + z_B)^2]\sqrt{I}$$
$$= +2A z_A z_B \sqrt{I}$$

Equation (4.44) now becomes

$$\log_{10} k = \log_{10} k_0 + 2A z_A z_B \sqrt{I}$$ (4.45)

and is known as the Brønsted–Bjerrum relationship. Therefore a plot of $\log_{10} k$ against $\sqrt{I}$ will be linear with a slope equal to $2A z_A z_B$.

Equation (4.45) indicates that a plot of $\log_{10}(k/k_0)$ versus $\sqrt{I}$ is linear with slope equal to $2Az_A z_B$. Therefore, as illustrated in Fig. 4.13, the rate increases with increasing ionic strength when both the ionic species have the same sign, while the rate decreases with increasing ionic strength when the ionic species have opposite sign. However, for a reaction such as the base-catalysed hydrolysis of ethyl ethanoate with $z_A z_B = 0$, the rate is independent of ionic strength.

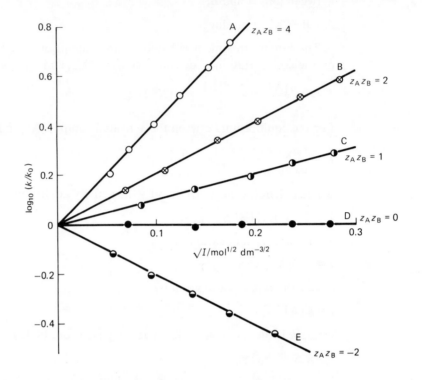

Figure 4.13   Variation of $\log_{10}(k/k_0)$ with $\sqrt{I}$ for a number of ionic reactions: A, $[Co(NH_3)_5 Br]^{2+} + Hg^{2+}$; B, $CH_2 Br COO^- + S_2 O_3^{2-}$; C, $CH_2 ClCOO^- + OH^-$; D, $CH_3 COOC_2 H_5 + OH^-$; E, $[Co(NH_3)_5 Br]^{2+} + OH^-$

4.11   Worked Examples

4.11.1 Rate Equation

The following kinetic data were obtained for the reaction between nitrogen oxide and hydrogen at 700°C

$$2NO + 2H_2 \rightarrow N_2 + 2H_2 O$$

Initial concentration/mol dm^{-3}		*Initial rate*/mol dm^{-3} s^{-1}
NO	H$_2$	
0.025	0.01	2.4×10^{-6}
0.025	0.005	1.2×10^{-6}
0.0125	0.01	0.6×10^{-6}

Deduce the order of the reaction with respect to each reactant and calculate the rate constant at 700°C.

Answer

The rate of reaction J is given by

$$J = -\frac{1}{2}\frac{dc_{NO}}{dt} = -\frac{1}{2}\frac{dc_{H_2}}{dt} = +\frac{dc_{N_2}}{dt} = +\frac{1}{2}\frac{dc_{H_2O}}{dt}$$

The rate equation for the reaction expressed in terms of initial concentrations is given by

$$J = kc_{NO}^x c_{H_2}^y$$

where x and y are the order of reaction with respect to NO and H_2, respectively, $x + y$ is the overall order of reaction and k is the rate constant.

Taking logarithms,

$$\ln J = \ln k + x \ln c_{NO} + y \ln c_{H_2}$$

From the first and second sets of data, c_{NO} is constant so that

$$\ln J = \text{constant} + y \ln c_{H_2}$$

or

$$\ln\left(\frac{J_1}{J_2}\right) = y \ln\left(\frac{(c_{H_2})_1}{(c_{H_2})_2}\right)$$

Substituting the appropriate numerical values,

$$\ln\left(\frac{2.4 \times 10^{-6}}{1.2 \times 10^{-6}}\right) = y \ln\left(\frac{0.01}{0.005}\right)$$

giving

$$y = 1.0$$

Therefore the reaction is first-order with respect to hydrogen.

For the first and last sets of data, c_{H_2} is constant so that

$$\ln\left(\frac{J_1}{J_3}\right) = x \ln\left(\frac{(c_{NO})_1}{(c_{NO})_3}\right)$$

Substituting the appropriate data gives

$$\ln\left(\frac{2.4 \times 10^{-6}}{0.6 \times 10^{-6}}\right) = x \ln\left(\frac{0.025}{0.0125}\right)$$

giving

$$x = 2.0$$

Therefore the reaction is second-order with respect to nitrogen oxide with the overall order $x + y = 3$, i.e. the reaction is overall third-order so that the rate equation is

$$J = kc_{NO}^2 c_{H_2}$$

From the first set of readings, the rate constant can be obtained as

$$2.4 \times 10^{-6} / \text{mol dm}^{-3} \text{ s}^{-1} = k \left[(0.025)^2 /(\text{mol dm}^{-3})^2\right] (0.01/\text{mol dm}^{-3})$$

giving

$$k = 0.384 \text{ dm}^6 \text{ mol}^{-2} \text{ s}^{-1}$$

[Note: This is an example of a reaction which illustrates the point made in Section 4.2.2 that order of a reaction must be determined experimentally and not assumed from the stoichiometric equation.]

4.11.2 First-Order Rate Constant

The decomposition of dinitrogen pentoxide in tetrachloromethane at 45°C takes place according to the equation

$$2N_2O_5 \rightarrow 4NO_2 + O_2$$

From the volumes of oxygen liberated after various times t, the following concentrations of N_2O_5 were obtained:

$[N_2O_5]$/mol dm^{-3}	2.33	1.91	1.36	1.11	0.72	0.55
Time/s	0	319	867	1196	1877	2315

By plotting the appropriate graph, show that the reaction is first-order and determine the first-order rate constant.

(University of Salford, BSc, 1st year)

Answer

The integrated rate equation for a first-order reaction (equation (4.10)) becomes

$$kt = \ln\left([A]_0/[A]\right) = \ln[N_2O_5]_0 - \ln[N_2O_5]$$

Therefore, a plot of $\ln[N_2O_5]$ against t should be linear, with slope $= -k$.

Time/s	0	319	867	1196	1877	2315
$[N_2O_5]$/mol dm^{-3}	2.33	1.91	1.36	1.11	0.72	0.55
$\ln([N_2O_5]$/mol dm$^{-3})$	0.846	0.647	0.307	0.104	−0.328	−0.598

Since a plot of $\ln[N_2O_5]$ versus t (Fig. 4.14) is linear, the reaction is first-order.

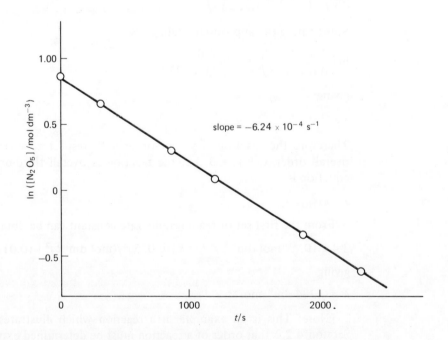

Figure 4.14 $\ln[N_2O_5]$ versus t for first-order decomposition of N_2O_5.

From the graph

slope $= -k = -6.24 \times 10^{-4}$ s^{-1}

i.e.

$k = 6.24 \times 10^{-4}$ s^{-1}

A mechanism for this reaction which leads to first-order kinetics is described in Section 4.9. The first-order rate constant in equation (4.34) is therefore given by

$$\frac{2k_1 k_2}{k_{-1} + 2k_2} = 6.24 \times 10^{-4} \text{ s}^{-1}$$

4.11.3 Second-Order Rate Constant

In studying the rate of decomposition of a reactant A, its concentration was found to decrease from its initial value of 0.8 mol dm^{-3} in the following way:

$[A]$/mol dm^{-3}	0.6	0.4	0.2	0.1
Time, t/min	4.17	12.5	37.5	87.5

What is the order of the reaction and what is the rate constant?

(University of Sheffield, BSc, 1st year)

Answer

It is apparent from the experimental data that the reaction is not first-order, since the time for $[A]$ to be reduced by a factor of 2 (e.g. from 0.4 to 0.2 mol dm^{-3} or from 0.2 to 0.1 mol dm^{-3}) is not constant. In other words, the half-life is not independent of concentration.

If the reaction is second-order, equation (4.14) will be obeyed, i.e.

$$kt = \frac{1}{[A]} - \frac{1}{[A]_0}$$

where $[A]_0$ is the initial concentration of A and $[A]$ is the concentration at time t. Therefore a plot of $1/[A]$ against t will be linear with slope equal to k.

t/min	0	4.17	12.5	37.5	87.5
mol dm^{-3}/$[A]$	1.25	1.67	2.50	5.00	10.00

The graph (Fig. 4.15) confirms that the reaction is second-order with

slope $= k = 0.100$ (mol dm^{-3})$^{-1}$ min^{-1}

giving

$k = 1.67 \times 10^{-3}$ dm^3 mol^{-1} s^{-1}.

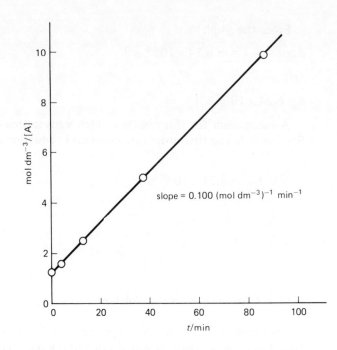

Figure 4.15 Second-order plot for decomposition of A.

4.11.4 Rate Constant

A solution of potassium peroxydisulphate was added to excess acidified potassium iodide (0.1 mol dm^{-3}) solution and the kinetics of the second-order reaction was followed by withdrawing samples at various times and titrating the liberated iodine with sodium thiosulphate solution. The following results were obtained at 298 K.

Titre/cm^3	0.00	5.80	9.80	12.60	14.30	15.80	16.80	18.80
Time/min	0	5	10	15	20	25	30	∞

Calculate the rate constant for the reaction at 298 K.

Answer

For the second-order reaction

$$S_2O_8^{2-} + 2I^- \rightarrow 2SO_4^{2-} + I_2$$

the rate J is given by

$$J = k_2 [S_2O_8^{2-}][I^-]$$

but in excess potassium iodide, it will be effectively first-order, i.e.

$$J = k'[S_2O_8^{2-}]$$

with k_2 being a second-order rate constant. k', the pseudo-first-order rate constant to be determined, is equal to $k_2[I^-]$. Since one molecule of iodine is produced for each molecule of peroxydisulphate reacting, the titre reading, which is proportional to the concentration of iodine produced, can be used to determine the rate constant k' from the integrated form of the rate equation. If V_∞ is the titre reading when the reaction has gone to completion, it is clearly proportional to the

134

initial concentration a. Similarly, the titre reading V_t at any time t is proportional to the concentration x at time t. The rate equation (4.6) becomes

$$k't = \ln\left(\frac{V_\infty}{V_\infty - V_t}\right)$$

or

$$\ln(V_\infty - V_t) = \ln V_\infty - k't$$

Therefore a plot of $\ln(V_\infty - V_t)$ against t will be linear with slope equal to $-k'$. From the data:

$(V_\infty - V_t)/cm^3$	18.80	13.00	9.00	6.20	4.50	3.00	2.00
$\ln[(V_\infty - V_t)/cm^3]$	2.934	2.565	2.197	1.825	1.504	1.099	0.693
t/min	0	5	10	15	20	25	30

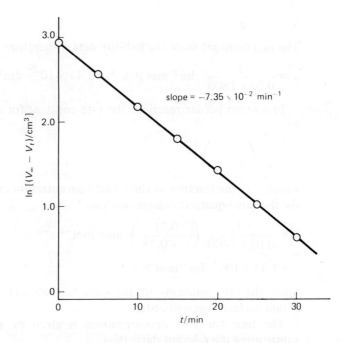

Figure 4.16   First-order rate constant by sampling method.

A plot of $\ln(V_\infty - V_t)$ against t is shown in Fig 4.16. From the graph

$$\text{slope} = -k' = -7.35 \times 10^{-2}\ min^{-1}$$

giving

$$k' = 1.23 \times 10^{-3}\ s^{-1}$$

The overall second-order rate constant is given by

$$k' = k_2[I^-]$$

Therefore

$$k_2 = \frac{k'}{[I^-]} = \frac{1.23 \times 10^{-3}\ s^{-1}}{0.1\ mol\ dm^{-3}} = 1.23 \times 10^{-2}\ dm^3\ mol^{-1}\ s^{-1}$$

4.11.5 Fractional Life

Ethyl ethanoate and sodium hydroxide in solution in an ethanol–water mixture at 303 K exhibit a hydrolysis reaction. In an experiment in which 0.05 mol dm^{-3} of each reactant were present at time $t = 0$, the time for half-change was 1800 s and the time for three-quarters change was 5400 s. Deduce the order of the reaction and calculate the rate constant. At what time was 10 per cent reaction complete?

(University of Bristol, BSc, Part I)

Answer

In a first-order reaction, the time for three-quarters change is double that for the half change. As this is not the case here, the reaction is not first-order.

If the reaction is second-order, the half-life $t_{0.5}$ is related to the rate constant k by

$$t_{0.5} = 1/ka$$

The rate constant from the half-life data is therefore

$$k = \frac{1}{0.05 \times 1800} \text{ dm}^3 \text{ mol}^{-1} \text{ s}^{-1} = 1.11 \times 10^{-2} \text{ dm}^3 \text{ mol}^{-1} \text{ s}^{-1}$$

In a second-order reaction, the rate constant for a change of fraction y is given by

$$k = \frac{1}{at} \left(\frac{y}{1 - y} \right) \tag{1}$$

where y is the fraction of the initial concentration at time t. Substituting the data for the three-quarters change, we have

$$k = \frac{1}{0.05 \times 5400} \left(\frac{0.75}{1 - 0.75} \right) \text{ dm}^3 \text{ mol}^{-1} \text{ s}^{-1}$$

$$= 1.11 \times 10^{-2} \text{ dm}^3 \text{ mol}^{-1} \text{ s}^{-1}$$

Since the rate constants are the same for half and three-quarters change, the reaction is clearly second-order.

The time for 10% decomposition is given by rearranging equation (1) and substituting the relevant data; thus

$$t = \frac{1}{ka} \left(\frac{y}{1 - y} \right) = \frac{1}{1.11 \times 10^{-2} \times 0.05} \left(\frac{0.10}{1 - 0.10} \right) \text{ s}$$

$$= 200 \text{ s}$$

4.11.6 Rate Constant from Absorbance

A first-order reaction A $\rightarrow$ B was followed kinetically by noting the increasing optical absorbance due to product B as a function of time. From the data below, calculate the value of the first-order rate constant.

Time/s	0	30	60	90	150	210	∞
Absorbance	0.000	0.106	0.194	0.268	0.380	0.459	0.640

(University of Durham, BSc, 1st year)

Answer

If A_∞ is the absorbance when the reaction has gone to completion, and A_t is the absorbance at any time t, then the difference $A_\infty - A_t$ is proportional to the concentration of the reactant at any time t while $A_\infty - A_0$ is proportional to the initial concentration a.

Therefore equation (4.9) can be expressed in the form

$$kt = \ln\left(\frac{A_\infty - A_0}{A_\infty - A_t}\right)$$

or

$$\ln(A_\infty - A_t) = \ln(A_\infty - A_0) - kt$$

and a plot of $\ln(A_\infty - A_t)$ versus t will be linear with slope equal to $-k$.

t/s	0	30	60	90	150	210
$(A_\infty - A_t)$	0.640	0.534	0.446	0.372	0.260	0.181
$\ln(A_\infty - A_t)$	−0.446	−0.627	−0.807	−0.989	−1.347	−1.709

A plot of $\ln(A_\infty - A_t)$ versus time is plotted in Fig. 4.17. From the graph

$$\text{slope} = -k = -0.00601 \text{ s}^{-1}$$

giving

$$k = 6.01 \times 10^{-3} \text{ s}^{-1}$$

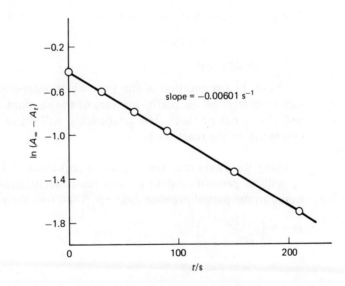

Figure 4.17   First-order plot for reaction from absorbance versus time measurements.

4.11.7 Gas-Phase Decomposition

The decomposition of 1-chloropropane occurs according to the stoichiometry

$$CH_3 CH_2 CH_2 Cl(g) \rightarrow CH_3 CH{=}CH_2(g) + HCl(g)$$

and has been studied by measurement of the pressure increase in a constant-volume system. Starting with an initial pressure of 112 mmHg pure 1-chloropropane at 713 K, the following pressures p were observed at the times t given:

t/min	15	30	45	60	75
p/mmHg	136	155	170	181	191

Confirm that the decomposition obeys first-order kinetics and calculate the rate constant.

(University of Liverpool, BSc, Part I)

Answer

Let p_0 be the initial pressure of 1-chloropropane at time $t = 0$. Let y be the decrease in 1-chloropropane pressure at any time t. The partial pressures of the reactants and products at time t are given by

1-chloropropane $p_{C_3H_7Cl} = p_0 - y$

propene $p_{C_3H_6} = y$

hydrogen chloride $p_{HCl} = y$

with the total pressure p at time t given therefore by

$$p = p_{C_3H_7Cl} + p_{C_3H_6} + p_{HCl} = (p_0 - y) + y + y$$
$$= p_0 + y$$

i.e.

$$y = p - p_0$$

The partial pressure of reactant $p_{C_3H_7Cl}$ at time t is therefore

$$p_{C_3H_7Cl} = p_0 - (p - p_0)$$
$$= 2p_0 - p$$

[Note: In any question of this type where total pressure is measured, it is necessary to determine the partial pressure of the reactant in terms of the total pressure and the initial pressure. The relationship will differ in accordance with the stoichiometry of the reaction.]

Using the first-order rate equation (equation (4.11)) the initial concentration c_0 will be proportional to p_0 and the concentration c at time t will be proportional to the partial pressure $2p_0 - p$. Therefore the rate constant k is given by

$$kt = \ln\left(\frac{p_0}{2p_0 - p}\right)$$

or

$$\ln(2p_0 - p) = \ln p_0 - kt$$

Therefore, if the reaction is first-order, a plot of $\ln(2p_0 - p)$ against t will be linear with slope equal to $-k$:

p/mmHg	136	155	170	181	191
$(2p_0 - p)$/mmHg	88	69	54	43	33
$\ln[(2p_0 - p)/\text{mmHg}]$	4.477	4.234	3.989	3.761	3.497
t/min	15	30	45	60	75

A plot of $\ln(2p_0 - p)$ against t is given in Fig. 4.18.

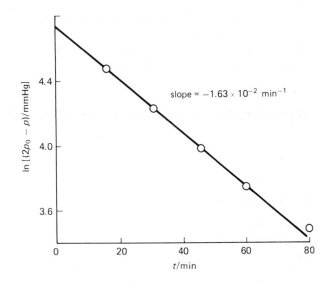

Figure 4.18 First-order plot for the thermal decomposition of 1-chloropropane.

Since the graph is linear for a substantial part of the decomposition, the reaction is first-order. From the graph

$$-k = -1.63 \times 10^{-2} \text{ min}^{-1}$$

giving

$$k = 1.63 \times 10^{-2} \text{ min}^{-1}$$

4.11.8 Gas Evolution Method

The following data refer to the decomposition of benzenediazonium chloride in aqueous solution at $50°C$:

$$C_6H_5N_2Cl \rightarrow C_6H_5Cl + N_2$$

Time/min	6	9	12	14	18	22	26	∞
N_2 evolved/cm^3	19.3	26.0	32.6	36.0	41.3	45.0	48.4	58.3

Find the order, the rate constant and the half-life of the reaction.

(GRSC, Part I)

Answer

If the reaction is first-order, equation (4.9) will be obeyed. If V_∞ is the volume of nitrogen evolved when the reaction goes to completion and V_t is the volume evolved in time t, then, since a is proportional to V_∞ and x is proportional to V_t, equation (4.9) becomes

$$kt = \ln\left(\frac{V_\infty}{V_\infty - V_t}\right)$$

or

$$\ln(V_\infty - V_t) = \ln V_\infty - kt$$

139

A plot of $\ln(V_\infty - V_t)$ against t will, therefore, be linear with slope equal to $-k$.

$(V_\infty - V_t)/\mathrm{cm}^3$	39.0	32.3	25.7	22.3	17.0	13.3	9.9
$\ln[(V_\infty - V_t)/\mathrm{cm}^3]$	3.664	3.476	3.246	3.105	2.833	2.588	2.293
t/min	6	9	12	14	18	22	26

A plot of $\ln(V_\infty - V_t)$ against t is given in Fig. 4.19. Since the plot is linear, the reaction is first-order with

$$\text{slope} = -k = -0.0688 \ \mathrm{min}^{-1}$$

i.e.

$$k = 1.1 \times 10^{-3} \ \mathrm{s}^{-1}$$

and half-life

$$t_{0.5} = (\ln 2)/k = \frac{0.693}{1.1 \times 10^{-3}} \ \mathrm{s}$$

$$= 630 \ \mathrm{s}$$

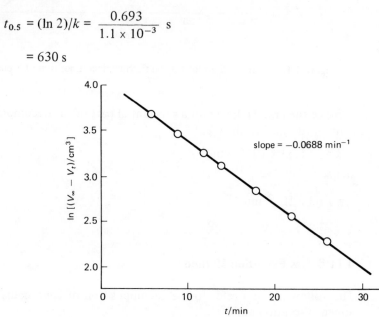

Figure 4.19 First-order plot for the decomposition of benzenediazonium chloride at 50°C.

4.11.9 Hydrolysis Reaction

The hydrolysis of methyl ethanoate is catalysed by hydrogen ions. The concentration of ester was measured as a function of time t at different hydrogen-ion concentrations, as follows:

$[\mathrm{H}^+] = 0.3 \ \mathrm{mol \ dm}^{-3}$

t/s	0	1500	3000	4500
$[\text{ester}]/\mathrm{mol \ dm}^{-3}$	1.00	0.64	0.41	0.26

$[\mathrm{H}^+] = 0.6 \ \mathrm{mol \ dm}^{-3}$

t/s	0	1000	2000	3000
$[\text{ester}]/\mathrm{mol \ dm}^{-3}$	1.00	0.55	0.30	0.17

Calculate the order with respect to each reactant and hence calculate the rate constant.

Answer

The acid-catalysed hydrolysis of an ester would normally be expected to be second-order with the rate equation given by

$$J = k_2 [H^+] [ester]$$

where k_2 is the second-order rate constant. When $[H^+]$ is constant, the rate equation becomes

$$J = k'[ester]$$

where k' is the pseudo-first-order rate constant and is equal to $k_2 [H^+]$.

Therefore, at constant $[H^+]$, the rate will follow first-order kinetics and a plot of ln[ester] versus t will be linear for each set of data, with slope equal to $-k'$.

$[H^+] = 0.3$ mol dm^{-3}

t/s	0	1500	3000	4500
$\ln([ester]/\text{mol dm}^{-3})$	0.00	−0.446	−0.892	−1.347

$[H^+] = 0.6$ mol dm^{-3}

t/s	0	1000	2000	3000
$\ln([ester]/\text{mol dm}^{-3})$	0.00	−0.598	−1.204	−1.772

A plot of ln[ester] versus t (Fig. 4.20) is linear for both sets of data, indicating that the hydrolysis is first-order.

At $[H^+] = 0.3$ mol dm^{-3}, slope $= -3.0 \times 10^{-4}$ s^{-1} so that $k' = 3.0 \times 10^{-4}$ s^{-1}, giving

$$k_2 = \frac{3.0 \times 10^{-4}}{0.3} = 1.0 \times 10^{-3} \text{ dm}^3 \text{ mol}^{-1} \text{ s}^{-1}$$

At $[H^+] = 0.6$ mol dm^{-3}, slope $= -6.0 \times 10^{-4}$ s^{-1} so that $k' = 6.0 \times 10^{-4}$ s^{-1}, giving

$$k_2 = \frac{6.0 \times 10^{-4}}{0.6} = 1.0 \times 10^{-3} \text{ dm}^3 \text{ mol}^{-1} \text{ s}^{-1}$$

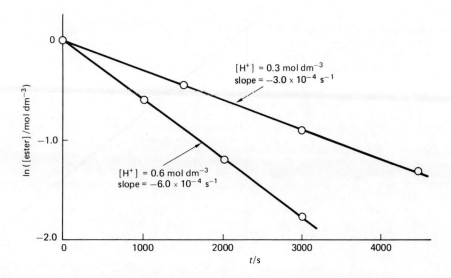

Figure 4.20   First-order plot for hydrolysis of methyl ethanoate.

141

The consistency in the values of k_2 from both sets of data indicates that the initial assumption was correct and that the reaction follows the overall rate equation

$$J = k_2 [H^+] [\text{ester}]$$

with $k_2 = 1.0 \times 10^{-3}$ dm^3 mol^{-1} s^{-1}.

4.11.10 Activation Energy

The rate constants k for the gas-phase decomposition of ethane were as follows:

$10^5 \, k/s$	2.5	4.7	8.2	12.3	23.1	35.3	57.6	92.4	141.5
$Temperature/K$	823	833	843	853	863	873	883	893	903

From the data, determine the activation energy for this decomposition.

(Brunel University, BTech, 2nd year)

Answer

The Arrhenius equation in its logarithmic form (equation (4.19)) is

$$\ln k = \ln A - E^{\ddagger}/RT$$

where A is the frequency factor and $E^{\ddagger}$ is the activation energy. A plot of $\ln k$ against $1/T$ will, therefore, be linear with slope equal to $-E^{\ddagger}/R$.

$\ln(k/s^{-1})$	−10.597	−9.965	−9.409	−9.003	−8.373	−7.949	−7.459	−6.987	−6.561
$10^3 \, K/T$	1.215	1.200	1.186	1.172	1.159	1.145	1.132	1.120	1.107

A plot of $\ln k$ against $1/T$ is given in Fig. 4.21. From the graph

$$\text{slope} = -E^{\ddagger}/R = -3.66 \times 10^4 \text{ K}$$

giving

$$E^{\ddagger} = 8.314 \times 3.66 \times 10^4 \text{ J mol}^{-1}$$

$$= 304 \text{ kJ mol}^{-1}$$

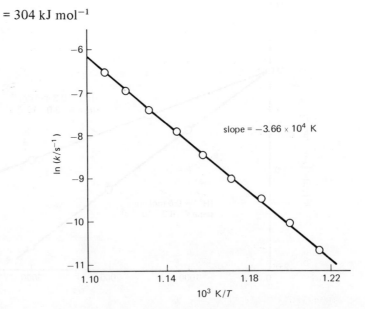

Figure 4.21 $\ln k$ versus $1/T$ plot for decomposition of ethane.

4.11.11 Rate of Decomposition

The decomposition of compound A in solution is a first-order process with an activation energy of 52.3 kJ mol^{-1}. A 10 per cent solution of A is 10 per cent decomposed in 10 min at 10°C. How much decomposition of A should be observed with a 20 per cent solution after 20 min at 20°C.

(GRSC, Part I)

Answer

Since this is a first-order reaction, equation (4.6) can be used. In the first experiment, the concentration x has decreased to be 10% of the initial concentration a at time t = 10 min. Substituting in equation (4.6) we have

$$k \times 10 = \ln \left(\frac{a}{a - 0.1a} \right)$$

i.e.

$$k = \frac{1}{10} \ln \left(\frac{10}{9} \right) = 0.01054 \text{ min}^{-1} \text{ at } 10°C$$

The rate constant at 20°C can now be calculated from equation (4.20), i.e.

$$\ln \left(\frac{k_{20°C}}{k_{10°C}} \right) = \frac{E^{\ddagger}}{R} \left(\frac{T_2 - T_1}{T_1 T_2} \right)$$

$$= \frac{52300 \times (293 - 283)}{8.314 \times 283 \times 293}$$

$$= 0.7586$$

Therefore the rate constant at 20°C is given by

$$\ln k_{20°C} = \ln (0.01054) + 0.7586$$

$$= -3.7940$$

giving

$$k_{20°C} = 0.0225 \text{ min}^{-1}$$

For a first-order reaction, the fraction y of the reactant decomposed at time t is given by

$$kt = \ln \left(\frac{1}{1 - y} \right)$$

For the reaction at 20°C with t = 20 min,

$$0.0225 \times 20 = \ln \left(\frac{1}{1 - y} \right)$$

giving

$$\frac{1}{1 - y} = 1.569$$

and

$$y = 0.363$$

Therefore the solution is 36.3% decomposed at 20°C after 20 min.

4.11.12 Collision Theory

The bimolecular decomposition of hydrogen iodide is given by

$$2HI \rightarrow H_2 + I_2$$

It is found that, at 700 K and 1 atm pressure, the collision rate is 1.02×10^{34} m^{-3} s^{-1}. From simple collision theory, calculate the reaction rate and the rate constant at 700 K, given that the activation energy is 184 kJ mol^{-1}.

Answer

The collision rate Z, which is the number of collisions per unit volume of gas per unit time, determines the frequency factor A in the Arrhenius equation. Since two molecules of HI are decomposed with each effective collision (i.e. when the activation energy is acquired), the reaction rate v is given by

$$v = 2Z \exp(-E^{\ddagger}/RT)$$

Substituting,

$$v = 2 \times (1.02 \times 10^{34}) \times \exp\left(\frac{-184\,000}{8.314 \times 700}\right) \text{ molecule m}^{-3} \text{ s}^{-1}$$

$$= 3.79 \times 10^{20} \text{ molecule m}^{-3} \text{ s}^{-1}$$

The rate constant k is given by the rate equation

$$v = k[HI]^2$$

At 1 atm and 700 K, the concentration of HI in molecule m^{-3} is given by

$$[HI] = pN_A/RT$$

where p is the pressure in N m^{-2} and N_A is the Avogadro constant, so that

$$[HI] = \frac{1.013 \times 10^5 \times 1 \times 6.023 \times 10^{23}}{8.314 \times 700} \text{ molecule m}^{-3}$$

$$= 1.05 \times 10^{25} \text{ molecule m}^{-3}$$

The rate constant k is therefore given by

$$k = \frac{v}{[HI]^2} = \frac{3.79 \times 10^{20}}{(1.05 \times 10^{25})^2} \text{ m}^3 \text{ molecule}^{-1} \text{ s}^{-1}$$

$$= 3.44 \times 10^{-30} \text{ m}^3 \text{ molecule}^{-1} \text{ s}^{-1}$$

Multiplying by the Avogadro constant gives k in the normal molar units, i.e.

$$k = 2.07 \times 10^{-6} \text{ m}^3 \text{ mol}^{-1} \text{ s}^{-1} = 2.07 \times 10^{-3} \text{ dm}^3 \text{ mol}^{-1} \text{ s}^{-1}$$

[Note: A comparison of Z and v shows that about only one in 10^{14} collisions is effective in leading to reaction.]

4.11.13 Entropy of Activation

A certain unimolecular reaction may proceed by a direct path or by a catalysed one. The entropy of activation for the direct path exceeds that for the catalysed path by 40 J K^{-1} mol^{-1}, and the activation energy for the direct path exceeds that for the catalysed path by 20 kJ mol^{-1}. Calculate the ratio of rate constants at 25°C.

Answer

The rate constant k is related to the entropy of activation $\Delta S^\ddagger$ and the activation energy $E^\ddagger$ by equation (4.25), viz.

$$k = \exp(1)\ \frac{kT}{h}\ \exp(\Delta S^\ddagger/R)\exp(-E^\ddagger/RT)$$

Taking logarithms,

$$\ln k = \text{constant} + \frac{\Delta S^\ddagger}{R} - \frac{E^\ddagger}{RT}$$

Using subscripts d and c to represent the direct and catalysed paths, respectively, we have

$$\ln\left(\frac{k_d}{k_c}\right) = \frac{40}{8.314} - \frac{20\,000}{8.314 \times 298}$$

$$= 4.8112 - 8.0724$$

$$= -3.2612$$

giving

$$k_d/k_c = 3.83 \times 10^{-2}$$

4.11.14 Lindemann Theory

The following values of the overall rate constant k' were obtained for the decomposition of 1,1-dimethylcyclopropane:

Initial pressure/mmHg	1.43	0.83	0.50	0.36	0.25	0.19	0.15
$10^4\ k'/\text{s}^{-1}$	4.39	4.20	4.08	4.00	3.85	3.71	3.53

Show that the results are consistent with Lindemann theory and calculate the limiting value of k' at high pressure.

Answer

From equation (4.30), a plot of $1/k'$ against $1/p$ should be linear.

mmHg/p	0.70	1.20	2.00	2.78	4.00	5.26	6.67
$10^{-4}\ \text{s}/k'$	0.228	0.238	0.245	0.250	0.260	0.270	0.283

The graph (Fig. 4.22) is linear except at low values of $1/p$. Extrapolation of the linear part of the graph gives

$$\text{intercept} = 1/k_\infty$$

$$= 0.230 \times 10^4\ \text{s}$$

so that

$$k_\infty = 4.35 \times 10^{-4}\ \text{s}^{-1}$$

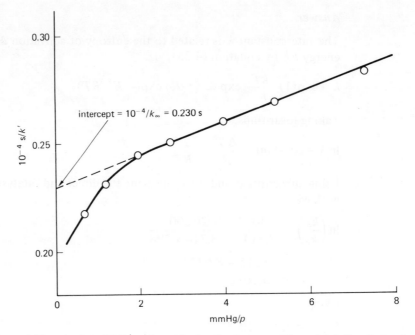

Figure 4.22 A plot of $1/k'$ against $1/p$ for the decomposition of 1,1-dimethylcyclopropane.

4.11.15 Rate of an Ionic Reaction

The second-order reaction between bromoethanoate ions and thiosulphate(VI) ions in which the potassium salts were used

$$BrCH_2 COO^- + S_2 O_3{}^{2-} \rightarrow S_2 O_3 CH_2 COO^{2-} + Br^-$$

was carried out with equal concentrations of both ions. The rate constants were found to be:

$10^3 \times$ *initial concentration*/mol dm^{-3}	0.5	0.7	1.0	1.4	2.0
Rate constant, k/dm^3 mol^{-1} min^{-1}	0.298	0.309	0.324	0.343	0.366

Calculate the rate constant when the activity coefficients are unity.

Answer

The Brønsted–Bjerrum relationship (equation (4.45)) predicts that a plot of $\log_{10} k$ versus $\sqrt{I}$ will be linear. The ionic strength of the reaction mixture is given by

$$I = \tfrac{1}{2} \sum c_i z_i^2$$
$$= \tfrac{1}{2} [(c_{K^+} \times 1^2) + (c_{BrCH_2 COO^-} \times 1^2) + (2c_{K^+} \times 1^2) + (c_{S_2 O_3^{2-}} \times 2^2)]$$
$$= 4c$$

$\log_{10}(k/\text{dm}^3\text{ mol}^{-1}\text{ min}^{-1})$	−0.526	−0.510	−0.489	−0.465	−0.437
I/mol dm^{-3}	0.0020	0.0028	0.0040	0.0056	0.0080
$(I$/mol dm$^{-3})^{1/2}$	0.0447	0.0529	0.0632	0.0748	0.0894

A plot of $\log_{10} k$ against $\sqrt{I}$ is given in Fig. 4.23. The graph is linear with slope = 2.01 dm$^{3/2}$ mol$^{-1/2}$, in good agreement with the theoretical value of

$$2 \times 2 \times 0.51 \text{ dm}^{3/2} \text{ mol}^{-1/2} = 2.04 \text{ dm}^{3/2} \text{ mol}^{-1/2}$$

146

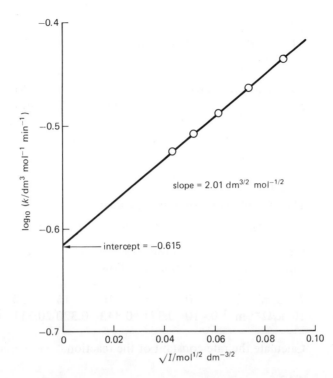

Figure 4.23 Plot of $\log_{10} k$ against $\sqrt{I}$ for the reaction between bromoethanoate and thiosulphate(VI) ions.

From the intercept

$$\log_{10} k_0 = -0.615$$

giving

$$k_0 = 0.243 \ \text{dm}^3 \ \text{mol}^{-1} \ \text{min}^{-1}$$

4.12 Unworked Examples

4.12.1
The decay of the radio-isotope ^{24}Na was measured as follows:

Time/h	0	4	8	12	16	20	24
Activity/min^{-1}	478	395	329	272	226	187	155

Calculate the rate constant of the decay and the half-life of the isotope.

4.12.2
Two substances A and B undergo a bimolecular reaction step. The following table gives the concentrations of A at various times for an experiment carried out at a constant temperature of 17°C:

10^4 [A]/mol dm^{-3}	10.00	7.94	6.31	5.01	3.98
Time/min	0	10	20	30	40

The initial concentration of B is 2.5 mol dm^{-3}. Calculate the second-order rate constant for the reaction.

(University of Manchester, BSc, 1st year)

4.12.3

When ammonia decomposes on a tungsten wire, the total pressure varies with time as follows:

Total pressure/mmHg	228	250	273	318
Time/s	200	400	600	1000

What is the order of the reaction and calculate the rate constant on the basis of mol dm^{-3} as the concentration unit.

4.12.4

The saponification of ethyl ethanoate,

$$CH_3COOC_2H_5 + OH^- \rightarrow CH_3COO^- + C_2H_5OH$$

proceeds by a second-order reaction. The conductivity of the solution was measured as a function of time as follows:

Time/min	0	5	10	15	20	25	30	35	40
$10^4 \kappa/\Omega^{-1} m^{-1}$	0.410	0.371	0.342	0.320	0.311	0.305	0.299	0.290	0.280

Calculate the rate constant of the reaction.

4.12.5

The gas-phase decomposition of di(1,1-dimethylethyl) peroxide is a first-order reaction given by

$$(CH_3)_3COOC(CH_3)_3 \rightarrow 2CH_3COCH_3 + C_2H_6$$

The following results were obtained for the total pressure p measured at constant volume at 147°C at times t:

t/min	0	6	10	14	22	30	38	46
p/mmHg	179.5	198.65	210.5	221.2	242.3	262.1	280.1	297.1

Calculate the rate constant of the reaction.

4.12.6

The rate of decomposition of dinitrogen oxide N_2O at the surface of an electrically heated gold wire has been followed as a function of pressure:

Time/min	0	30	52	100
Pressure/mmHg	200	232	252	272

(a) Assuming that the products are exclusively nitrogen and oxygen, calculate the final pressure and hence the half-life.
(b) At the same temperature, but at an initial pressure of 400 mmHg, the half-life was found to be 52 min. What is the order of the reaction?

(University of Birmingham, BSc, 1st year)

4.12.7

The optical rotations α for the mutarotation of α-glucose at 20°C are as follows

α/deg	20.26	18.92	16.82	15.22	14.06	13.18	10.60
Time/min	10	20	40	60	80	100	∞

Show that the reaction is first-order and calculate the overall rate constant.

4.12.8

The rate constant k for the first-order decomposition of 2-chloropropane into propene and hydrogen chloride was found to vary with temperature T as follows:

$10^3 k/s^{-1}$	0.162	0.238	0.311	0.475	0.706	0.901	1.225
T/K	640.6	646.7	651.2	657.5	665.1	669.0	674.9

Calculate the activation energy and the frequency factor.

4.12.9

For a certain first-order reaction, the time required to reduce the initial concentration to one-half is 5000 s at 325 K and 1000 s at 335 K. Calculate the rate constant at both temperatures and hence determine the activation energy.

(Brunel University, BTech, part I)

4.12.10

The Arrhenius equations for the rate of decomposition of dibutyl mercury and diethyl mercury are

$$k/s^{-1} = 10^{15.2} \exp(-193\,000 \text{ J mol}^{-1}/RT)$$

and

$$k/s^{-1} = 10^{14.1} \exp(-180\,000 \text{ J mol}^{-1}/RT)$$

respectively. Find the temperature at which the rate constants are equal.

4.12.11

The reaction between nitroethane and OH^- ions in aqueous solution proceeds according to the rate equation

$$-\frac{d[C_2H_5NO_2]}{dt} = -\frac{d[OH^-]}{dt} = k[C_2H_5NO_2][OH^-]$$

Experiments at $0°C$ with initial concentrations $[C_2H_5NO_2] = 0.01$ mol dm^{-3} and $[OH^-] = 0.01$ mol dm^{-3} have a value of 150 s for the reaction half-life. Calculate the rate constant at $0°C$. Experiments at $25°C$ gave a value of 5.90 dm^3 mol^{-1} s^{-1} for the reaction rate constant; calculate the activation energy of the reaction.

(GRSC, Part I)

4.12.12

The frequency factor for the decomposition of ethenoxyethane is 2.7×10^{11} s^{-1}. Calculate the entropy of activation at 803 K and comment on the value obtained.

(GRSC, Part II)

4.12.13

The following values of the overall rate constant k' were obtained for the uni-molecular decomposition of ethoxyethane:

Initial concentration/mmol dm^{-3}	1.20	1.89	3.55	5.42	8.18
$10 k'/s^{-1}$	2.48	3.26	4.61	5.54	6.29

Use the data to demonstrate the validity of Lindemann theory and obtain the limiting value of k' at high pressure.

4.12.14

The proposed mechanism for the decomposition of ethanal catalysed by iodine is given by

$$I_2 \rightarrow 2I\bullet$$

$$I\bullet + CH_3CHO \rightarrow HI + CH_3CO\bullet$$

$$CH_3CO\bullet \rightarrow CH_3\bullet + CO$$

$$CH_3\bullet + I_2 \rightarrow CH_3I + I\bullet$$

$$CH_3\bullet + HI \rightarrow CH_4 + I\bullet$$

$$CH_3I + HI \rightarrow CH_4 + I_2$$

Derive an expression for the rate of this reaction in terms of the rate of formation of carbon monoxide.

4.12.15

Assuming that gaseous ozone decomposes by the following mechanism

$$O_3 \underset{k_{-1}}{\overset{k_1}{\rightleftharpoons}} O_2 + O\colonbullet$$

$$O\colonbullet + O_3 \xrightarrow{k_2} 2O_2$$

derive an expression for the rate of decomposition in the presence of oxygen using a steady-state method. Show that the mechanism would be consistent with the observation that the reaction is second-order in ozone and inhibited by oxygen.

4.12.16

The reaction between peroxydisulphate ions and iodide ions is as follows

$$S_2O_8{}^{2-} + 2I^- \rightarrow 2SO_4{}^{2-} + I_2$$

Using an initial concentration of 1.5×10^{-4} mol dm^{-3} potassium peroxydisulphate, the following values of the rate constant k were obtained at the concentrations of potassium iodide given:

10^3 [KI]/mol dm^{-3}	1.6	2.0	3.2	4.0	6.0	8.0	10.0
$10k$/dm^3 mol^{-1} min^{-1}	1.03	1.05	1.12	1.16	1.18	1.26	1.32

Estimate $z_A z_B$ for this reaction and calculate the rate constant when the activity coefficients are unity.

5 Ions in Solution

5.1 Introduction

This chapter deals with the electrical behaviour of ions in bulk solution, while the next chapter considers electrode processes.

The information relating to ions in solution that can be obtained from conductance and related studies is described. The material included in Chapter 7 of *Work Out Chemistry 'A' Level* on acids and bases, pH, buffer solutions and indicators is consolidated and expanded. Applications of basic thermodynamic principles (as developed in Chapter 2) to electrolyte solutions is considered. The electrostatic interactions between ions in solution is strong compared with the corresponding van der Waals' interaction, as a result of which electrolyte solutions tend to show substantial deviations from ideal behaviour. Methods of accounting for this are considered.

5.2 Ionic Solutions

5.2.1 The Role of the Solvent

In the solid state, many substances exist as ionic crystals, i.e. positive and negative ions coexist in a regular pattern which forms a crystal lattice. The electrostatic (or coulombic) force between charges Q_1 and Q_2 separated by a distance r in vacuum is given by

$$F = \frac{Q_1 Q_2}{4\pi\epsilon_0 r^2} \tag{5.1}$$

where ϵ_0 is the permittivity of a vacuum (see Section 1.4). For charges of opposite sign, F is negative (attraction), and for charges of like sign, F is positive (repulsion). In air, the result is approximately the same. The corresponding energy is given by

$$E = -\int_{\infty}^{r} F \, dr = \frac{Q_1 Q_2}{4\pi\epsilon_0 r} \tag{5.2}$$

In any crystal, the nearest neighbours to a particular ion will be ions of opposite charge, so, although both electrostatic attractions and repulsions exist, the attractions outweigh the repulsions sufficiently to maintain the crystal structure against the randomising effect of thermal energy.

In a polar solvent, such as water, the above electrostatic interaction is reduced to $E = Q_1 Q_2 / 4\pi\epsilon r$, where ϵ is the permittivity of the solvent. The permittivity of water is approximately 80 times greater than that of air, i.e. the electrostatic interactions between the ions is a factor of 80 less, and this is often insufficient to retain the integrity of the crystal lattice against the randomising effect of thermal energy. As a consequence, the crystal dissolves and the constituent ions are distributed throughout the solution in a fashion that is partly random (as dictated by thermal motion) and partly ordered (as dictated by the now weaker electrostatic interaction).

Other substances, e.g. hydrogen chloride and ethanoic acid, are non-ionic by themselves, but ionise when dissolved in a polar solvent, such as water. Hydrogen chloride dissolved in water (hydrochloric acid) dissociates completely into hydrogen and chloride ions, whereas ethanoic acid in water dissociates only partially into hydrogen and ethanoate ions and forms an equilibrium mixture of ionic and unionised species.

5.2.2 Strong and Weak Electrolytes

Electrolytes can be classified as **strong** or **weak**. This has nothing to do with their concentration but relates to their extent of ionisation. A strong electrolyte is one that is completely ionised at all concentrations. A weak electrolyte is one that is only partly ionised, with the degree of ionisation α decreasing as the concentration of electrolyte is increased.

5.2.3 Equilibrium Constants

Consider, for example, the partial ionisation of a weak acid HA and represent this by a simple equation

$$HA \rightleftharpoons H^+ + A^- \tag{5.3}$$

The thermodynamic equilibrium constant (which in this case is an acid dissociation constant, K_a) is given in terms of activities by

$$K_a = a_{H^+} a_{A^-}/a_{HA} \tag{5.4}$$

and is a true constant at a given temperature.

A similar expression in terms of concentrations,

$$K_a = [H^+][A^-]/[HA] \tag{5.5}$$

will only approximate to constancy, owing to deviations from ideal behaviour.

If c is the total (unionised plus ionised) concentration of acid and α is the degree of ionisation, then, following the procedure outlined in Section 2.12.4,

$$[HA] = (1 - \alpha)c \qquad \text{and} \qquad [H^+] = [A^-] = \alpha c$$

giving

$$K_a = \alpha^2 c/(1 - \alpha) \tag{5.6}$$

Similar consideration applies to the ionisation of a weak base, where K_b will denote a base dissociation constant.

Consider next the partial dissolution of a salt MA of low solubility

$$MA \rightleftharpoons M^+ + A^- \tag{5.7}$$

The equilibrium constant is given by

$$K_s = a_{M^+} a_{A^-}/a_{MA} \tag{5.8}$$

but since MA is in the form of a pure solid, $a_{MA} = 1$, and

$$K_s = a_{M^+} a_{A^-} \approx [M^+][A^-] \tag{5.9}$$

and is called the **solubility product**.

5.2.4 Ion Hydration, Hydrogen Ions

The water molecule has an appreciable dipole moment and ions in aqueous solution tend to be strongly hydrated as a result of charge–dipole interaction. Cations tend to be more strongly hydrated than anions.

It is convenient and customary to denote hydrogen ions as H^+, even though H^+ strictly represents a proton. In reality, hydrogen ions exist as hydrated protons, i.e. as H_3O^+.

In view of this, it would seem appropriate to modify the previous ionic equilibria (equations (5.3) and (5.7)) so that the ionic species on the right-hand side are recognised as being hydrated and a corresponding number of water molecules is included on the left-hand side. This means that $(a_{H_2O})^n$ would appear in the denominator of the equilibrium constant expression (equations (5.4) and (5.8)). However, if the solution is reasonably dilute, the water will approximate to being in its standard state of unit activity (pure water), i.e. $(a_{H_2O})^n = 1$, and the inclusion of this term is unnecessary. Even for concentrated solutions, where this argument may be questionable, $(a_{H_2O})^n$ is still not included in the equilibrium constant expression; however, the activities are calculated from the experimental data in such a way that equations (5.4) and (5.9) still hold true.

5.2.5 Ionisation of Water

For the equilibrium

$$H_2O \rightleftharpoons H^+ + OH^-$$

we have

$$K_w = a_{H^+} a_{OH^-} / a_{H_2O}$$

but, since, for pure water, $a_{H_2O} = 1$,

$$K_w = a_{H^+} a_{OH^-} \approx [H^+][OH^-] \tag{5.10}$$

where K_w is called the **ionic product** of water.

5.2.6 Units of K

If the above equilibrium constants are expressed in terms of activities, they are dimensionless, even though they relate to a standard value of concentration (usually $c^\ominus = 1$ mol dm^{-3}) (see Section 1.5.3). If expressed in terms of concentrations, the equilibrium constant will be in an appropriate power of a concentration unit; for example,

$$K_w = a_{H^+} a_{OH^-} = 10^{-14} \qquad \text{at 298 K}$$

but

$$[H^+][OH^-] = 10^{-14} \text{ (mol dm}^{-3})^2 \qquad \text{at 298 K}$$

5.3 Electrolytic Conduction

When an electric potential difference is applied between two electrodes immersed in an ionic solution, a current flows. The conductance of the solution is due to the movement of positive ions towards the negative electrode (cathode) and of negative ions towards the positive electrode (anode). The conductivity of an ionic solution increases with increasing temperature owing to the decrease in viscosity. This contrasts with the conductivity of metals, etc., which decreases with increasing temperature because the increased thermal motion of the crystal lattice opposes the passage of electrons.

5.3.1 Conductance and Conductivity

The electrical resistance R of a conductor is directly proportional to its length l and inversely proportional to its cross-sectional area A, i.e.

$$R = \rho l/A \tag{5.11}$$

where ρ is the resistivity.

Conductance G is the reciprocal of resistance, and **conductivity** κ is the reciprocal of resistivity, i.e.

$$G = 1/R \qquad \text{and} \qquad \kappa = l/RA \tag{5.12}$$

The conductivity of an electrolyte solution is usually measured using a 'dip-type' conductivity cell. l/A represents the effective distance between the electrodes divided by the effective area of the electrodes and is called the cell constant K, i.e. $K = R\kappa$. It is measured by calibration with a solution of known conductivity.

Example 5.1

In a conductivity cell containing KCl (aq, 0.01 mol dm^{-3}) at 298 K the resistance is 150 Ω, while for HCl (aq, 0.01 mol dm^{-3}) at 298 K the resistance is 51.4 Ω. The conductivity of the KCl solution is 1.41×10^{-3} Ω^{-1} cm^{-1}. Calculate the cell constant and the conductivity of the HCl solution.

$K = \kappa(\text{KCl})R(\text{KCl})$

$\quad = 1.41 \times 10^{-3}$ Ω^{-1} cm^{-1} $\times 150$ $\Omega = 0.2115$ cm^{-1}

$\kappa(\text{HCl}) = \dfrac{K}{R(\text{HCl})} = \dfrac{0.2115 \text{ cm}^{-1}}{51.4 \text{ }\Omega} = 4.11 \times 10^{-3}$ Ω^{-1} cm^{-1}

$$(\text{or } 4.11 \times 10^{-3} \text{ S cm}^{-1}) \qquad \blacksquare$$

5.3.2 Molar Conductivity

The conductivity of an electrolyte solution increases with increasing concentration and at maximum increases in proportion to the concentration. It is, therefore, appropriate to consider electrolyte conductance in terms of **molar conductivity** Λ, defined as

$$\Lambda = \kappa/c \tag{5.13}$$

Example 5.2

At 298 K, the conductivity of KCl (aq, 5.0×10^{-4} mol dm^{-3}) is 7.44×10^{-3} S m^{-1} and that of the water from which this solution was made is 0.06×10^{-3} S m^{-1}. Calculate the molar conductivity of KCl in this solution.

$\kappa(\text{KCl}) = \kappa(\text{solution}) - \kappa(\text{water})$

$\quad = (7.44 - 0.06) \times 10^{-3} = 7.38 \times 10^{-3}$ S m^{-1}

Therefore

$$\Lambda = \frac{\kappa}{c} = \frac{7.38 \times 10^{-3} \text{ S m}^{-1}}{5.0 \times 10^{-4} \times 10^3 \text{ mol m}^{-3}}$$

$$= 1.476 \times 10^{-2} \text{ S m}^2 \text{ mol}^{-1}$$ ∎

5.3.3 Limiting Molar Conductivity

In the case of a strong electrolyte, Λ depends on concentration to a small extent, reflecting deviation from ideality due to interactions between the ions. Λ increases to a steady value Λ^∞ on approaching zero concentration (infinite dilution).

Kohlrausch established the empirical relationship

$$\Lambda = \Lambda^\infty - k\sqrt{c} \qquad (5.14)$$

where k is a constant. The relationship can be established theoretically on the basis of the Debye–Hückel model of strong electrolytes (see Section 5.6.2). Λ^∞ of a strong electrolyte is, therefore, best determined by extrapolating a plot of Λ versus $\sqrt{c}$ to zero c. It represents the molar conductivity of the electrolyte under conditions of complete ionisation and zero ionic interactions.

The extrapolation of Λ to zero concentration to give a reliable value of Λ^∞ for a weak electrolyte is impracticable (see Fig. 5.1), owing to the substantial increase in the degree of ionisation that is involved. An alternative method of determining Λ^∞ must be sought.

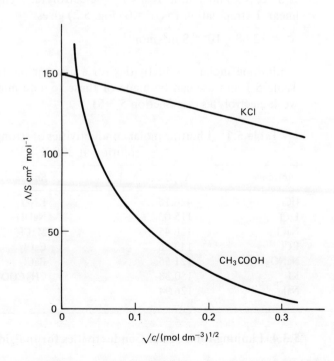

Figure 5.1 Variation of molar conductivity with $\sqrt{c}$ for aqueous solutions of potassium chloride (strong electrolyte) and ethanoic acid (weak electrolyte) at 298 K.

Example 5.3

The molar conductivity of aqueous sodium iodide at 298 K varies with concentration as follows:

$c/\text{mol m}^{-3}$	0.50	1.00	5.00	10.0	20.0
$(c/\text{mol m}^{-3})^{1/2}$	0.707	1.00	2.236	3.162	4.472
$10^3\,\Lambda/\text{S m}^2\,\text{mol}^{-1}$	12.54	12.43	12.13	11.92	11.67

Determine the limiting molar conductivity.

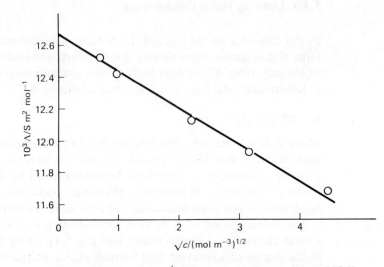

Figure 5.2 Λ versus $\sqrt{c}$ for aqueous sodium iodide at 298 K.

Since sodium iodide is a strong electrolyte, a plot of Λ against $\sqrt{c}$ should be linear. Extrapolation to $\sqrt{c} = 0$ (Fig. 5.2) gives

$$\Lambda^{\infty} = 12.68 \times 10^{-3}\ \text{S m}^2\ \text{mol}^{-1} \qquad\blacksquare$$

Limiting molar conductivities for a number of strong electrolytes are given in Table 5.1 and use can be made of these to determine the molar conductivities of weak electrolytes (see Section 5.3.5).

Table 5.1 Limiting molar conductivities of strong electrolytes in aqueous solution at 298 K

Substance	$\Lambda^{\infty}/\text{S cm}^2\,\text{mol}^{-1}$	Substance	$\Lambda^{\infty}/\text{S cm}^2\,\text{mol}^{-1}$
HCl	426.16	KNO_3	144.96
LiCl	115.03	NaOH	247.80
NaCl	126.45	$MgCl_2$	129.40
KCl	149.86	$CaCl_2$	135.84
$NaNO_3$	121.55	$BaCl_2$	139.98
KI	150.38	CH_3COONa	91.0
NaI	126.94		

5.3.4 Limiting Ionic Molar Conductivities for Individual Ionic Species

The limiting molar conductivity of an electrolyte is made up of contributions from each of the individual ions in the solution. To illustrate this point, consider the differences in the values of $\Lambda^\infty_{298\ K}$ /S cm^2 mol^{-1} (see Table 5.1) for the following pairs of aqueous electrolytes:

KCl	149.86	KNO$_3$	144.96	KI	150.38
NaCl	126.45	NaNO$_3$	121.55	NaI	126.94
	23.41		23.41		23.44

Since there is a common anion in each of the above pairs, the constant difference represents the difference between the contributions of K$^+$ and Na$^+$ to Λ^∞ of the respective electrolyte.

If Λ^∞_+ and Λ^∞_- are the limiting molar conductivities of the cation and the anion, respectively, in an electrolyte, the total molar conductivity (Kohlrausch's law of independent ion migration) is given by

$$\Lambda^\infty = \Lambda^\infty_+ + \Lambda^\infty_- \tag{5.15}$$

The molar conductivity of the ionic species is a measure of the amount of current carried by the ions in question. Comparison of the molar conductivities of ions is, therefore, more meaningful when related to constant charge, e.g. when $\Lambda^\infty(Na^+)$ is compared with $\frac{1}{2}\Lambda^\infty(Mg^{2+})$ rather than with $\Lambda^\infty(Mg^{2+})$.

5.3.5 Limiting Molar Conductivities of Weak Electrolytes

These cannot be measured directly but can be determined by making use of equation (5.15).

(a) By direct substitution of known values of limiting molar conductivities of ions. For example, $\Lambda^\infty(H^+)$ is 349.8 S cm^2 mol^{-1} and $\Lambda^\infty(CH_3COO^-)$ is 40.9 S cm^2 mol^{-1} at 298 K. Therefore, the limiting molar conductivity of ethanoic acid is given by

$$\Lambda^\infty(CH_3COOH) = 349.8 + 40.9 = 390.7 \text{ S cm}^2 \text{ mol}^{-1}$$

(b) From known values of Λ^∞ for strong electrolytes whose molar conductivity can be determined from a plot of Λ against $\sqrt{c}$ as in Example 5.3. For example, since

$$\Lambda^\infty(CH_3COOH) = \Lambda^\infty(H^+) + \Lambda^\infty(CH_3COO^-)$$

its value can also be obtained from

$$\Lambda^\infty(CH_3COOH) = \Lambda^\infty(HCl) + \Lambda^\infty(CH_3COONa) - \Lambda^\infty(NaCl)$$

$$= \Lambda^\infty(H^+) + \Lambda^\infty(Cl^-) + \Lambda^\infty(Na^+) + \Lambda^\infty(CH_3COO^-)$$

$$- \Lambda^\infty(Na^+) - \Lambda^\infty(Cl^-)$$

From the values in Table 5.1,

$$\Lambda^\infty(CH_3COOH) = (426.16 + 91.0 - 126.45) \text{ S cm}^2 \text{ mol}^{-1}$$

$$= 390.7 \text{ S cm}^2 \text{ mol}^{-1}$$

5.4 Transport of Ions

5.4.1 Ionic Mobility

The mobility u_i of an ion i is given by

$$u_i = v_i/E \tag{5.16}$$

where v_i is the velocity of the ion in an electric field (i.e. potential gradient) of strength E. The basic SI unit of ionic mobility is, therefore, m s^{-1}/V m^{-1} = m^2 s^{-1} V^{-1}.

Mobility and molar conductivity are related by the expression

$$\Lambda_i = F u_i \tag{5.17}$$

where F is Faraday's constant.

Example 5.4

Given the mobility of the K$^+$ ion in aqueous solution at 291 K is 6.7×10^{-8} m^2 s^{-1} V^{-1}, calculate the molar conductivity.

$$\Lambda(K^+) = 96\,487 \text{ C mol}^{-1} \times 6.7 \times 10^{-8} \text{ m}^2 \text{ s}^{-1} \text{ V}^{-1}$$

$$= 64.6 \times 10^{-4} \text{ S m}^2 \text{ mol}^{-1} = 64.6 \text{ S cm}^2 \text{ mol}^{-1} \qquad \blacksquare$$

Some limiting ionic mobilities and corresponding molar conductivities at 298 K for some cations and anions are set out in Table 5.2.

Table 5.2 Limiting ionic mobilities and molar conductivities at 298 K

Cation	H$^+$	Na$^+$	K$^+$	$\frac{1}{2}$Mg^{2+}	
u_+/cm^2 s^{-1} V^{-1} $\times 10^{-4}$	36.4	5.20	7.62	4.75	
Λ_+^∞/S cm^2 mol^{-1}	349.8	50.11	73.52	53.06	
Anion	OH$^-$	Cl$^-$	NO$_3^-$	$\frac{1}{2}$SO$_4^{2-}$	CH$_3$COO$^-$
u_-/cm^2 s^{-1} V^{-1} $\times 10^{-4}$	20.05	7.90	7.40	8.27	3.8
Λ_-^∞/S cm^2 mol^{-1}	197.6	76.34	71.44	80.0	40.9

5.4.2 Transport Numbers

The **transport number** of an ion is defined as the **fraction of the total current carried by that ion**. Since ions in an electrolyte can differ in both their size and their charge, they do not all migrate at the same speed. However, all the ions share in carrying the current.

If t_+ is the transport number of the cation and t_- is the transport number of the anion in a single electrolyte, from the above definition it follows that

$$t_+ + t_- = 1 \tag{5.18}$$

For example, in HCl (aq, 0.1 mol dm^{-3}), $t_+ = 0.83$. It follows therefore that $t_- = 0.17$ in this solution.

The transport number is also related to ionic conductivity by

$$t_+ = \Lambda_+/\Lambda \qquad \text{and} \qquad t_- = \Lambda_-/\Lambda \tag{5.19}$$

The transport numbers therefore provide a means for calculating the molar ionic conductivities of individual ions.

The quantity of electricity carried by individual ions is related to the ionic velocity v by

$$t_+ = \frac{c_+ v_+}{c_+ v_+ + c_- v_-} \qquad \text{and} \qquad t_- = \frac{c_- v_-}{c_+ v_+ + c_- v_-} \tag{5.20}$$

where c_+ and c_- are the concentrations of the cation and anion, respectively.

Electrolysis experiments are used to determine transport numbers and readers should familiarise themselves with the experimental details of the two most commonly used methods, which are the Hittorf method and the moving-boundary method. The moving-boundary technique provides the most direct method of determining ionic mobilities.

If a current I is flowing through a tube of uniform cross section A containing two electrolyte solutions, the electric mobilities of the ions can be obtained from measurement of the velocity with which the boundary between the two electrolytes moves. The electric field strength is given by

$$E = I/A\kappa \tag{5.21}$$

The time dt taken for the boundary to move distance dx is given by

$$v_i = dx/dt$$

so that

$$u_i = \frac{v_i}{E} = \frac{dx/dt}{E} = \frac{(dx/dt)A\kappa}{I} \tag{5.22}$$

Example 5.5

In a moving-boundary experiment with KCl (aq, 0.1 mol dm^{-3}), the boundary moves 4.64 cm during 67 min when the current is 5.21×10^{-3} A. The cross-sectional area of the tube is 0.23 cm^2 and the conductivity of the electrolyte is 1.29 S m^{-1} at 298 K. Calculate the electric field strength and the ionic mobility.

From equation (5.21)

$$E = \frac{I}{A\kappa} = \frac{5.21 \times 10^{-3} \text{ A}}{(0.230 \times 10^{-4} \text{ m}^2) \times (1.29 \text{ S m}^{-1})}$$

$$= 176 \text{ V m}^{-1}$$

The ionic mobility u_i of the ion is given by

$$u_i = \frac{v_i}{E} = \frac{0.0464 \text{ m}}{(67 \times 60) \text{ s} \times 176 \text{ V m}^{-1}}$$

$$= 6.56 \times 10^{-8} \text{ m}^2 \text{ V}^{-1} \text{ s}^{-1} \qquad \blacksquare$$

In a mixed electrolyte, the transport number of a particular ion will be dependent not only on its individual charge but also on its concentration in the mixture. In general, for an ion i,

$$t_i = \frac{c_i \Lambda_i}{\Sigma c_i \Lambda_i} \tag{5.23}$$

Example 5.6

In a mixture of HCl (aq, 0.1 mol dm^{-3}) and KCl (aq, 3.0 mol dm^{-3}), the molar conductivities of the H$^+$, K$^+$ and Cl$^-$ ions are (in S cm^2 mol^{-1}) 349.9, 73.5 and 76.4 respectively. Calculate the value of the transport number of H$^+$.

Using equation (5.23)

$$t_{H^+} = \frac{0.1 \times 349.9}{(0.1 \times 349.9) + (0.1 \times 76.4) + (3.0 \times 73.5) + (3.0 \times 76.4)}$$

$$= 0.07 \qquad \blacksquare$$

Equation (5.23), therefore, provides a method of calculating the limiting ionic conductivities of individual ions. Using either the Hittorf or the moving-boundary technique, values of Λ_i^∞ and t_i^∞ are determined by extrapolation of a series of measurements over a range of low concentrations.

5.5 Applications of Conductivity Measurements

5.5.1 Dissociation Constant of a Weak Acid

For the partial ionisation of a weak acid,

$$HA \rightleftharpoons H^+ + A^-$$

the respective concentrations are given by

$$[HA] = (1 - \alpha)c \qquad \text{and} \qquad [H^+] = [A^-] = \alpha c$$

where α is the degree of ionisation. Assuming the speed of the ions does not change with dilution, Λ is a measure of the number of ions present. The dissociation constant K_a (in terms of concentration) is given by equation (5.6), i.e.

$$K_a = \alpha^2 c/(1 - \alpha)$$

This expression is termed Ostwald's dilution law.

As dilution increases, the equilibrium is displaced to the right with more HA dissociating into ions. At infinite dilution, the ionisation is complete and Λ^∞ is a measure of the total number of ions produced. In these circumstances, the degree of ionisation α is given by

$$\alpha = \Lambda/\Lambda^\infty \tag{5.24}$$

Substituting in equation (5.6) gives

$$K_a = \frac{(\Lambda/\Lambda^\infty)^2 c}{1 - (\Lambda/\Lambda^\infty)} \tag{5.25}$$

For aqueous ethanoic acid solutions, Table 5.3 shows that a constant value of K_a is obtained from conductivity measurements undertaken over a wide range of concentration (It is assumed that $\Lambda^\infty = 390.7$ S cm^2 mol^{-1} is known.)

Table 5.3

Concentration/mol dm^{-3}	Λ/S cm^2 mol^{-1}	$\alpha = \Lambda/\Lambda^\infty$	$K_a \times 10^5$/mol dm^{-3}
0.001	48.63	0.1245	1.77
0.005	22.80	0.05836	1.81
0.01	16.20	0.04150	1.80
0.02	11.57	0.02961	1.81
0.05	7.36	0.01884	1.81
0.10	5.20	0.01331	1.80

Rearranging equation (5.25) gives

$$\Lambda c = K_a[(\Lambda^\infty)^2/\Lambda] - K_a\Lambda^\infty \tag{5.26}$$

Therefore a plot of Λc against $1/\Lambda$ should be linear with slope equal to $K_a(\Lambda^\infty)^2$. Hence K_a can be obtained provided Λ^∞ is known. This method is used to determine K_a of nitric acid in methanol in Worked Example 5.9.5.

5.5.2 Ionic Product of Water

The ionic product of water K_w (see Section 5.2.5) is given by equation (5.10), i.e.

$$K_w = a_{H^+}a_{OH^-} \approx [H^+][OH^-]$$

K_w can be determined from conductivity measurements as follows.

Example 5.7

At 298 K, the conductivity of pure water is 5.8×10^{-6} S m^{-1} and the limiting molar conductivities of the hydrogen and hydroxyl ions are 0.034 98 and 0.019 76 S m^2 mol^{-1}, respectively. Calculate the ionic product of pure water at 298 K.

For pure water

$$c_{H^+} = c_{OH^-} = c$$

where the concentration c is given from equation (5.13) by

$$c = \frac{\kappa}{\Lambda} = \frac{\kappa}{\Lambda(H^+) + \Lambda(OH^-)} = \frac{5.8 \times 10^{-6} \text{ S m}^{-1}}{0.05474 \text{ S m}^2 \text{ mol}^{-1}}$$

$$= 1.060 \times 10^{-4} \text{ mol m}^{-3} = 1.060 \times 10^{-7} \text{ mol dm}^{-3}$$

Therefore

$$K_w = c_{H^+} c_{OH^-} = (1.060 \times 10^{-7} \text{ mol dm}^{-3})^2$$

$$= 1.12 \times 10^{-14} \text{ (mol dm}^{-3})^2 \qquad \blacksquare$$

5.5.3 Solubility of a Sparingly Soluble Salt

The conductivity κ of a saturated solution of a sparingly soluble salt can be determined by subtracting the measured conductivity of the pure solvent from the measured conductivity of the saturated solution, i.e.

$$\kappa(\text{salt}) = \kappa(\text{solution}) - \kappa(\text{solvent})$$

The molar conductivity of the salt in saturated solution is given by

$$\Lambda(\text{salt}) = \kappa(\text{salt})/c$$

where c is the concentration. Since the salt is sparingly soluble, its saturated solution can be considered to be infinitely dilute, i.e.

$$\Lambda(\text{salt}) = \Lambda^\infty(\text{salt}) = \Lambda_+^\infty + \Lambda_-^\infty \qquad (5.27)$$

and so

$$c = \frac{\kappa(\text{salt})}{\Lambda_+^\infty + \Lambda_-^\infty} \qquad (5.28)$$

If the limiting ionic conductivities of the ions are known from measurements with soluble strong electrolytes, the solubility c can therefore be determined, as can the solubility product (see equation (5.9)). This method is illustrated in Worked Example 5.9.6.

5.5.4 Conductiometric Titration

The exceptionally high limiting molar ionic conductivities of the H$^+$ ion (350 S cm^2 mol^{-1}) and the OH$^-$ ion (198 S cm^2 mol^{-1}) mean that acid–base titrations can readily be undertaken in a conductivity cell. As the titration proceeds with the addition of, say, base, the concentration of the various ions in the solution in the cell changes, producing a change in the conductivity of the solution. The total conductivity is influenced predominantly by the contributions of the H$^+$ and OH$^-$ ions compared with ions such as Na$^+$ and Cl$^-$ which would be present in a titration using HCl and NaOH solutions. In order to compensate for the fact that, as the titration proceeds, the volume is increasing steadily (this itself will decrease the conductivity as illustrated in Table 5.3), it is found that a plot of total volume × conductivity against the volume of base added gives the best results.

The graphs in Figs 5.3a and b illustrate the types of plots obtained in some types of acid–base titrations. It is an excellent method to use when the solutions are highly coloured, making the use of normal indicators impracticable. The technique can also be extended to titrations in which precipitation occurs.

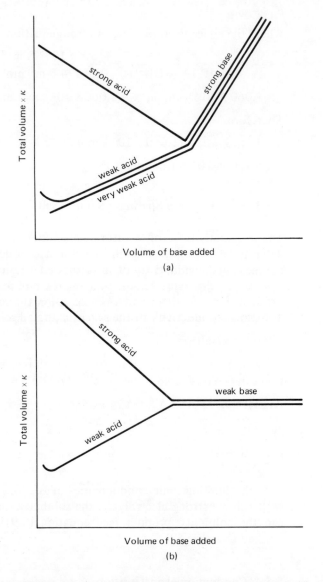

(a)

(b)

Figure 5.3 (a) Conductiometric titrations of acids with strong bases. (b) Conductiometric titrations of acids with weak bases.

5.6 Thermodynamics of Electrolyte Solutions

5.6.1 Activities and Activity Coefficients

Ions in solution attract and repel each other owing to the net electric charge that they carry. The electrostatic forces between ions will, of course, increase with

162

increasing electrolyte concentration and consequent decreasing inter-ionic distances. In general, these electrostatic forces are significantly stronger than the van der Waals' attractive forces that exist between species (charged or uncharged) in solution. It follows that deviations from ideal solution behaviour will, in general, be more pronounced in solutions of electrolytes than in solutions of non-electrolytes.

As with non-electrolytes, it is convenient to consider real versus ideal behaviour in terms of activities and activity coefficients (see Section 2.12.2), i.e.

$$a_+ = \frac{m_+}{m^{\ominus}} \gamma_+ \qquad \text{and} \qquad a_- = \frac{m_-}{m^{\ominus}} \gamma_- \qquad (5.29)$$

where a, m and γ represent activity, molality and activity coefficient, respectively. $m^{\ominus}$ is an arbitrarily chosen standard value of molality (invariably 1 mol kg^{-1}). Similar expressions can be written in terms of concentration, with $c^{\ominus} = 1$ mol dm^{-3}.

A fundamental complication which exists in the study of ions in solution is that it is impossible to study a single ionic species without at the same time studying neutralising ions of opposite charge. Experiments yield mean activities and mean activity coefficients. These are arbitrarily taken as the geometric means of the corresponding 'single-ion values', e.g.

$$a_{\pm}(\text{NaCl}) \qquad = (a_{\text{Na}^+} a_{\text{Cl}^-})^{1/2}$$

$$a_{\pm}(\text{Na}_2\text{SO}_4) = (a_{\text{Na}^+}^2 a_{\text{SO}_4^{2-}})^{1/3}$$

and similarly for the mean ionic activity coefficients.

It is for this same reason that expressions for K_a, K_s, K_w, etc., contain the product $a_+ a_-$ in them and that single-ion thermodynamic quantities (enthalpy, entropy, free energy, electrode potential, etc.) are related to an arbitrary (hydrogen ion) zero (see equations (2.25) and (2.63) and Table 6.1).

5.6.2 Debye–Hückel Theory of Strong Electrolytes

A given ion in an electrolyte solution will attract ions of opposite charge towards it and repel ions of like charge away from it. This, together with the randomising effect of thermal energy, will mean that the nearest neighbours to a given ion will tend to be ions of opposite charge and the ion is considered as being surrounded by an 'ionic atmosphere' of opposite net charge. (The same basic concept applies to the diffuse electric double layer described in Section 7.5.1.) The Debye–Hückel theory is based on this model.

The electric potential at a given distance from an ion includes two contributions: that due to the reference ion itself and that (of opposite sign) due to the ionic atmosphere. The latter of these is related to the activity coefficient of the reference ion. On the basis of several significant assumptions, the following expression, known as the Debye–Hückel limiting law, can be derived (see an appropriate textbook for details):

$$\log_{10} \gamma_i = - A z_i^2 \sqrt{I} \qquad (5.30)$$

where γ_i is the activity coefficient and z_i the charge number (valency) of the ionic species i, A is a constant dependent on the permittivity of the solution and the temperature, and I is the ionic strength of the solution. I depends on all the ions in the solution and is given by

$$I = \tfrac{1}{2} \sum c_i z_i^2 \qquad (5.31)$$

For an aqueous solution at 298 K, A is equal to 0.509 (mol dm^{-3})$^{-1/2}$.

163

The mean ionic activity coefficient of an electrolyte with positive ion(s) of charge number z_+ and negative ion(s) of charge number z_- is given by

$$\log_{10} \gamma_\pm = -A \, |z_+ z_-| \sqrt{I} \qquad (5.32)$$

where, again, I is the ionic strength of the solution, which depends on all the ions present. $|z_+ z_-|$ means that the product of the ion charge numbers is assigned a positive value despite the fact that z_- is usually defined as negative. Equation (5.32) is sometimes expressed in the alternative form

$$\log_{10} \gamma_\pm = +A z_+ z_- \sqrt{I}$$

with z_- now taken as negative. Either way, $\log_{10} \gamma_\pm$ is negative and $\gamma_\pm$ is predicted to be less than unity.

Example 5.8

For $CaCl_2$ (aq, 0.001 mol dm^{-3}) at 298 K, calculate
(a) the ionic strength,
(b) the activity coefficients of the Ca^{2+} and Cl^- ions,
(c) the mean ionic activity coefficient, and
(d) check the answers to (b) and (c) for consistency.

(a) $I = \frac{1}{2}(c_{Ca^{2+}} z^2_{Ca^{2+}} + c_{Cl^-} z^2_{Cl^-})$

$\qquad = \frac{1}{2}(1 \times 0.001 \times 2^2 + 2 \times 0.001 \times 1^2)$ mol dm^{-3}

$\qquad = 0.003$ mol dm^{-3}

(b) (i) $\log_{10} \gamma_{Ca^{2+}} = -0.509 \times 2^2 \times \sqrt{0.003}$

$\qquad$ giving

$\qquad \gamma_{Ca^{2+}} = 0.774$

$\quad$ (ii) $\log_{10} \gamma_{Cl^-} = -0.509 \times 1^2 \times \sqrt{0.003}$

$\qquad$ giving

$\qquad \gamma_{Cl^-} = 0.938$

(c) $\log_{10} \gamma_\pm = -0.509 \times 2 \times 1 \times \sqrt{0.003}$

$\qquad$ giving

$\qquad \gamma_\pm = 0.880$

(d) $\gamma_\pm = (\gamma_{Ca^{2+}} \, \gamma^2_{Cl^-})^{1/3} = [0.774 \times (0.938)^2]^{1/3}$

$\qquad = 0.880$ (as in (c)) $\qquad\qquad\qquad\qquad\qquad\qquad\qquad\blacksquare$

The Debye–Hückel limiting law is based on a considerably simplified model of the electrolyte solution. Table 5.4 shows a comparison of predicted and experimental activity coefficients for a 1–1 electrolyte.

Table 5.4

Concentration/mol dm^{-3}	0.001	0.01	0.1
$\gamma_\pm$ (Debye–Hückel limiting law)	0.965	0.890	0.690
$\gamma_\pm$ (experimental for HCl(aq))	0.965	0.905	0.794

For 1–1 electrolytes, the limiting law is reasonably applicable up to a concentration of about 0.01 mol dm^{-3} and it overestimates deviation from ideality. For electrolytes containing multivalent ions, theory and experiment tend to be much

more at variance and the limiting law tends to underestimate deviation from ideality.

Modified equations based on more sophisticated models of electrolyte solution have been proposed. An equation that allows for the finite size of the ions takes the form

$$\log_{10}\gamma_\pm = \frac{-A\,|z_+z_-|\sqrt{I}}{1+\sqrt{I}} \tag{5.33}$$

Another, which allows for solvent polarisation and the fact that solvation gives an effective increase in concentration, is

$$\log_{10}\gamma_\pm = -A\,|z_+z_-|\sqrt{I} + CI \tag{5.34}$$

where C is an empirical constant. This equation accounts for the experimental observation that in a $\log_{10}\gamma_\pm$ versus $\sqrt{I}$ plot (see Fig. 5.4), $\log_{10}\gamma_\pm$ not only deviates from linearity but the slope reverses and becomes positive with increasing $\sqrt{I}$.

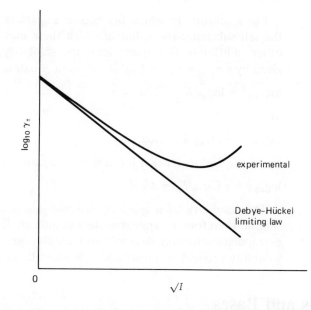

Figure 5.4 $\log_{10}\gamma_\pm$ versus $\sqrt{I}$ from Debye–Hückel limiting law (equation (5.32)).

Despite the limitations of Debye–Hückel theory, even the limiting law (equation (5.30)) is useful in explaining and processing electrochemical data, especially where an extrapolation to zero concentration is involved. Examples in this and the next chapter illustrate this point.

5.6.3 Conductivity of Strong Electrolytes

The existence of an 'ion atmosphere' of opposite net charge around each of the ions in an electrolyte solution causes a lowering of ionic mobility in two ways:
(a) Since the ions in the ion atmosphere are solvated, their migration causes a movement of solvent molecules which opposes the migration of the reference ion. This known as the **electrophoretic effect**.
(b) The reference ion and its ion atmosphere migrate in opposite directions. Since a small relaxation time is involved, the reference ion will be off-centre with

165

respect to its ion atmosphere. It will, therefore, be retarded by the resulting net backward attraction. This is known as the **relaxation effect**.

An equation, due to Onsager, which accounts for these effects for a dilute solution of a strong electrolyte takes the form

$$\Lambda = \Lambda^\infty - (A + B\,\Lambda^\infty)\sqrt{c} \tag{5.35}$$

where A and B are constants. This resembles Kohlrausch's empirical equation (equation (5.14)).

5.6.4 Solubility and Ionic Strength

The solubility product of a sparingly soluble 1–1 salt is given by

$$K_s = a_+ a_- = (c_+ c_-)\gamma_\pm^2$$

Therefore

$$\log_{10}(c_+ c_-) = \log_{10} K_s - 2\log_{10}\gamma_\pm \tag{5.36}$$

For a solution in which the ions of a sparingly soluble salt originate only from the salt substance itself, but in which there may be significant concentrations of other indifferent (i.e. inert) ions, the solubility of the sparingly soluble salt is given by $s = c_+ = c_-$, and substitution in equation (5.36) gives

$$\log_{10} s^2 = \log_{10} K_s - 2\log_{10}\gamma_\pm$$

or

$$\log_{10} s = \tfrac{1}{2}\log_{10} K_s - \log_{10}\gamma_\pm \tag{5.37}$$

Using the Debye–Hückel limiting law (equation (5.32)) to substitute for $\log_{10}\gamma_\pm$,

$$\log_{10} s = \tfrac{1}{2}\log_{10} K_s + A\sqrt{I} \tag{5.38}$$

The solubility of a sparingly soluble salt in a solution of an inert electrolyte should, therefore, be approximately as indicated, and this equation can be used to extrapolate solubility data to zero ionic strength in order to obtain a value for the solubility product, as illustrated in Worked Example 5.9.8.

5.7 Acids and Bases

5.7.1 Lowry–Brønsted Theory

The Lowry–Brønsted definitions of acid and base are as follows:
(a) An **acid** is a proton donor, e.g. $HA \rightarrow H^+ + A^-$, with the acid dissociation constant K_a given by equation (5.5) as

$$K_a = [H^+][A^-]/[HA]$$

(b) A **base** is a proton acceptor, e.g. $B + H^+ \rightarrow BH^+$, with the base dissociation constant K_b given by

$$K_b = [BH^+]/[B][H^+] \tag{5.39}$$

It should be noted that for the reverse processes in the above reactions, A^- acts as a Lowry–Brønsted base

$$H^+ + A^- \rightarrow HA$$

and BH^+ acts as a Lowry–Brønsted acid

$$BH^+ \rightarrow H^+ + B$$

Two substances that relate to each other by the exchange of a proton are said to be **conjugate**. Since in ionic solutions free protons are not obtained as a product, the proton transfer that does take place is normally between conjugate acids and bases, e.g.

$$HA + B \rightleftharpoons BH^+ + A^- \tag{5.40}$$

Acid HA and base A^- are conjugate. Acid BH^+ and base B are conjugate.

5.7.2 The Role of the Solvent

The acidic and basic properties of a species become apparent in a solution because the solvent itself can act as a proton acceptor or base (i.e. be protophilic) or as a proton donor or acid (i.e. be protogenic).

In aqueous solution of an acid HA, water acts as a proton acceptor (i.e. a base), e.g.

$$HA + H_2O \rightarrow H_3O^+ + A^- \tag{5.41}$$

The stronger the protophilic action of the solvent, the further the position of equilibrium in the above reaction will be to the right. In aqueous solution this equilibrium is almost completely to the right, so that strong acids (e.g. $HClO_4$, HBr, H_2SO_4, HCl, HNO_3) appear to be equally strong.

However, in a weakly protophilic solvent (e.g. ethanoic acid) the equilibrium is not very far to the right, with the above examples being listed in decreasing order of strength and $HClO_4$ being over 50 times as strong as HNO_3 in ethanoic acid solvent.

Similarly for bases in aqueous solution,

$$B + H_2O \rightarrow BH^+ + OH^- \tag{5.42}$$

In this case, water can act as a proton donor or acid. In strongly protogenic (acidic) solvents (e.g. HF, HCl), many substances that are normally acids (e.g. HNO_3) behave as bases, e.g.

$$\underset{\text{base}}{HNO_3} + \underset{\text{solvent (acid)}}{HF} \rightleftharpoons \underset{\text{acid}}{H_2NO_3^+} + \underset{\text{base}}{F^-}$$

5.7.3 Relationship Between K_a, K_b and K_w

For the equilibrium, $H_2O \rightleftharpoons H^+ + OH^-$ (see Section 5.2.5), $K_w = [H^+][OH^-]$ and is equal to 10^{-14} at 298 K.

In aqueous solution, the acid HA and its conjugate base A^- both interact with the water (the water is acting as a amphiprotic solvent in such circumstances), as follows:

$$HA + H_2O \rightleftharpoons H_3O^+ + A^-$$
$$A^- + H_2O \rightleftharpoons HA + OH^- \tag{5.43}$$

with

$$K_a = [H^+][A^-]/[HA]$$
$$K_b = [HA][OH^-]/[A^-] \tag{5.44}$$

Multiplying equations (5.44) gives

$$K_a K_b = \frac{[H^+][A^-]}{[HA]} \times \frac{[HA][OH^-]}{[A^-]} = [H^+][OH^-]$$

i.e.

$$K_w = K_a K_b \qquad\qquad (5.45)$$

5.8 pH, Hydrolysis, Buffer Solutions

5.8.1 p-Values (pH, pK_a, pK_b, pK_w, etc.)

In order to avoid quoting negative powers of 10, it is convenient to express ionic equilibrium constants in logarithmic form:

$$pH = \log_{10}(1/[H^+]) = -\log_{10}[H^+]$$

$$pK_a = -\log_{10} K_a$$

$$pK_w = -\log_{10} K_w = 14 \qquad \text{(at 298 K)}$$

Examples of pK_a and pK_b in aqueous solution at 298 K are given in Table 5.5.

Table 5.5

Acids	pK_a	Bases	pK_b
Ethanoic	4.75	Ammonia	4.77
Chloroethanoic	2.85	Methylamine	3.36
Dichloroethanoic	1.3	Phenylamine	9.39
Trichloroethanoic	0.7	Pyridine	8.80

Example 5.9

Calculate the pH of ethanoic acid (aq, 0.1 mol dm^{-3}), if the acid dissociation constant is 1.8×10^{-5} mol dm^{-3}.

From equation (5.5)

$$K_a = [H^+][A^-]/[HA]$$

At equilibrium, $[H^+] = [A^-]$. If the degree of ionisation is small, the equilibrium concentration [HA] of unionised acid approximates to the total concentration, i.e. $c = [HA] + [A^-] \approx [HA]$. Therefore,

$$K_a = [H^+]^2/[HA] = [H^+]^2/c$$

i.e.

$$[H^+] = \sqrt{(K_a c)}$$

Taking logarithms,

$$\log_{10}[H^+] = \tfrac{1}{2}\log_{10} K_a + \tfrac{1}{2}\log_{10} c$$
$$= \tfrac{1}{2}\log_{10}(1.8 \times 10^{-5}) + \tfrac{1}{2}\log_{10} 0.1 = -2.87$$

Therefore,

$$pH = 2.87 \qquad\qquad \blacksquare$$

Note that the above pH can be expressed as

$$pH = \tfrac{1}{2} pK_a - \tfrac{1}{2}\log_{10} c$$

5.8.2 Neutralisation and Hydrolysis

Neutralisation is the reaction of an acid and a base to give a salt and water. When a strong acid reacts with a strong base, the salts are fully ionised, and if equivalent amounts of acid and base are used, the solution will be neutral.

However, when a salt of a weak base and a strong acid (e.g. ammonium chloride) is formed, the solution is found to be acidic. This arises from the ability of the ammonium ion to donate a proton to the water via

$$NH_4^+ + H_2O \rightleftharpoons H_3O^+ + NH_3$$

When a salt of a weak acid and a strong base (e.g. sodium ethanoate) is formed, the solution is found to be alkaline. This arises from the ability of the ethanoate ion to accept a proton from the water via

$$CH_3COO^- + H_2O \rightleftharpoons CH_3COOH + OH^-$$

and produce hydroxyl ions. This tendency of a salt when dissolved in water to react with the solvent and thereby reverse the neutralisation process is termed **hydrolysis**.

For a general case, both the above reactions are examples of neutralisation where

$$\underset{\text{acid}}{HA} + \underset{\text{base}}{B} \rightleftharpoons \underset{\text{acid}}{BH^+} + \underset{\text{base}}{A^-} \tag{5.46}$$

where BH^+ and A^- can be regarded as the ions of the salt produced by neutralisation. In aqueous solution, BH^+ and A^- hydrolyse as follows

$$BH^+ + H_2O \rightarrow B + H_3O^+$$

$$A^- + H_2O \rightarrow HA + OH^-$$

The first of these reactions is favoured when the base is weak (as in ammonium chloride), and this leads to the production of protons and acidic solutions. The second of these reactions is favoured when the acid is weak (as in sodium ethanoate), and this leads to alkaline solutions.

5.8.3 Hydrolysis Equations

Following the above general idea, it is possible to derive expressions for K_h as follows.

(a) *Hydrolysis of a Salt of a Weak Acid and a Strong Base*

From the second of equations (5.43), the hydrolysis constant K_h is given by

$$K_h = \frac{[HA][OH^-]}{[A^-]} = \frac{[H^+][OH^-] \times [HA]}{[H^+][A^-]} = \frac{K_w}{K_a} \tag{5.47}$$

But at equilibrium, $[HA] = [OH^-]$; therefore,

$$K_h = \frac{[OH^-]^2}{[A^-]} = \frac{[OH^-]^2}{c} = \frac{K_w^2}{[H^+]^2 c} \tag{5.48}$$

Combining equations (5.47) and (5.48) gives

$$\frac{K_w^2}{[H^+]^2 c} = \frac{K_w}{K_a}$$

i.e.

$$[H^+] = \sqrt{(K_a K_w /c)}$$

Taking logarithms,

$$\log_{10} [H^+] = \tfrac{1}{2} \log_{10} K_a + \tfrac{1}{2} \log_{10} K_w - \tfrac{1}{2} \log_{10} c \qquad (5.49)$$

or

$$pH = \tfrac{1}{2} pK_a + \tfrac{1}{2} pK_w + \tfrac{1}{2} \log_{10} c$$

(b) *Hydrolysis of a Salt of a Strong Acid and a Weak Base*

A similar derivation based on equation (5.42) gives

$$K_h = K_w / K_b$$

$$\log_{10} [H^+] = \tfrac{1}{2} \log_{10} K_w - \tfrac{1}{2} \log_{10} K_b + \tfrac{1}{2} \log_{10} c$$

and

$$pH = \tfrac{1}{2} pK_w - \tfrac{1}{2} pK_b - \tfrac{1}{2} \log_{10} c \qquad (5.50)$$

The use of the above relationships in the study of hydrolyses is illustrated in Worked Examples 5.9.12 and 5.9.13.

5.8.4 Buffer Solutions

Buffer solutions represent a specific application of the above. They can be prepared to have a definite known pH which does not change significantly on dilution or on addition of small quantities of acid or base. This action is known as **buffer action**, and such mixtures can be used for resisting pH changes and providing solutions of known pH.

Examples of buffer solutions are the following.

(a) *Mixture of Weak Acid* HA *and One of its Salts with Strong Base* A⁻

In such a mixture, changes to pH are resisted by the following reactions taking place

$$H_3 O^+ + A^- \rightarrow HA + H_2 O$$

$$OH^- + HA \rightarrow A^- + H_2 O$$

Since for the weak acid,

$$K_a = \frac{[H^+][A^-]}{[HA]} \approx \frac{[H^+][salt]}{[acid]}$$

then

$$\log_{10} [H^+] = \log_{10} K_a + \log_{10} ([acid]/[salt])$$

giving

$$pH = pK_a + \log_{10} ([salt]/[acid]) \qquad (5.51)$$

This is known as the Henderson equation.

(b) *Mixture of Weak Base* B *and One of its Salts with Strong Acid* BH⁺

For this mixture

$$K_b = \frac{[BH^+][OH^-]}{[B]} \approx \frac{[OH^-][salt]}{[base]}$$

$$pOH = pK_b + \log_{10} ([salt]/[base])$$

and

$$pH = pK_w - pK_b - \log_{10} ([salt]/[base]) \tag{5.52}$$

The approximations made in the derivation of the Henderson equation mean that, for the best results, the pH range is limited to about pH 4–10. Two examples of buffer solutions are

- Ethanoic acid/sodium ethanoate   pH 3.7–5.6
- Boric(III) acid/disodium tetraborate (borax)   pH 6.7–9.2

5.9 Worked Examples

5.9.1 Molar Conductivity

A solution of KCl (aq, 0.02 mol dm^{-3}), which has a conductivity of 0.00277 S cm^{-1}, was found to have a resistance of 83 Ω. When potassium sulphate (aq, 0.005 mol dm^{-3}) solution was substituted, the resistance was 326 Ω. What is the cell constant and what is the conductivity and molar conductivity of the potassium sulphate solution?

Answer

The cell constant K is given by

$$K = \kappa R = 0.002\,77 \text{ S cm}^{-1} \times 83 \ \Omega = 0.230 \text{ cm}^{-1}$$

For $K_2 SO_4$

$$\kappa = K/R = \frac{0.230 \text{ cm}^{-1}}{326 \ \Omega}$$

$$= 7.055 \times 10^{-4} \text{ S cm}^{-1}$$

The molar conductivity Λ is given by

$$\Lambda = \frac{7.055 \times 10^{-4} \text{ S cm}^{-1}}{0.005 \times 10^{-3} \text{ mol cm}^{-3}}$$

$$= 141 \text{ S cm}^2 \text{ mol}^{-1}$$

5.9.2 Limiting Molar Conductivity of a Strong Electrolyte

From the data below, test whether Kohlrausch's law is obeyed and where possible determine the limiting molar conductivity.

c/mol dm^{-3}	Λ/S cm^2 mol^{-1}			
	HCl	KCl	NaCl	$CH_3 COOH$
0.0005	422.7	147.8	124.5	67.30
0.001	421.4	147.0	123.7	48.63
0.005	415.8	143.6	120.7	22.80
0.01	412.0	141.3	118.5	16.20
0.05	399.1	133.4	111.1	7.36
0.10	391.3	129.0	106.7	5.20

Answer

Kohlrausch's law (equation (5.14)) states that, for strong electrolytes, the molar conductivity Λ is given by

$$\Lambda = \Lambda^{\infty} - k\sqrt{c}$$

Therefore a plot of Λ against $\sqrt{c}$ should be linear if this relationship is obeyed.

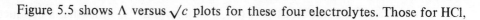

$c/\text{mol dm}^{-3}$	0.0005	0.001	0.005	0.01	0.05	0.10
$\sqrt{c}/(\text{mol dm}^{-3})^{1/2}$	0.0224	0.0316	0.0707	0.100	0.224	0.316
$\Lambda_{HCl}/\text{S cm}^2\text{ mol}^{-1}$	422.7	421.4	415.8	412.0	399.1	391.3
$\Lambda_{KCl}/\text{S cm}^2\text{ mol}^{-1}$	147.8	147.0	143.6	141.3	133.4	129.0
$\Lambda_{NaCl}/\text{S cm}^2\text{ mol}^{-1}$	124.5	123.7	120.7	118.5	111.1	106.7
$\Lambda_{CH_3COOH}/\text{S cm}^2\text{ mol}^{-1}$	67.30	48.63	22.80	16.20	7.36	5.20

Figure 5.5 shows Λ versus $\sqrt{c}$ plots for these four electrolytes. Those for HCl,

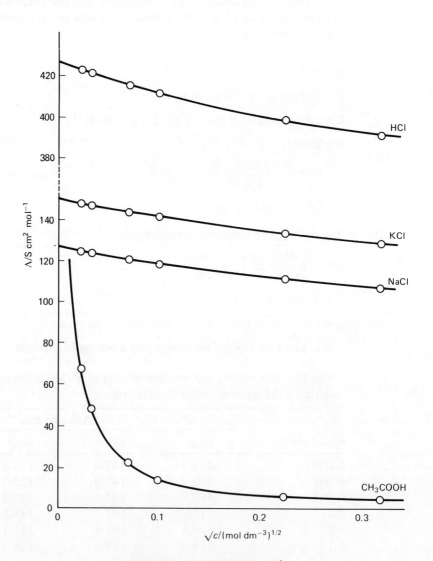

Figure 5.5 Plots of Λ versus $\sqrt{c}$.

KCl and NaCl are linear (except at higher concentrations) as anticipated for strong electrolytes, and extrapolate to zero concentration to give

$$\Lambda_{HCl}^{\infty} = 426.2 \text{ S cm}^2 \text{ mol}^{-1}$$

$$\Lambda_{KCl}^{\infty} = 149.9 \text{ S cm}^2 \text{ mol}^{-1}$$

$$\Lambda_{NaCl}^{\infty} = 126.5 \text{ S cm}^2 \text{ mol}^{-1}$$

The Λ versus $\sqrt{c}$ plot for ethanoic acid is not linear and cannot be extrapolated reliably to zero concentration in order to determine Λ^{∞}.

5.9.3 Limiting Molar Conductivity of a Weak Electrolyte

Given the following limiting molar conductivities,

sodium benzoate (NaB)	$8.24 \times 10^{-3} \text{ S m}^2 \text{ mol}^{-1}$
hydrochloric acid	$4.262 \times 10^{-2} \text{ S m}^2 \text{ mol}^{-1}$
sodium chloride	$1.265 \times 10^{-2} \text{ S m}^2 \text{ mol}^{-1}$

calculate the limiting molar conductivity of aqueous benzoic acid (HB).

Answer

$$\Lambda^{\infty} (HB) = \Lambda^{\infty} (H^+) + \Lambda^{\infty} (B^-)$$

However $\Lambda^{\infty}(HB)$ can also be obtained from the data by adding to each side of the above the Λ^{∞} of a salt of a strong acid and a strong base such as sodium chloride, so that

$$\Lambda^{\infty} (HB) + \Lambda^{\infty} (NaCl) = \Lambda^{\infty} (H^+) + \Lambda^{\infty} (B^-) + \Lambda^{\infty} (Na^+) + \Lambda^{\infty} (Cl^-)$$

$$= \Lambda^{\infty} (HCl) + \Lambda^{\infty} (NaB)$$

Therefore

$$\Lambda^{\infty} (HB) = \Lambda^{\infty} (HCl) + \Lambda^{\infty} (NaB) - \Lambda^{\infty} (NaCl)$$

Substituting,

$$\Lambda^{\infty} (HB) = (42.62 + 8.24 - 12.65) \times 10^{-3} \text{ S m}^2 \text{ mol}^{-1}$$

$$= 3.82 \times 10^{-2} \text{ S m}^2 \text{ mol}^{-1}$$

5.9.4 Conductivity and Ionic Mobility

At 298 K, the limiting molar conductivities at infinite dilution of potassium chloride and sodium nitrate are $0.014\,985 \text{ S m}^2 \text{ mol}^{-1}$ and $0.012\,159 \text{ S m}^2 \text{ mol}^{-1}$, respectively. The transport numbers of the potassium and sodium ions in these solutions are 0.4906 and 0.4124, respectively. Calculate the limiting molar conductivities of potassium nitrate and sodium chloride.

(GRSC, Part I)

Answer

The limiting molar conductivities of the four ions are obtained as follows:

$$\Lambda^{\infty} (K^+) = \Lambda^{\infty} (KCl) \times t(K^+)$$

$$= 0.014\,985 \times 0.4906 \text{ S m}^2 \text{ mol}^{-1}$$

$$= 7.352 \times 10^{-3} \text{ S m}^2 \text{ mol}^{-1}$$

$$\Lambda^\infty(Cl^-) = \Lambda^\infty(KCl) \times t(Cl^-)$$
$$= 0.014\,985 \times (1 - 0.4906) \text{ S m}^2 \text{ mol}^{-1}$$
$$= 7.633 \times 10^{-3} \text{ S m}^2 \text{ mol}^{-1}$$

$$\Lambda^\infty(Na^+) = \Lambda^\infty(NaNO_3) \times t(Na^+)$$
$$= 0.012\,159 \times 0.4124 \text{ S m}^2 \text{ mol}^{-1}$$
$$= 5.014 \times 10^{-3} \text{ S m}^2 \text{ mol}^{-1}$$

$$\Lambda^\infty(NO_3^-) = \Lambda^\infty(NaNO_3) \times t(NO_3^-)$$
$$= 0.012\,159 \times (1 - 0.4124) \text{ S m}^2 \text{ mol}^{-1}$$
$$= 7.145 \times 10^{-3} \text{ S m}^2 \text{ mol}^{-1}$$

Therefore

$$\Lambda^\infty(KNO_3) = \Lambda^\infty(K^+) + \Lambda^\infty(NO_3^-)$$
$$= (7.352 + 7.145) \times 10^{-3} \text{ S m}^2 \text{ mol}^{-1}$$
$$= 1.450 \times 10^{-2} \text{ S m}^2 \text{ mol}^{-1}$$

and

$$\Lambda^\infty(NaCl) = \Lambda^\infty(Na^+) + \Lambda^\infty(Cl^-)$$
$$= (5.014 + 7.633) \times 10^{-3} \text{ S m}^2 \text{ mol}^{-1}$$
$$= 1.265 \times 10^{-2} \text{ S m}^2 \text{ mol}^{-1}$$

5.9.5 Dissociation Constant from Conductivity Data

The molar conductivity of nitric acid in methanol at 298 K is tabulated below as a function of the concentration:

$c/\text{mol dm}^{-3} \times 10^{-4}$	0	0.966	3.075	4.730	7.084	9.163
$\Lambda/\text{S m}^2 \text{ mol}^{-1} \times 10^{-4}$	203.0	178.7	151.0	137.6	124.6	116.3

Investigate the applicability of Ostwald's dilution law to this system.

(GRSC, Part I)

Answer

The dissociation of nitric acid can be represented thus

$$HNO_3 \rightleftharpoons H^+ + NO_3^-$$

In methanol, nitric acid acts as a weak electrolyte, and therefore Ostwald's dilution law (equation (5.6)) applies and the dissociation constant K_a (calculated in terms of concentrations) is given by equation (5.26), i.e.

$$\Lambda c = K_a[(\Lambda^\infty)^2/\Lambda] - K_a\Lambda^\infty$$

A plot of Λc against $1/\Lambda$ should, therefore, give a straight line of slope $K_a(\Lambda^\infty)^2$.

$10^4 c/\mathrm{mol\ dm^{-3}}$	$\Lambda c \times 10^6 /(\mathrm{S\ m^2\ mol^{-1}})\,(\mathrm{mol\ dm^{-3}})$	$\mathrm{S\ m^2\ mol^{-1}}/\Lambda$
0	0	49.3
0.966	1.73	56.0
3.075	4.64	66.2
4.730	6.51	72.7
7.084	8.83	80.3
9.163	10.66	86.0

The graph (Fig. 5.6) is a straight line, for which

$$\text{slope} = K_a (\Lambda^\infty)^2 = 2.88 \times 10^{-7}\ (\mathrm{mol\ dm^{-3}})\,(\mathrm{S\ m^2\ mol^{-1}})^2$$

and

$$K_a = \frac{2.88 \times 10^{-7}}{(0.0203)^2}\ \mathrm{mol\ dm^{-3}}$$

$$= 7.0 \times 10^{-4}\ \mathrm{mol\ dm^{-3}}$$

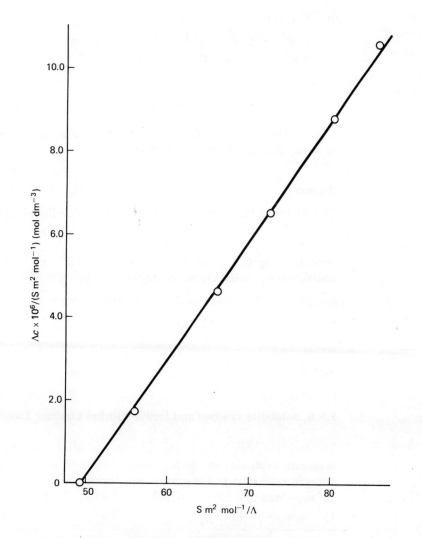

Figure 5.6   Plot of Λc versus $1/\Lambda$.

5.9.6 Conductivity and Solubility

The conductivity of silver chloride at 298 K is measured to be 2.28×10^{-4} S m^{-1}. The molar conductivities of Ag$^+$ and Cl$^-$ ions are 0.00619 S m^2 mol^{-1} and 0.00752 S m^2 mol^{-1}, respectively. What is the solubility and the solubility product?

Answer

Applying equation (5.28) to the above gives

$$c = \frac{\kappa_{AgCl}}{\Lambda_{Ag^+}^\infty + \Lambda_{Cl^-}^\infty}$$

$$= \frac{2.28 \times 10^{-4}}{0.00619 + 0.00752} \text{ mol m}^{-3}$$

$$= 1.66 \times 10^{-2} \text{ mol m}^{-3}$$

$$= 1.66 \times 10^{-5} \text{ mol dm}^{-3}$$

The solubility product K_s is given by

$$K_s = c_{Ag^+} c_{Cl^-}$$

$$= (1.66 \times 10^{-5})^2 \text{ (mol dm}^{-3})^2$$

$$= 2.8 \times 10^{-10} \text{ (mol dm}^{-3})^2$$

5.9.7 Debye–Hückel Limiting Law

Use the Debye–Hückel limiting law to calculate the activity coefficient of BaSO$_4$ in a 0.01 mol dm^{-3} solution of NaNO$_3$.

Answer

In a 0.01 mol dm^{-3} solution of NaNO$_3$, the solubility of BaSO$_4$ will be sufficiently small to assume that the ionic strength of the solution is determined solely by the NaNO$_3$. For a 1-1 electrolyte (e.g. NaNO$_3$), the ionic strength is equal to the concentration (i.e. when $z_+ = z_- = 1$, $I = \frac{1}{2} \Sigma c_i z_i^2 = c$). Therefore the activity coefficient $\gamma_\pm$ of BaSO$_4$ in NaNO$_3$ is given by

$$\log_{10} \gamma_\pm = -0.509 \times |z_{Ba^{2+}} z_{SO_4^{2-}}| (c/\text{mol dm}^{-3})^{1/2}$$

$$= -0.509 \times 2 \times 2 \sqrt{0.01} = -0.2036$$

giving

$$\gamma_\pm = 0.626$$

5.9.8 Solubility Product and Debye–Hückel Limiting Law

The following data refer to the solubility of silver chloride in aqueous solutions of magnesium sulphate at 298 K:

$10^5 s_{AgCl}$/mol dm^{-3}	1.43	1.48	1.51	1.55	1.60	1.65
$10^2 c_{MgSO_4}$/mol dm^{-3}	0.1	0.2	0.3	0.4	0.6	1.0

Determine the solubility product of AgCl in aqueous solution at 298 K.

Answer

The solubility product K_s of AgCl is given by

$$K_s = a_{Ag^+} a_{Cl^-} = \frac{c_{Ag^+} c_{Cl^-}}{(c^{\ominus})^2} \gamma_{\pm}^2$$

In pure water or in a solution of an indifferent electrolyte,

$$c_{Ag^+} = c_{Cl^-} = s_{AgCl}$$

Therefore

$$K_s = (s_{AgCl}/\text{mol dm}^{-3})^2 \gamma_{\pm}^2$$

or

$$\log_{10}(s_{AgCl}/\text{mol dm}^{-3}) = \tfrac{1}{2} \log_{10} K_s - \log_{10} \gamma_{\pm}$$

Substituting from the limiting law (equation (5.30)), we have

$$\log_{10}(s_{AgCl}/\text{mol dm}^{-3}) = \tfrac{1}{2} \log_{10} K_s + 0.509 \sqrt{I}/(\text{mol dm}^{-3})^{1/2}$$

Since $c_{MgSO_4} \gg c_{AgCl}$, it can be assumed that the ionic strength I is determined solely by the concentration of $MgSO_4$, i.e.

$$I = \tfrac{1}{2}(c_{Mg^{2+}} z_{Mg^{2+}}^2 + c_{SO_4^{2-}} z_{SO_4^{2-}}^2) = 4c_{MgSO_4}$$

Therefore a plot of $\log_{10}(s_{AgCl}/\text{mol dm}^{-3})$ against $\sqrt{I}/(\text{mol dm}^{-3})^{1/2}$ should be linear with the intercept at $I = 0$ giving $\tfrac{1}{2} \log_{10} K_s$.

$10^2 c_{MgSO_4}/\text{mol dm}^{-3}$	0.1	0.2	0.3	0.4	0.6	1.0
$10^2 I/\text{mol dm}^{-3}$	0.40	0.80	1.20	1.60	2.40	4.00
$\sqrt{I}/(\text{mol dm}^{-3})^{1/2}$	0.063	0.089	0.110	0.126	0.155	0.200
$s_{AgCl}/\text{mol dm}^{-3} \times 10^{-5}$	1.43	1.48	1.51	1.55	1.60	1.65
$\log_{10}(s_{AgCl}/\text{mol dm}^{-3})$	−4.845	−4.830	−4.821	−4.810	−4.796	−4.783

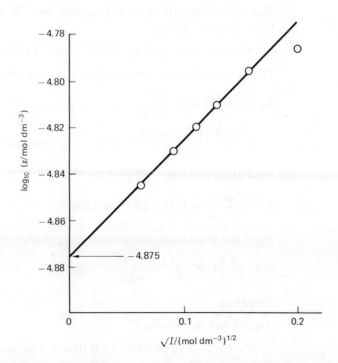

Figure 5.7   Plot of $\log_{10} s_{AgCl}$ versus $\sqrt{I}$ to determine solubility product.

From the graph (Fig. 5.7)

intercept $= \frac{1}{2} \log_{10} K_s = -4.875$

giving

$K_s = 1.78 \times 10^{-10} \ (mol \ dm^{-3})^2$

5.9.9 pH and Dissociation Constant of a Weak Acid

The molar conductivity of ethanoic acid (aq, $0.0025 \ mol \ dm^{-3}$) is $0.003\,165$ S $m^2 \ mol^{-1}$ at 298 K and the limiting molar conductivity at infinite dilution is $0.039\,07$ S $m^2 \ mol^{-1}$. From these data, determine at 298 K
(a) the pH of the ethanoic acid solution and the dissociation constant;
(b) the molar conductivity and pH of ethanoic acid (aq, $0.01 \ mol \ dm^{-3}$).

Answer

(a) The dissociation of ethanoic acid and the equilibrium concentrations can be represented as follows:

$$HAc \rightleftharpoons H^+ + Ac^-$$
$$(1 - \alpha)c \quad \alpha c \quad \alpha c$$

where the degree of ionisation α is given by

$$\alpha = \frac{\Lambda}{\Lambda^\infty} = \frac{0.003165}{0.03907} = 0.0810$$

Therefore

$$c_{H^+} = \alpha c = 0.081 \times 0.0025 \ mol \ dm^{-3}$$
$$= 2.025 \times 10^{-4} \ mol \ dm^{-3}$$

The ionic strength αc is sufficiently low for the activity coefficient to be taken as unity, giving

$$pH = - \log_{10} c_{H^+} = - \log_{10} (2.025 \times 10^{-4}) = 3.69$$

The classical dissociation constant K_a is given by

$$K_a = \frac{c_{H^+} c_{Ac^-}}{c_{HA}} = \frac{\alpha^2 c}{1 - \alpha}$$

$$= \frac{(0.081)^2 \times 0.0025}{1 - 0.081} = 1.78 \times 10^{-5} \ mol \ dm^{-3}$$

(b) For CH_3COOH (aq, $0.01 \ mol \ dm^{-3}$),

$$K_a = \frac{\alpha^2 c}{1 - \alpha} = 1.78 \times 10^{-5} \ mol \ dm^{-3}$$

Since α is small compared to unity, $K_a \approx \alpha^2 c$

$$\alpha = \sqrt{\frac{K_a}{c}} = \sqrt{\frac{1.78 \times 10^{-5}}{0.01}} = 0.0422$$

Therefore

$$\Lambda(0.01 \ mol \ dm^{-3}) = \alpha \Lambda^\infty$$

$$= 0.0422 \times 0.03907 \ S \ m^2 \ mol^{-1}$$

$$= 1.65 \times 10^{-3} \ S \ m^2 \ mol^{-1}$$

and

$$pH = -\log_{10}(c_{H^+}/\text{mol dm}^{-3})$$

$$= -\log_{10}(0.0422 \times 0.01)$$

$$= 3.37$$

5.9.10 pH of a Buffer Solution

Calculate the pH of a mixture of 100 cm^3 of ethanoic acid (aq, 0.2 mol dm^{-3}) and 100 cm^3 of sodium ethanoate (aq, 0.5 mol dm^{-3}), given that the dissociation constant of ethanoic acid is 1.8×10^{-5} mol dm^{-3}.

Answer

For this buffer solution,

$$K_a = [H^+][Ac^-]/[HAc]$$

Therefore

$$[H^+] = K_a[HAc]/[Ac^-]$$

or in the terms used in the Henderson equation,

$$pH = -\log_{10}\left(\frac{1}{K_a}\frac{[\text{acid}]}{[\text{salt}]}\right) = \log_{10}\left(\frac{1}{K_a}\frac{[\text{salt}]}{[\text{acid}]}\right)$$

Substituting,

$$pH = \log_{10}\left(\frac{1}{1.8 \times 10^{-5}} \times \frac{0.5}{0.2}\right)$$

$$= 5.14$$

5.9.11 pH of a Phosphate Buffer Solution

Calculate the pH of an aqueous phosphate buffer solution at 298 K, which is 0.02 mol dm^{-3} with respect to both K_2HPO_4 and KH_2PO_4. The second thermodynamic constant of phosphoric acid, K_{a2}, is 8.00×10^{-8}. Use the Debye–Hückel equation in the form

$$\log_{10}\gamma_i = -\frac{Az_i^2\sqrt{I}}{1+\sqrt{I}}$$

where $A = 0.51$ dm$^{3/2}$ mol$^{-1/2}$ to estimate the activity coefficients.

Answer

The second dissociation constant of phosphoric acid is represented by the equation

$$H_2PO_4^- \rightleftharpoons H^+ + HPO_4^{2-}$$

and the equilibrium constant is given by

$$K_{a2} = \frac{a_{H^+}\,a_{HPO_4^{2-}}}{a_{H_2PO_4^-}} = \frac{a_{H^+}\,c_{HPO_4^{2-}}}{c_{H_2PO_4^-}}\,\frac{\gamma_{HPO_4^{2-}}}{\gamma_{H_2PO_4^-}}$$

where a represents relative activity, c the concentration and γ the activity coefficient. Since the K_2HPO_4 and KH_2PO_4 concentrations are equal,

$$K_{a2} = a_{H^+} \frac{\gamma_{HPO_4^{2-}}}{\gamma_{H_2PO_4^-}}$$

The ionic strength of the solution is calculated as follows:

$$I = \tfrac{1}{2} \sum c_i z_i^2 = \tfrac{1}{2}(c_{K^+} + c_{H_2PO_4^-} + 2^2 \times c_{HPO_4^{2-}})$$
$$= \tfrac{1}{2}[(3 \times 0.02) + 0.02 + (4 \times 0.02)] \text{ mol dm}^{-3}$$
$$= 0.08 \text{ mol dm}^{-3}$$

Therefore

$$\log_{10}\gamma_{HPO_4^{2-}} = \frac{-0.51 \times 2^2 \times \sqrt{0.08}}{1 + \sqrt{0.08}}$$

and

$$\log_{10}\gamma_{H_2PO_4^-} = \frac{-0.51 \times 1^2 \times \sqrt{0.08}}{1 + \sqrt{0.08}}$$

from which

$$\frac{\gamma_{HPO_4^{2-}}}{\gamma_{H_2PO_4^-}} = 0.460$$

Therefore,

$$a_{H^+} = \frac{8.0 \times 10^{-8}}{0.460}$$

giving

$$pH = -\log_{10} a_{H^+} = 6.76$$

5.9.12 pH of a Salt of a Weak Acid and a Strong Base

Calculate the pH of sodium ethanoate (aq, 0.05 mol dm^{-3}) at 298 K, given that the dissociation constant of ethanoic acid is 1.8×10^{-5} mol dm^{-3} and the ionic product of water is 1.0×10^{-14} (mol dm^{-3})^2 at that temperature.

Answer

Sodium ethanoate is a salt of a weak acid and a strong base with equation (5.43) taking the form

$$CH_3COO^- + H_2O \rightleftharpoons CH_3COOH + OH^-$$

and the pH being given by equation (5.49), i.e.

$$\log_{10}[H^+] = \tfrac{1}{2}\log_{10}K_a + \tfrac{1}{2}\log_{10}K_w - \tfrac{1}{2}\log_{10}c$$
$$= \tfrac{1}{2}(\log_{10} 1.8 \times 10^{-5} + \log_{10} 1.0 \times 10^{-14} - \log_{10} 0.05)$$
$$= \tfrac{1}{2}(-4.74 - 14.00 + 1.30) = -8.72$$

giving

$$pH = 8.72$$

5.9.13 Hydrolysis of a Salt of a Strong Acid and a Weak Base

The hydrolysis constant of phenylamine hydrochloride $C_6H_5NH_3Cl$ is 2.63×10^{-5} in water at 298 K. Calculate the degree of hydrolysis of a 0.1 mol dm^{-3} solution of phenylamine hydrochloride and the base dissociation constant of phenylamine in water at 298 K. The ionic product of water at 298 K is 1.01×10^{-14}.

(Liverpool Polytechnic, BSc, 1st year)

Answer

The hydrolysis reaction is that of a salt of a strong acid and a weak base and the equilibrium concentrations for the above can be represented by

$$C_6H_5NH_3^+ + H_2O \rightleftharpoons C_6H_5NH_2 + H_3O^+$$
$$(1-\alpha)c \qquad\qquad \alpha c \qquad \alpha c$$

where α is the degree of hydrolysis and c is the stoichiometric concentration of the salt.

Therefore the hydrolysis constant K_h is given by

$$K_h = \frac{a_{C_6H_5NH_2}\, a_{H_3O^+}}{a_{C_6H_5NH_3^+}} \approx \frac{c_{C_6H_5NH_2}\, c_{H_3O^+}}{c_{C_6H_5NH_3^+}\, c^{\ominus}}$$

$$= \frac{\alpha^2 c}{(1-\alpha)\, c^{\ominus}}$$

where $c^{\ominus}$ is 1 mol dm^{-3} and ensures that K_h remains dimensionless as it is when defined in terms of activities.

Assuming $1 - \alpha \approx 1$ and rearranging,

$$\alpha = \sqrt{(K_h/c)}$$

$$= \sqrt{\frac{2.63 \times 10^{-5}}{0.1}} = 0.0162$$

The base dissociation constant K_b of phenylamine in water is related to K_w by equation (5.50); therefore

$$K_b = K_w/K_h$$

Substituting,

$$K_b = \frac{1.01 \times 10^{-14}}{2.63 \times 10^{-5}} = 3.84 \times 10^{-10}$$

5.10 Unworked Examples

5.10.1
In a conductivity cell at 298 K, the electrodes have an effective area of 1.0×10^{-4} m^2 and the effective distance between them is 3.0×10^{-2} m. When an electrolyte of concentration 0.02 mol dm^{-3} is placed in the cell, it shows a resistance of $60\ \Omega$. What is the resistivity, conductivity and molar conductivity of the electrolyte?

5.10.2
A conductance cell was calibrated with 0.02 mol dm^{-3} KCl ($\kappa = 0.002\,768$ S cm^{-1}) and the resistance at 298 K was $457.3\ \Omega$. When $CaCl_2$ (aq, 0.01 mol dm^{-3}) was used, the measured resistance was $1050\ \Omega$. Calculate (a) the cell constant, (b) the conductivity of $CaCl_2$ and (c) the molar conductivity of $CaCl_2$.

5.10.3

The limiting molar conductivities of sodium ethanoate, hydrochloric acid and sodium chloride, in units of $S\ m^2\ mol^{-1}$, are 0.917×10^{-2}, 4.255×10^{-2} and 1.264×10^{-2}, respectively. Calculate (a) the limiting molar conductivity of ethanoic acid, and (b) the degree of dissociation in $0.01\ mol\ dm^{-3}$ ethanoic acid if the molar conductivity at that concentration is $16.3 \times 10^{-4}\ S\ m^2\ mol^{-1}$.

5.10.4

The molar conductivity of a $0.01\ mol\ dm^{-3}$ solution of a weak acid, HA, at 298 K is $5.17 \times 10^{-4}\ S\ m^2\ mol^{-1}$. At this temperature, the limiting molar conductivities of H^+ and A^- are $3.50 \times 10^{-2}\ S\ m^2\ mol^{-1}$ and $0.40 \times 10^{-2}\ S\ m^2\ mol^{-1}$, respectively. Calculate the degree of dissociation and the dissociation constant for HA.

5.10.5

The conductivity of ethanoic acid (aq, $1.58 \times 10^{-2}\ mol\ dm^{-3}$) is $0.0215\ S\ m^{-1}$. The limiting ionic conductivities of the hydrogen and ethanoate ions are $34.98 \times 10^{-3}\ S\ m^2\ mol^{-1}$ and $4.09 \times 10^{-3}\ S\ m^2\ mol^{-1}$, respectively. Calculate the degree of dissociation and the dissociation constant for ethanoic acid.

5.10.6

At 298 K, the molar conductivities of aqueous ethanoic acid solutions at different concentrations are as follows:

$c/mol\ dm^{-3}$	0	0.0004	0.0009	0.0025	0.010	0.040
$\Lambda/S\ cm^2\ mol^{-1}$	390.7	73.9	51.15	31.65	16.21	8.19

Find an approximate value of the dissociation constant from the above data.

5.10.7

The resistivity of pure water was found to be $1.61 \times 10^7\ \Omega\ cm$. The limiting molar conductivities of the hydrogen and hydroxide ions are $349.8\ S\ cm^2\ mol^{-1}$ and $198.6\ S\ cm^2\ mol^{-1}$, respectively. What is the ionic product of water?

5.10.8

The conductivity of a saturated solution of barium sulphate at 298 K is found to be $4.20 \times 10^{-4}\ S\ m^{-1}$. The water has a conductivity of $1.05 \times 10^{-4}\ S\ m^{-1}$. The limiting molar conductivity of $BaSO_4$ is $2.865 \times 10^{-2}\ S\ m^2\ mol^{-1}$. What is the solubility of barium sulphate? ($M_r\ (BaSO_4) = 233$.)

5.10.9

The solubility of thallium(I) iodate in KCl(aq, $0.02\ mol\ kg^{-1}$) was found to be $2.10 \times 10^{-3}\ mol\ kg^{-1}$. Given that the solubility product of thallium(I) iodate is 3.02×10^{-6}, calculate the mean ionic activity coefficient of the thallium(I) iodate in the above solution. Use the Debye–Hückel limiting law to calculate the solubility of thallium(I) iodate in pure water.

5.10.10

The conductivity of a solution of $0.001\ mol\ dm^{-3}\ Na_2SO_4$ is $2.6 \times 10^{-2}\ S\ m^{-1}$. Given the molar conductivity of Na^+ is $5.0 \times 10^{-3}\ S\ m^2\ mol^{-1}$, calculate the molar conductivity of the sulphate ion.

When this sodium sulphate solution is saturated with calcium sulphate, the conductivity rises to $7.0 \times 10^{-2}\ S\ m^{-1}$. Calculate the solubility product of $CaSO_4$ given that the molar conductivity of $\frac{1}{2}Ca^{2+}$ is $6.0 \times 10^{-3}\ S\ m^2\ mol^{-1}$.

5.10.11

25 cm^3 of 0.1 mol dm^{-3} methanoic acid was neutralised with sodium hydroxide solution, and a further 25 cm^3 of acid added. The pH was measured and found to be 3.82. Calculate (a) the pH of 0.1 mol dm^{-3} methanoic acid, (b) the pH of 0.0005 mol dm^{-3} methanoic acid solution, and (c) the pH of 0.1 mol dm^{-3} methanoic acid solution which has been 75 per cent neutralised with sodium hydroxide solution.

(University of Salford, BSc, 2nd year)

5.10.12

100 cm^3 of 0.1 mol dm^{-3} aqueous 2-hydroxypropanoic acid is neutralised with aqueous sodium hydroxide and then a further 100 cm^3 of 2-hydroxypropanoic acid solution added. The pH of the resulting solution is 3.85. Calculate the approximate values of (a) K_a for 2-hydroxypropanoic acid; (b) the pH of 0.1 mol dm^{-3} aqueous 2-hydroxypropanoic acid; (c) the pH of 0.1 mol dm^{-3} aqueous sodium 2-hydroxypropanoate. Assume pK_w is 14.

(Liverpool Polytechnic, GRSC, Part I)

5.10.13

At 298 K the thermodynamic dissociation constant K_a of ethanoic acid in water is 1.75×10^{-5} and the ionic product of water is 1.01×10^{-14}. Using the Debye–Hückel limiting equation to estimate activity coefficients, calculate the pH of a 0.01 mol dm^{-3} aqueous solution of sodium ethanoate at this temperature.

5.10.14

What is the conductivity at 298 K of distilled water in equilibrium with air at one atmosphere assuming that the air contains 0.050 volume per cent of CO_2? The only ions that need to be considered are $H^+(aq)$ and $HCO_3^-(aq)$, their molar conductivities being 349.7×10^{-4} S m^2 mol^{-1} and 44.5×10^{-4} S m^2 mol^{-1}, respectively. At 298 K and at a partial pressure of 1 atm CO_2, 1 dm^3 of water dissolves 0.8266 dm^3 CO_2. The first dissociation constant of carbonic acid, $H_2CO_3(aq)$, is 4.7×10^{-7} mol dm^{-3}.

(GRSC, Part I)

5.10.15

If a very small amount of phenolphthalein is added to a 0.15 mol dm^{-3} solution of sodium benzenecarboxylic acid, what fraction of the indicator will exist in the coloured form. State any assumptions made.

K_a(benzenecarboxylic acid) $= 6.20 \times 10^{-5}$
K_w $= 1.01 \times 10^{-14}$
K_{In}(phenolphthalein) $= 3.16 \times 10^{-10}$

(University of Salford, BSc, Part I)

5.10.16

Calculate the degree of hydrolysis and the pH of (a) 0.1 mol dm^{-3} ammonium chloride solution, and (b) 0.1 mol dm^{-3} sodium ethanoate solution at 298 K given the following:

K_a(ethanoic acid) $= 1.75 \times 10^{-5}$
K_w(water) $= 1.01 \times 10^{-14}$
K_b(ammonium hydroxide) $= 1.77 \times 10^{-5}$

6 Electrode Processes

6.1 Introduction

In Chapter 5, aspects of electrochemistry which deal with the nature and processes in electrolytic solutions were covered. In this chapter, another important branch of electrochemistry is considered, namely the processes that occur when electrodes are immersed in solutions and are connected via an external circuit.

6.1.1 Electrochemical Cells

An electrochemical cell consists of two electrodes dipping either into a common electrolyte or into two different electrolytes that are in electrical contact with one another. When it acts as a source of electrical energy, it is referred to as a **galvanic cell**. When it is driven by an external source of electric current and **electrolysis** occurs, it is referred to as an **electrolytic cell**.

6.1.2 Electrodes

Electrodes are either **reactive** or **inert**. The former consists of a metal that will participate in the cell reaction by donating metal ions to the solution or by accepting and discharging metal ions from the solution. The latter (e.g. platinum, carbon) are resistant to physical or chemical change but transfer electrons to and from the solution.

6.1.3 Electrode Reactions

Consider a typical electrochemical cell, such as the Daniell cell illustrated in Fig. 6.1. The external circuit has in it a voltmeter of very high resistance (e.g. an appropriate digital voltmeter) such that negligible current flows through it and a load (e.g. a heating element or an electric motor) through which a significant current will flow when connected. The cell itself consists of two **half-cells**, a zinc rod dipping in a solution of a zinc salt and a copper rod dipping in a solution of a copper salt. The other component of the cell is the salt bridge which contains a concentrated solution of electrolyte (e.g. KCl) and is a means for providing electrical connection between the solutions in the two half-cells; it is also a device for minimising any potential difference between these solutions.

Consider first the situation when there is no external circuit. The following electrode processes will occur in forward and backward directions:

(1) $Cu - 2e \rightleftharpoons Cu^{2+}$
(2) $Zn - 2e \rightleftharpoons Zn^{2+}$

For this particular system, forward reaction (2) is favoured over forward reaction (1), and vice versa for the reverse reactions. It follows that the copper electrode will acquire a positive charge and the zinc electrode a negative charge. With no

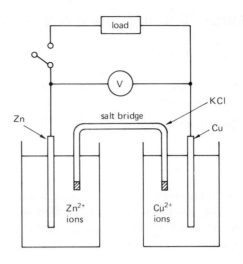

Figure 6.1 Daniell cell.

external circuit, this charge separation will very quickly reach a limit because the positive copper electrode will repel further Cu^{2+} ions approaching it and the negative zinc electrode will attract back any Zn^{2+} ions leaving it. If the external circuit through the load is now completed, positive charge can flow in it from the Cu electrode to the Zn electrode (i.e. electrons flow from Zn to Cu) and the electrode processes (or **half-reactions**),

$$Cu^{2+} + 2e \rightarrow Cu$$

$$Zn - 2e \rightarrow Zn^{2+}$$

can take place continuously as the cell discharges. The overall **cell reaction** is the sum of the two half-reactions, i.e.

$$Cu^{2+} + Zn \rightarrow Cu + Zn^{2+}$$

The electrodes of an electrochemical cell are designated **anode** and **cathode** such that

oxidation occurs at the **anode**

reduction occurs at the **cathode**

Therefore, in the discharging Daniell cell, the zinc electrode is the anode and the copper electrode is the cathode.

6.1.4 Electromotive Force

The high-resistance voltmeter shown in Fig. 6.1 permits the potential difference between the Cu and Zn electrodes to be measured. The limiting value of this electric potential difference for zero current through the cell (i.e. with the external load disconnected) is called the **electromotive force** (e.m.f.), symbol E or E_{cell}. In this limiting situation, a condition of thermodynamic reversibility exists.

6.2 Conventions Relating to Electrochemical Cells

6.2.1 Cell Notation

The Daniell cell discussed in the previous section is represented, generally, by the shorthand notation

$$Zn(s) \mid Zn^{2+}(aq) \mid Cu^{2+}(aq) \mid Cu(s)$$

or, in more abbreviated form, as

$$Zn \mid Zn^{2+} \mid Cu^{2+} \mid Cu$$

The single vertical lines represent phase boundaries.

The boundary between the two solutions is denoted by double vertical lines when a salt bridge (which virtually eliminates liquid junction potential – see Section 6.2.5) is used, i.e.

$$Zn \mid Zn^{2+} \parallel Cu^{2+} \mid Cu$$

The Daniell cell could, alternatively, be set up with a porous membrane separating the solutions containing Zn^{2+} and Cu^{2+} ions; this boundary would be denoted by a single vertical line or by a broken vertical line, e.g. $Zn \mid Zn^{2+} \vdots Cu^{2+} \mid Cu$.

If it is desired to state the solution concentrations (or molalities), the notation would, for example, be

$$Zn(s) \mid Zn^{2+}(aq, 0.1 \text{ mol kg}^{-1}) \parallel Cu^{2+}(aq, 0.2 \text{ mol kg}^{-1}) \mid Cu(s)$$

6.2.2 Electrode Potentials

The cell e.m.f. can be thought of as the difference between the e.m.f.'s of the two half-cells. Although not incorrect, the term e.m.f. tends not to be applied to half-cells; rather the term **reversible electrode potential** (usually abbreviated to **electrode potential**) is used.

By convention, **the cell e.m.f. is given as the potential of the right-hand electrode minus that of the left-hand electrode.** Therefore, if the Daniell cell is written as

$$Zn \mid Zn^{2+} \parallel Cu^{2+} \mid Cu$$

then

$$E_{cell} = E_{right} - E_{left}$$
$$= E_{Cu} - E_{Zn}$$

If, for example, the e.m.f. of this cell is found to be 1.1 V, with the Cu electrode the positive pole, this means that E_{Cu} is 1.1 V more positive than E_{Zn}.

The above cell could, alternatively, be written as

$$Cu \mid Cu^{2+} \parallel Zn^{2+} \mid Zn$$

in which case

$$E_{cell} = E_{Zn} - E_{Cu} = -1.1 \text{ V}$$

It is not possible to measure the potential of a single electrode. In order that values might be assigned for the potentials of single electrodes, an arbitrarily chosen reference point is required. To this end the potential of the **standard hydrogen electrode (S.H.E.)** (discussed in Section 6.2.4) is taken to be zero at all temperatures.

The reversible potentials of the copper and zinc electrodes are therefore the same as the e.m.f.'s of the cells S.H.E. ∥ Cu^{2+} | Cu and S.H.E. ∥ Zn^{2+} | Zn, respectively.

The copper and zinc systems are quoted above in terms of the respective **reduction** processes. By the above convention, **all electrode potentials are reduction potentials**. The notations for the electrode potentials of the copper and zinc systems are

$$E_{Cu^{2+}|Cu} \qquad \text{and} \qquad E_{Zn^{2+}|Zn}$$

or

$$E(Cu^{2+}|Cu) \qquad \text{and} \qquad E(Zn^{2+}|Zn)$$

6.2.3 Standard Electrode Potentials

As with any other thermodynamic quantity, a standard electrode potential $E^\ominus$ is the value of the electrode potential when all relevant factors relate to a standard state of unit activity. This will involve unit activity of solute (see Sections 2.5.3 and 2.7.3), unit activity of metal (i.e. pure metal) and a gas fugacity of 1 atm.

A range of values with the corresponding half-cell reactions is given in Table 6.1.

The **more positive** the electrode potential, the **more likely** is the **reduction** process, and the **more negative** the electrode potential, the **more likely** is the **oxidation** process. When two half-cells are joined to make a galvanic cell, **reduction** will take place in the **half-cell** with the **more positive** of the two electrode potentials and **oxidation** in the **half-cell** with the **more negative** of the two electrode potentials.

6.2.4 Inert Electrodes

These consist of a solid (ideally platinum) which does not take part in the electrode process itself, but which acts as an electrical contact and a means for transferring electrons to or from an electrolyte solution. Two types can be recognised.

(a) *Gas Electrodes*

The best known of these is the hydrogen electrode (Fig. 6.2). Hydrogen is bubbled over a platinum electrode where some of the gas forms an adsorbed monomolecular layer on the metal surface. The half-cell reaction is, therefore,

$$H^+(aq) + e \rightleftharpoons \tfrac{1}{2} H_2(g)$$

and the notation for the half-cell is

$$H^+ | H_2, Pt$$

Other gas electrodes, e.g. the chlorine electrode, $Cl^- | Cl_2$, Pt, can be set up in a similar fashion.

Notation for the electrode (reduction) potentials will be $E_{H^+|H_2}$, $E_{Cl_2|Cl^-}$, etc.

The standard hydrogen electrode is of particular interest in view of its zero role. It will, in theory, consist of hydrogen gas at a fugacity of 1 atm bubbled over a platinum electrode immersed in a solution in which the activity of the hydrogen ions is equal to unity.

This presents difficulties of both an experimental and theoretical nature. On the experimental side, (a) the electrode develops an overpotential very easily, and (b) precautions must be taken to exclude impurities that may also adsorb on the

Table 6.1 Standard electrode (reduction) potentials[a] at 298 K

Electrode	$E^{\ominus}/V$	Half-cell reaction
$Li^+ \mid Li$	−3.045	$Li^+ + e \rightarrow Li$
$K^+ \mid K$	−2.925	$K^+ + e \rightarrow K$
$Rb^+ \mid Rb$	−2.925	$Rb^+ + e \rightarrow Rb$
$Na^+ \mid Na$	−2.714	$Na^+ + e \rightarrow Na$
$Mg^{2+} \mid Mg$	−2.37	$\frac{1}{2}Mg^{2+} + e \rightarrow \frac{1}{2}Mg$
$Pu^{3+} \mid Pu$	−2.07	$\frac{1}{3}Pu^{3+} + e \rightarrow \frac{1}{3}Pu$
$Th^{4+} \mid Th$	−1.90	$\frac{1}{4}Th^{4+} + e \rightarrow \frac{1}{4}Th$
$Np^{3+} \mid Np$	−1.86	$\frac{1}{3}Np^{3+} + e \rightarrow \frac{1}{3}Np$
$Al^{3+} \mid Al$	−1.66	$\frac{1}{3}Al^{3+} + e \rightarrow \frac{1}{3}Al$
$Zn^{2+} \mid Zn$	−0.763	$\frac{1}{2}Zn^{2+} + e \rightarrow \frac{1}{2}Zn$
$Fe^{2+} \mid Fe$	−0.440	$\frac{1}{2}Fe^{2+} + e \rightarrow \frac{1}{2}Fe$
$Cr^{3+}, Cr^{2+} \mid Pt^{b,c}$	−0.41	$Cr^{3+} + e \rightarrow Cr^{2+}$
$Cd^{2+} \mid Cd$	−0.403	$\frac{1}{2}Cd^{2+} + e \rightarrow \frac{1}{2}Cd$
$Tl^+ \mid Tl$	−0.3363	$Tl^+ + e \rightarrow Tl$
$Br^- \mid PbBr_2(s), Pb$	−0.280	$\frac{1}{2}PbBr_2 + e \rightarrow \frac{1}{2}Pb + Br^-$
$Co^{2+} \mid Co$	−0.277	$\frac{1}{2}Co^{2+} + e \rightarrow \frac{1}{2}Co$
$Ni^{2+} \mid Ni$	−0.250	$\frac{1}{2}Ni^{2+} + e \rightarrow \frac{1}{2}Ni$
$I^- \mid AgI(s), Ag$	−0.151	$AgI + e \rightarrow Ag + I^-$
$Sn^{2+} \mid Sn$	−0.140	$\frac{1}{2}Sn^{2+} + e \rightarrow \frac{1}{2}Sn$
$Pb^{2+} \mid Pb$	−0.126	$\frac{1}{2}Pb^{2+} + e \rightarrow \frac{1}{2}Pb$
$D^+ \mid D_2, Pt$	−0.0034	$D^+ + e \rightarrow \frac{1}{2}D_2$
$H^+ \mid H_2, Pt$	0.0000	$H^+ + e \rightarrow \frac{1}{2}H_2$
$Ti^{4+}, Ti^{3+} \mid Pt$	0.04	$Ti^{4+} + e \rightarrow Ti^{3+}$
$Br^- \mid AgBr(s), Ag$	0.095	$AgBr + e \rightarrow Ag + Br^-$
$Sn^{4+}, Sn^{2+} \mid Pt$	0.15	$\frac{1}{2}Sn^{4+} + e \rightarrow \frac{1}{2}Sn^{2+}$
$Cu^{2+}, Cu^+ \mid Pt$	0.153	$Cu^{2+} + e \rightarrow Cu^+$
$Cl^- \mid AgCl(s), Ag$	0.2224	$AgCl + e \rightarrow Ag + Cl^-$
$Cl^- \mid Hg_2Cl_2(s), Hg^d$	0.268	$\frac{1}{2}Hg_2Cl_2 + e \rightarrow Hg + Cl^-$
$Cu^{2+} \mid Cu$	0.337	$\frac{1}{2}Cu^{2+} + e \rightarrow \frac{1}{2}Cu$
$H^+ \mid C_2H_4(g), C_2H_6(g), Pt$	0.52	$H^+ + \frac{1}{2}C_2H_4(g) + e \rightarrow \frac{1}{2}C_2H_6(g)$
$Cu^+ \mid Cu$	0.521	$Cu^+ + e \rightarrow Cu$
$I^- \mid I_2(s), Pt$	0.5355	$\frac{1}{2}I_2 + e \rightarrow I^-$
$H^+, quinhydrone(s) \mid Pt$	0.6996	$\frac{1}{2}C_6H_4O_2 + H^+ + e \rightarrow \frac{1}{2}C_6H_6O_2$
$Fe^{3+}, Fe^{2+} \mid Pt$	0.771	$Fe^{3+} + e \rightarrow Fe^{2+}$
$Hg_2^{2+} \mid Hg$	0.789	$\frac{1}{2}Hg_2^{2+} + e \rightarrow Hg$
$Ag^+ \mid Ag$	0.7991	$Ag^+ + e \rightarrow Ag$
$Hg^{2+}, Hg_2^{2+} \mid Pt$	0.920	$Hg^{2+} + e \rightarrow \frac{1}{2}Hg_2^{2+}$
$Pu^{4+}, Pu^{3+} \mid Pt$	0.97	$Pu^{4+} + e \rightarrow Pu^{3+}$
$Br^- \mid Br_2(l) \mid Pt$	1.0652	$\frac{1}{2}Br_2(l) + e \rightarrow Br^-$
$Tl^{3+}, Tl^+ \mid Pt$	1.250	$\frac{1}{2}Tl^{3+} + e \rightarrow \frac{1}{2}Tl^+$
$Cl^- \mid Cl_2(g) \mid Pt$	1.3595	$\frac{1}{2}Cl_2(g) + e \rightarrow Cl^-$
$Pb^{2+} \mid PbO_2 \mid Pb$	1.455	$\frac{1}{2}PbO_2 + 2H^+ + e \rightarrow \frac{1}{2}Pb^{2+} + H_2O$
$Au^{3+} \mid Au$	1.50	$\frac{1}{3}Au^{3+} + e \rightarrow \frac{1}{3}Au$
$Ce^{4+}, Ce^{3+} \mid Pt$	1.61	$Ce^{4+} + e \rightarrow Ce^{3+}$
$Co^{3+}, Co^{2+} \mid Pt$	1.82	$Co^{3+} + e \rightarrow Co^{2+}$
$F^- \mid F_2(g) \mid Pt$	2.87	$\frac{1}{2}F_2(g) + e \rightarrow F^-$
$HF(aq) \mid F_2(g) \mid Pt$	3.06	$H^+ + \frac{1}{2}F_2(g) + e \rightarrow HF(aq)$

[a]All ions are at unit activity in water, and all gases are at 1 atm.

[b]The symbol Pt represents an inert electrode like platinum.

[c]The order of writing the ions in the electrolyte solution is immaterial.

[d]The electromotive force of the normal calomel electrode is 0.2802 V and of the calomel electrode containing saturated KCl is 0.2415 V.

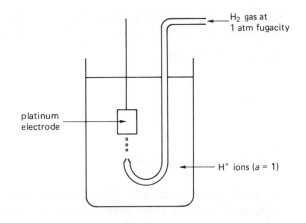

Figure 6.2 A standard hydrogen electrode.

platinum surface. On the theoretical side (as explained in the last chapter), single ion species cannot be considered in isolation and the activity of hydrogen ions will depend on the nature of the associated anions. An extrapolation of data to zero concentration where the activity coefficient of the hydrogen ions approaches unity is, therefore, necessary in order to put the standard hydrogen electrode zero convention into effect. It is not surprising, therefore, that the standard hydrogen electrode is not a routine piece of laboratory equipment. Instead, secondary standards are used, the most popular being the calomel electrode, which is described in Section 6.2.6.

(b) *Redox Electrodes*

Consider the reaction

$$Fe^{3+}(aq) + e \rightleftharpoons Fe^{2+}(aq)$$

This can be exploited as a half-cell reaction using an inert platinum electrode, i.e.

$$Fe^{3+}, Fe^{2+} | Pt$$

6.2.5 Liquid Junction Potentials

If a Daniell cell or any similar cell is set up with a porous diaphragm between the electrolyte solutions, it is found that the junction between the two electrolytes is itself a source of e.m.f. arising from the free-energy change occurring as ions migrate across the boundary. If both ions diffuse at the same speed, no change in potential will arise, but if one ion travels faster than the other (as is usually the case), a separation of charge will occur giving rise to what is called the **liquid junction potential**. For most investigations it is preferable to minimise the liquid junction potential as it could be as much as 0.1 V. This is achieved by the use of a salt bridge containing a concentrated solution of an electrolyte such as potassium chloride or ammonium nitrate in which $t_+ \approx t_-$, as shown in Fig. 6.1, i.e. the cell is

$$Zn | ZnSO_4(aq) | KCl(aq) | CuSO_4(aq) | Cu$$

Nearly all of the diffusion will be done by the salt-bridge ions as they are so concentrated. Since the ions in the salt bridge travel at much the same speed, no liquid junction potential is set up. As previously stated, two vertical lines denote a salt bridge and the conventional notation for this cell is

$$Zn \mid Zn^{2+} \parallel Cu^{2+} \mid Cu$$

6.2.6 Secondary Electrodes

A well known example is the so-called silver–silver chloride electrode, which consists of a rod of silver coated with a thin layer of silver chloride dipping into a solution of known chloride concentration, i.e. $Cl^- \mid AgCl$, Ag. It is, from the electrode potential point of view, an $Ag^+ \mid Ag$ electrode. The solubility product of silver chloride in water at $25°C$ is of the order of 10^{-10} $(mol\ dm^{-3})^2$, i.e. for $[Ag^+] = [Cl^-]$ the concentration is of the order of 10^{-5} mol dm^{-3}. The difference, in practice, between the above electrodes is that for the $Ag^+ \mid Ag$ electrode, $[Ag^+]$ will usually be greater than 10^{-5} mol dm^{-3} and monitored directly, whereas for the $Cl^- \mid AgCl$, Ag electrode, $[Ag^+]$ will usually be less than 10^{-5} mol dm^{-3} and monitored indirectly via $[Cl^-]$ and $K_s(AgCl)$. The standard silver–silver chloride electrode has chloride ions at unit activity (see Section 6.3.4).

Another important secondary electrode, the potential of which also depends on chloride ion activity, is the calomel electrode, $Cl^- \mid Hg_2Cl_2$, Hg. A particularly useful version is the saturated calomel electrode (see Fig. 6.3) in which the activity of the chloride ions is that associated with a saturated solution of KCl at the temperature in question. It is very frequently used as a reference electrode, its potential at $25°C$ being 0.2415 V.

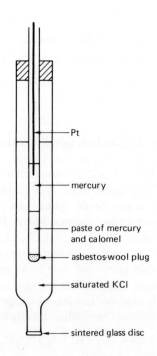

Figure 6.3   A saturated calomel electrode.

6.3 Thermodynamics of Electrochemical Cells

6.3.1 Cell Reactions

The potential difference between the electrodes of an electrochemical cell can be measured under conditions where zero or negligible current flows. Electrochemical cells, therefore, permit many reactions to be studied under thermodynamic reversible conditions.

With suitable ingenuity, an electrochemical cell can be devised for most reactions.

Example 6.1

Devise electrochemical cells in which the following overall reactions can occur.
(a) $2Na(s) + Cd^{2+}(aq) \rightarrow 2Na^+(aq) + Cd(s)$
(b) $Fe^{3+}(aq) + Cr^{2+}(aq) \rightarrow Fe^{2+}(aq) + Cr^{3+}(aq)$
(c) $Ag^+(aq) + I^-(aq) \rightarrow AgI(s)$
(d) $Ni(s) + Cl_2(g) \rightarrow NiCl_2(aq)$
(e) $HgO(s) + H_2(g) \rightarrow Hg(l) + H_2O(l)$

(a) This is analogous to the copper–zinc reaction in the Daniell cell but with the complication that an electrode of pure sodium would be attacked by water. An electrode of sodium dissolved in mercury could be used instead and a suitable cell would be

$$(\text{--}) \; Hg, Na \,|\, NaNO_3(aq) \,\|\, Cd(NO_3)_2(aq) \,|\, Cd \; (+)$$

(b) This is a reaction involving two redox systems and will take place in the cell

$$(\text{--}) \; Pt \,|\, Cr^{2+}(aq), Cr^{3+}(aq) \,\|\, Fe^{2+}(aq), Fe^{3+}(aq) \,|\, Pt \; (+)$$

At the +ve electrode	$Fe^{3+} + e \rightarrow Fe^{2+}$
At the −ve electrode	$Cr^{2+} - e \rightarrow Cr^{3+}$
Overall reaction	$Fe^{3+} + Cr^{2+} \rightarrow Fe^{2+} + Cr^{3+}$

(c) The negative pole will be a silver–silver iodide electrode, the reaction of which is

$$Ag + I^- - e \rightarrow AgI$$

Subtracting this from the equation for the overall reaction gives the reaction at the positive pole, i.e.

$$Ag^+ + e \rightarrow Ag$$

A suitable cell is, therefore,

$$(-) \; Ag, AgI(s) \,|\, KI(aq) \,\|\, AgNO_3(aq) \,|\, Ag \; (+)$$

(d) The positive pole is a chlorine gas electrode, $Cl^- \,|\, Cl_2(g)$, Pt, the reaction of which is

$$Cl_2 + 2e \rightarrow 2Cl^-$$

Subtracting this from the equation for the overall reaction gives the reaction at the negative electrode, i.e.

$$Ni - 2e \rightarrow Ni^{2+}$$

The overall reaction, therefore, takes place in the cells

$$(-) \ Ni(s) \ | \ NiCl_2 \ (aq) \ | \ Cl_2 \ (g), \ Pt \ (+)$$

$$(-) \ Ni(s) \ | \ NiSO_4 \ (aq) \ \| \ KCl(aq) \ | \ Cl_2 \ (g), \ Pt \ (+)$$

the former having the advantage of not requiring a salt bridge.

(e) Since hydrogen gas is involved in this reaction, one of the electrodes will be a hydrogen electrode. As some of the water is dissociated, the overall reaction can be written

$$HgO(s) + H_2 \ (g) + H_2O \rightarrow Hg(l) + 2H^+(aq) + 2OH^- (aq)$$

Subtracting the reaction at the hydrogen electrode (−ve pole), i.e. $H_2 \ (g) - 2e \rightarrow 2H^+$, gives the equation for the reaction at the other electrode

$$HgO(s) + H_2O + 2e \rightarrow Hg(l) + 2OH^- (aq)$$

This is the reaction of a mercury – mercury(II) oxide – aqueous electrolyte electrode (+ve pole). The complete cell is, therefore,

$$(-) \ Pt, \ H_2 \ (g) \ | \ aqueous \ electrolyte \ | \ HgO(s), \ Hg \ (+)$$

the aqueous electrolyte being one that has no direct chemical effect on the electrodes, e.g. KOH(aq), its only function being to provide H^+ and OH^- ions. ∎

6.3.2 ΔG, ΔS and ΔH

The reversible, isobaric work done converting chemical to electrical energy in an electrochemical cell is equal to the decrease in Gibbs free energy. Since work is equal to charge multiplied by potential difference,

$$\Delta G_{cell \ reaction} = -zFE_{cell} \tag{6.1}$$

or, for standard conditions,

$$\Delta G^{\ominus}_{cell \ reaction} = -zFE^{\ominus}_{cell} \tag{6.2}$$

where z is the number of electrons involved in the cell reaction and F is Faraday's constant ($F = N_A e = 96\ 487 \ C \ mol^{-1}$).

Applying equation (2.57) with equation (6.1),

$$\Delta S = -\left(\frac{\partial \Delta G}{\partial T}\right)_p = zF\left(\frac{\partial E}{\partial T}\right)_p \tag{6.3}$$

and, since

$$\Delta H = \Delta G + T\Delta S$$

then

$$\Delta H = -zFE + zFT\left(\frac{\partial E}{\partial T}\right)_p \tag{6.4}$$

Example 6.2

Use information provided in Table 6.1 to calculate $\Delta G^{\ominus}_{298 \ K}$ for the Daniell cell reaction, $Cu^{2+} + Zn \rightarrow Zn^{2+} + Cu$. If $(\partial E^{\ominus}/\partial T)_p = -1.08 \times 10^{-4}$ V K^{-1}, calculate $\Delta S^{\ominus}_{298 \ K}$ and $\Delta H^{\ominus}_{298 \ K}$.

$$E^{\ominus}_{298 \ K} = E^{\ominus}_{298 \ K} (Cu^{2+} \ | \ Cu) - E^{\ominus}_{298 \ K} (Zn^{2+} \ | \ Zn)$$

$$= +0.337 - (-0.763) = +1.100 \ V$$

$z = 2$, since two electrons are involved in each electrode reaction.

$$\Delta G^{\ominus}_{298\ K} = -zFE^{\ominus} = -2 \times 96\,487 \times 1.100 \text{ J mol}^{-1}$$

$$= -212.3 \text{ kJ mol}^{-1}$$

$$\Delta S^{\ominus}_{298\ K} = zF\left(\frac{\partial E}{\partial T}\right)_p = 2 \times 96\,487 \times (-1.08 \times 10^{-4}) \text{ J K}^{-1} \text{ mol}^{-1}$$

$$= -20.8 \text{ J K}^{-1} \text{ mol}^{-1}$$

$$\Delta H^{\ominus}_{298\ K} = \Delta G^{\ominus}_{298\ K} + T\Delta S^{\ominus}_{298\ K}$$

$$= [-212\,300 + 298 \times (-20.8)] \text{ J mol}^{-1}$$

$$= -218.5 \text{ kJ mol}^{-1} \qquad\qquad \blacksquare$$

6.3.3 Nernst Equation

The free energy and the standard free energy of a single substance of activity a are related by

$$G = G^{\ominus} + RT \ln a$$

Therefore, for a chemical reaction,

$$\Delta G = \Delta G^{\ominus} + RT \ln \left(\frac{\Pi(\text{activities of products})}{\Pi(\text{activities of reactants})}\right) \tag{6.5}$$

where Π represents the product of all terms concerned.

If the reaction in question is an electrochemical cell reaction, then using equations (6.1) and (6.2) to substitute for ΔG and $\Delta G^{\ominus}$ gives

$$-zFE = -zFE^{\ominus} + RT \ln \left(\frac{\Pi(\text{activities of products})}{\Pi(\text{activities of reactants})}\right)$$

or

$$E = E^{\ominus} - \frac{RT}{zF} \ln \left(\frac{\Pi(\text{activities of products})}{\Pi(\text{activities of reactants})}\right) \tag{6.6}$$

The contents of an electrochemical cell reach a state of equilibrium when the cell is fully discharged, i.e. $E = 0$, and therefore

$$0 = E^{\ominus} - (RT/zF) \ln K^{\ominus} \tag{6.7}$$

where $K^{\ominus}$ is the standard equilibrium constant of the cell reaction.

Equation (6.7) is, of course, much more simply the result of eliminating $\Delta G^{\ominus}$ from equation (6.2) and the standard reaction isotherm equation, $\Delta G^{\ominus} = -RT \ln K^{\ominus}$.

Example 6.3

Calculate the equilibrium constant at 298 K of the Daniell cell reaction, $Zn + Cu^{2+} \rightleftharpoons Zn^{2+} + Cu$, given that $E^{\ominus}$ (298 K) = + 1.100 V.

$$E^{\ominus} = (RT/zF) \ln K^{\ominus}$$

Therefore

$$1.100 = \frac{8.314 \times 298}{2 \times 96\,500} \ln K^{\ominus}$$

giving

$$K^{\ominus} = 1.6 \times 10^{37} \qquad\qquad \blacksquare$$

To derive an expression giving the variation of a single electrode potential with activity, consider, for example, the cell

$$\text{Pt, H}_2 \mid \text{H}^+ \parallel \text{M}^{z+} \mid \text{M}$$

for which the cell reaction is

$$\text{M}^{z+} + \tfrac{1}{2}z\text{H}_2 \rightarrow \text{M} + z\text{H}^+$$

and equation (6.6) takes the form

$$E = E^\ominus - \frac{RT}{zF} \ln\left(\frac{a(\text{M})\, a(\text{H}^+)^z}{a(\text{M}^{z+})\, a(\text{H}_2)^{z/2}} \right)$$

If the hydrogen electrode is a standard hydrogen electrode, E and $E^\ominus$ are the electrode potential and standard electrode potential of the electrode $\text{M}^{z+} \mid \text{M}$ and $a(\text{H}^+)$ and $a(\text{H}_2)$ are both unity. Therefore

$$E = E^\ominus - \frac{RT}{zF} \ln\left(\frac{a(\text{M})}{a(\text{M}^{z+})} \right) = E^\ominus + \frac{RT}{zF} \ln\left(\frac{a(\text{M}^{z+})}{a(\text{M})} \right)$$

or, in more general terms,

$$E = E^\ominus + \frac{RT}{zF} \ln\left(\frac{a(\text{oxidised form})}{a(\text{reduced form})} \right) \tag{6.8}$$

For the special case of $T = 298.15$ K, this expression becomes

$$E = E^\ominus + \frac{2.3026 \times 8.314 \times 298.15 \text{ V}}{z \times 96487} \log_{10}\left(\frac{a(\text{oxidised form})}{a(\text{reduced form})} \right)$$

$$= E^\ominus + \frac{0.05916 \text{ V}}{z} \log_{10}\left(\frac{a(\text{oxidised form})}{a(\text{reduced form})} \right) \tag{6.9}$$

Example 6.4

Calculate $E(298 \text{ K})$ for the electrode $\text{Cu}^{2+}(\text{aq}, a = 0.2) \mid \text{Cu(s)}$.

The reduced form is pure copper; therefore $a(\text{Cu}) = 1$, and

$$E = +0.337 + \frac{0.05916}{2} \log_{10} 0.2$$

$$= +0.337 - 0.021 = 0.316 \text{ V} \qquad \blacksquare$$

Example 6.5

Calculate $E(298 \text{ K})$ for the electrode $\text{Cl}^-(\text{aq}) \mid \text{Cl}_2(\text{g})$, Pt if the chlorine gas has a fugacity of 2 atm, the chloride ions an activity of 0.5 and $E^\ominus(\text{Cl}^-(\text{aq}) \mid \text{Cl}_2(\text{g}), \text{Pt}) = 1.3595$ V.

The electrode reaction is $\tfrac{1}{2}\text{Cl}_2 + \text{e} \rightarrow \text{Cl}^-$, and equation (6.9) will take the form

$$E = E^\ominus + 0.05916 \text{ V} \times \log_{10}\left(\frac{[f(\text{Cl}_2)]^{1/2}}{a(\text{Cl}^-)} \right)$$

$$= +1.3595 + 0.05916 \log_{10}\left(\frac{(2)^{1/2}}{0.5} \right)$$

$$= +1.3595 + 0.0267 = +1.3862 \text{ V} \qquad \blacksquare$$

Example 6.6

When Fe^{3+} and Sn^{2+} ions are mixed at 298 K, to what extent will Sn^{2+} be oxidised to Sn^{4+}?

The reaction in question is

$$2Fe^{3+} + Sn^{2+} \rightarrow 2Fe^{2+} + Sn^{4+}$$

At equilibrium,

$$E(Fe^{3+} \mid Fe^{2+}) = E(Sn^{4+} \mid Sn^{2+})$$

Therefore, using the standard potentials in Table 6.1, and equating activities with concentrations,

$$0.771 + 0.059 \log_{10}\left(\frac{[Fe^{3+}]}{[Fe^{2+}]}\right) = 0.15 + \frac{0.059}{2} \log_{10}\left(\frac{[Sn^{4+}]}{[Sn^{2+}]}\right)$$

i.e.

$$0.621 + \frac{0.059}{2} \log_{10}\left(\frac{[Fe^{3+}]}{[Fe^{2+}]}\right)^2 = \frac{0.059}{2} \log_{10}\left(\frac{[Sn^{4+}]}{[Sn^{2+}]}\right)$$

giving

$$\log_{10}\left(\frac{[Sn^{4+}][Fe^{2+}]^2}{[Sn^{2+}][Fe^{3+}]^2}\right) = \frac{0.621 \times 2}{0.059} = 21.0$$

or

$$\frac{[Sn^{4+}][Fe^{2+}]^2}{[Sn^{2+}][Fe^{3+}]^2} = K = 10^{21}$$

Thus, the reaction goes virtually to completion. ∎

6.3.4 Secondary Electrodes

Consider the silver–silver chloride electrode, $Cl^-(aq) \mid AgCl(s)$, Ag. This is a silver electrode, and just as for the $Ag^+(aq) \mid Ag$ electrode, the Nernst equation can be written as

$$E_{AgCl} = E_{Ag}^{\ominus} + (RT/F) \ln a_{Ag^+}$$

The activities of Ag^+ and Cl^- ions are related in terms of the solubility product of silver chloride by

$$K_s = a_{Ag^+} a_{Cl^-}$$

Therefore, substituting for a_{Ag^+},

$$E_{AgCl} = E_{Ag}^{\ominus} + (RT/F) \ln (K_s/a_{Cl^-})$$

$$= [E_{Ag}^{\ominus} + (RT/F) \ln K_s] - (RT/F) \ln a_{Cl^-}$$

Since the silver–silver chloride electrode is monitored in terms of the chloride ions, it is convenient to define the standard potential of this electrode as the potential when the activity of the chloride ions is unity, i.e.

$$E_{AgCl}^{\ominus} = E_{Ag}^{\ominus} + (RT/F) \ln K_s \tag{6.10}$$

and

$$E_{AgCl} = E_{AgCl}^{\ominus} - (RT/F) \ln a_{Cl^-} \tag{6.11}$$

6.4 Concentration Cells

If two half-cells of the same chemical nature are combined to form an electrochemical cell, an e.m.f. will arise if there is some difference in activity between them. This difference may be between the solutions or between the electrodes. These are known as concentration cells, of which the following are examples:

(a) $Ag(s) | AgNO_3(aq, a_1) \| AgNO_3(aq, a_2) | Ag(s)$

(b) $Ag, AgCl(s) | KCl(aq, a_1) \| KCl(aq, a_2) | AgCl(s), Ag$

(c) $Zn(s) | ZnSO_4(aq, a_1), Hg_2SO_4(s) | Hg | Hg_2SO_4(s), ZnSO_4(aq, a_2) | Zn(s)$

(d) $Pt, Cl_2(p_1) | HCl(aq) | Cl_2(p_2), Pt$

(e) $Zn/Hg(a_1) | ZnSO_4(aq) | Zn/Hg(a_2)$

Consider cell (a). Application of the Nernst equation gives

$$E = \left(E_{Ag}^{\ominus} + \frac{RT}{F} \ln [a(Ag^+)_2] \right) - \left(E_{Ag}^{\ominus} + \frac{RT}{F} \ln [a(Ag^+)_1] \right)$$

$$= \frac{RT}{F} \ln \left(\frac{a(Ag^+)_2}{a(Ag^+)_1} \right) \tag{6.12}$$

If it is assumed that the ratio of the silver ion activities is the same as the ratio of the mean ion activities for the two silver nitrate solutions, then

$$E = \frac{RT}{F} \ln \left(\frac{(a_\pm)_2}{(a_\pm)_1} \right) \tag{6.13}$$

If cell (a) is considered where the silver nitrate solutions are separated by a porous diaphragm rather than by a salt bridge, then a liquid junction potential will be set up, given by

$$E_1 = (t_{NO_3^-} - t_{Ag^+}) \frac{RT}{F} \ln \left(\frac{(a_\pm)_2}{(a_\pm)_1} \right) \tag{6.14}$$

The cell is referred to as a **concentration cell with transport**. The e.m.f. of the complete cell as such is, therefore, given by the sum of the e.m.f.'s in equations (6.13) and (6.14) (noting that $t_+ + t_- = 1$),

$$E = 2t_{NO_3^-} \frac{RT}{F} \ln \left(\frac{(a_\pm)_2}{(a_\pm)_1} \right) \tag{6.15}$$

For cell (b), with the salt bridge to eliminate liquid junction potential,

$$E = \frac{RT}{F} \ln \left(\frac{a(Cl^-)_1}{a(Cl^-)_2} \right) \approx \frac{RT}{F} \ln \left(\frac{(a_\pm)_1}{(a_\pm)_2} \right) \tag{6.16}$$

and for the cell with liquid junction potential,

$$E = 2t_{K^+} \frac{RT}{F} \ln \left(\frac{(a_\pm)_1}{(a_\pm)_2} \right) \tag{6.17}$$

Cells (c), (d) and (e) are examples of **concentration cells without transport** – no liquid junction potential can develop in these cells. Cell (c) is, in effect, two cells, back-to-back.

For cell (d), the electrode reaction is

$$\tfrac{1}{2}Cl_2 + e \rightarrow Cl^-$$

Therefore, assuming pressure and fugacities for $Cl_2(g)$ to be equal,

$$E = \left[E^{\ominus} + \frac{RT}{F} \ln \left(\frac{(p_2)^{1/2}}{a_{Cl^-}} \right) \right] - \left[E^{\ominus} + \frac{RT}{F} \ln \left(\frac{(p_1)^{1/2}}{a_{Cl^-}} \right) \right]$$

$$= \frac{RT}{F} \ln \left(\frac{p_2}{p_1} \right)^{1/2} = \frac{RT}{2F} \ln \left(\frac{p_2}{p_1} \right) \tag{6.18}$$

For cell (e)

$$E = \frac{RT}{2F} \ln \left(\frac{a_1}{a_2} \right) \tag{6.19}$$

6.5 Further Applications of e.m.f. Measurements

6.5.1 Solubility of a Sparingly Soluble Salt

The use of standard electrode potentials provides a much better method for determining the solubilities of sparingly soluble salts than, for example, the conductivity method described in Section 5.5.3.

Example 6.7

Use the standard electrode potentials of the $Ag^+ \mid Ag$ and $Cl^- \mid AgCl$, Ag electrodes (Table 6.1) to calculate the solubility product of silver chloride at 298 K.

Using equation (6.10)

$$E^{\ominus}_{AgCl} = E^{\ominus}_{Ag} + (RT/F) \ln K_s$$

Therefore

$$0.2224 \text{ V} = 0.7991 \text{ V} + 0.05916 \text{ V} \times \log_{10} K_s$$

giving

$$K_s = 1.8 \times 10^{-10} \qquad \blacksquare$$

6.5.2 Determination of Mean Ionic Activity Coefficients

Consider the cell

Pt, H_2 (1 atm) $\mid$ HCl(aq) $\mid$ AgCl(s), Ag

$$E = E_{AgCl} - E_{H_2}$$

But

$$E_{H_2} = (RT/F) \ln a_{H^+}$$

and

$$E_{AgCl} = E^{\ominus}_{AgCl} - (RT/F) \ln a_{Cl^-}$$

Combining these expressions,

$$E = E^{\ominus}_{AgCl} - (RT/F) \ln a_{H^+} a_{Cl^-}$$

$$= E^{\ominus}_{AgCl} - (RT/F) \ln (a_{\pm})^2$$

where $a_{\pm}$ is the mean ionic activity of hydrochloric acid and is equal to $m_{\pm} \gamma_{\pm}$. Therefore

$$E = E^{\ominus}_{AgCl} - (2RT/F) \ln (m_{\pm} \gamma_{\pm}) \tag{6.20}$$

For a 1–1 electrolyte, $m_+ = m_- = m$ and $m_{\pm}^2 = m^2$; therefore

$$E = E^{\ominus}_{AgCl} - \frac{2RT}{F} \ln m - \frac{2RT}{F} \ln \gamma_{\pm} \tag{6.21}$$

Hence provided the standard potential of the silver–silver chloride electrode is known, the value of $\gamma_\pm$ can be determined from the molality m and the measured cell e.m.f.

Example 6.8

An e.m.f. of 0.3524 V at 298 K is measured for the cell

Pt, H_2 (1 atm) | HCl(aq, 0.1 mol kg^{-1}) | AgCl(s), Ag

Calculate the mean ionic activity coefficient and the pH of the HCl(aq), given that $E^\ominus$(Cl$^-$ | AgCl(s), Ag) = + 0.2224 V.

From equation (6.21), we have for this cell

$$E = E^\ominus_{AgCl} - \frac{2RT}{F} \ln m - \frac{2RT}{F} \ln \gamma_\pm$$

Therefore, in aqueous solution at 298 K this becomes

$$0.3524 \text{ V} = 0.2224 \text{ V} - 0.1183 \log_{10} 0.1 - 0.1183 \log_{10} \gamma_\pm$$

giving

$$\log_{10} \gamma_\pm = \frac{0.2224 + 0.1183 - 0.3524}{0.1183}$$

$$= -0.09890$$

from which

$$\gamma_\pm = 0.796$$

In aqueous hydrochloric acid,

$$a_{H^+} = \gamma_\pm m_{H^+}$$

$$= 0.796 \times 0.1 = 0.0796$$

Therefore

$$\text{pH} = -\log_{10} a_{H^+} = -\log_{10} 0.0796$$

$$= 1.10 \qquad \blacksquare$$

6.5.3 Determination of Standard Electrode Potential

The derivation in Section 6.5.2 could, alternatively, be used to determine $E^\ominus$, provided the mean ionic activity coefficient can be determined.

Alternatively, and more realistically, if values of E can be measured over a range of concentrations, it is possible to determine both $E^\ominus$ and the mean activity coefficient graphically. Applying equation (6.21) in general terms gives

$$E + \frac{2RT}{F} \ln m = E^\ominus - \frac{2RT}{F} \ln \gamma_\pm \qquad (6.22)$$

Hence a plot of $E + (2RT/F) \ln m$ against m will be linear at low molalities and, by extrapolation to zero m, $E^\ominus$ can be obtained. At any molality, the ordinate minus $E^\ominus$ gives $(2RT/F) \ln \gamma_\pm$, from which $\gamma_\pm$ can be obtained as illustrated in Fig. 6.4.

A further refinement of this method is possible using the Debye–Hückel limiting equation (see Section 5.6.2). For a 1–1 electrolyte

$$\log_{10} \gamma_\pm = -A \sqrt{m} + Cm$$

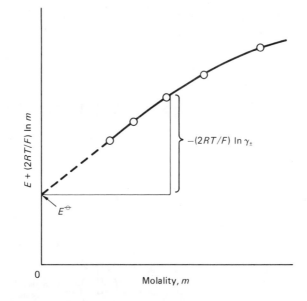

Figure 6.4 Determination of $E^{\ominus}$ and $\gamma_{\pm}$ by graphical method.

where A and C are constants. Hence a plot of the left-hand side of equation (6.22) against $\sqrt{m}$ will give a better linear plot and enable an accurate value of $E^{\ominus}$ to be read as the intercept at $\sqrt{m} = 0$. This is illustrated in Worked Example 6.6.12.

6.5.4 Determination of pH

The simple definition of pH (see Section 5.8.1) is

$$pH = - \log_{10} a_{H^+}$$

Since it is impossible to measure single-ion activities, this definition does not provide a basis for the experimental determination of pH.

The deduction of H^+ ion concentrations from conductivity measurements is limited to dilute solutions, so that for more concentrated solutions and under conditions where other ionic species are present, this method is not satisfactory.

In practice, e.m.f. measurement provides the most suitable method of determining pH. In principle, this could be achieved by means of a hydrogen electrode combined with a suitable reference electrode. However, there are impracticalities associated with the use of a hydrogen electrode, as outlined in Section 6.2.4.

It is, therefore, normal to use a **glass electrode**, which consists of a thin glass bulb or membrane (Fig. 6.5) containing a 1 mol dm^{-3} solution of HCl saturated with AgCl into which a silver wire is inserted (i.e. Ag|AgCl(s)|HCl(aq, 1 mol dm^{-3})|glass). The glass membrane separates the two different solutions, but is constructed so that it allows passage of only one type of ion, the hydrogen ion, ensuring that the electrode is responsive to H^+ ions only. One of its strengths is its insensitivity to oxidising and reducing agents and to other ionic species.

The potential of the silver–silver chloride electrode will be constant as it is in HCl of constant activity. The potential between the inner surface of the glass and the HCl will also be constant as the pH of this solution does not change. When this cell is dipped into a solution X of unknown pH, the potential of the outside of the glass depends on the pH of solution X, and therefore the overall e.m.f.

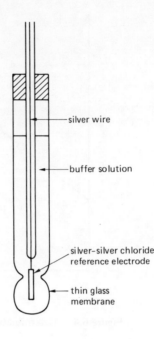

silver wire

buffer solution

silver–silver chloride reference electrode

thin glass membrane

Figure 6.5   Glass electrode.

of the system is dependent on the pH of solution X. When the glass electrode is connected to, say, a calomel electrode, a measurement of the pH is obtained from the e.m.f. of the cell

Ag | AgCl | Cl$^-$, H$^+$ | glass electrode | solution X | calomel electrode

The modern definition of pH, therefore, is based on the measurement of the e.m.f. of a cell which combines a suitable indicator electrode (e.g. a glass electrode) with a reference electrode (e.g. a calomel electrode). The pH of the solution under test is measured relative to conventionally agreed pH values for standard solutions such as

- potassium hydrogen phthalate (aq, 0.05 mol kg^{-1}, 298 K): pH = 4.008
- KH$_2$PO$_4$(0.025 mol kg^{-1}) + Na$_2$HPO$_4$(0.025 mol kg^{-1}); (aq, 298 K): pH = 6.865
- Na$_2$B$_4$O$_7$(aq, 0.01 mol kg^{-1}, 298 K): pH = 9.180

If E^S is the e.m.f. of the cell using the standard solution in which the activity of the H$^+$ ions is $a_{H^+}(S)$, then

$$E^X - E^S = \frac{RT}{F} \ln(a_{H^+}(S)) - \frac{RT}{F} \ln(a_{H^+}(X))$$

where E^X is the e.m.f. of the cell containing solution X with the H$^+$ ion activity equal to $a_{H^+}(X)$. At 298.15 K, therefore,

$$E^X - E^S = 0.059 \left[\log_{10}(a_{H^+}(S)) - \log_{10}(a_{H^+}(X))\right]$$

$$= 0.059 (pH_X - pH_S)$$

Rearranging gives

$$pH_X = pH_S + \frac{E^X - E^S}{0.059}$$

It should be noted that this is an **operational** definition of pH, since any unknown solution can be placed in this type of cell and its pH measured relative to that of one of the standard solutions.

6.5.5 Potentiometric Titrations

In any volumetric titration, the end-point corresponds to a sudden change in concentration of some ion. Since the e.m.f. of a cell also changes rapidly when this occurs, a plot of e.m.f. against volume v will indicate the end-point. In an acid–base titration, a rapid change in pH will occur at the end-point. As illustrated in Fig. 6.6 a better estimate of the end-point is given by plotting dE/dv against volume.

The technique can also be applied to precipitation titrations. For instance, titration of a mixture of I^-, Br^- and Cl^- with $AgNO_3$ produces the stepwise result shown in Fig. 6.7.

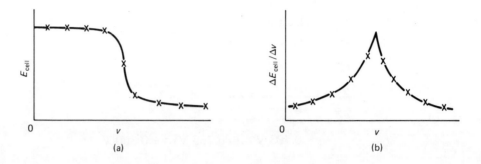

(a) (b)

Figure 6.6 Potentiometric acid–base titration.

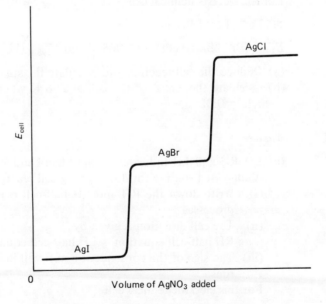

Figure 6.7 Potentiometric titration of mixed halides.

6.6 Worked Examples

6.6.1 Cell Reaction and e.m.f.

For the electrochemical cell

$$Zn(s) \mid Zn^{2+}(aq) \parallel Cd^{2+}(aq) \mid Cd(s)$$

(a) deduce the cell reaction, and

(b) calculate the standard e.m.f. given that

$$E^{\ominus}(Zn^{2+} \mid Zn) = -0.763 \text{ V and}$$

$$E^{\ominus}(Cd^{2+} \mid Cd) = -0.403 \text{ V}.$$

(Liverpool Polytechnic, BSc, 1st year)

Answer

At $-$ve electrode

$$Zn \rightarrow Zn^{2+} + 2e$$

At +ve electrode

$$Cd^{2+} + 2e \rightarrow Cd$$

Overall reaction is

$$Zn + Cd^{2+} \rightarrow Cd + Zn^{2+}$$

$$E^{\ominus}_{cell} = E^{\ominus}_{right} - E^{\ominus}_{left}$$

$$= -0.403 \text{ V} - (-0.763 \text{ V}) = +0.360 \text{ V}$$

6.6.2 Inert Electrodes

For the electrochemical cell

$$Pt \mid Fe^{3+}, Fe^{2+} \parallel Br^- \mid Br_2 (l) \mid Pt$$

$$E^{\ominus}_{298 \text{ K}}(Br^- \mid Br_2 (l) \mid Pt) = +1.065 \text{ V and } E^{\ominus}_{298 \text{ K}}(Fe^{3+} \mid Fe^{2+}) = +0.771 \text{ V}.$$

(a) Deduce the cell reaction and calculate the standard e.m.f. of the cell at 298 K.

(b) Calculate the e.m.f. of the cell at 298 K when $a_{Fe^{3+}} = 0.05$, $a_{Fe^{2+}} = 0.01$ and $a_{Br^-} = 0.02$.

Answer

(a) Let RH and LH indicate the right-hand and left-hand of the cell, respectively. A suggested routine for determining cell reactions and directions is:

(i) Write down the RH and LH half-cell reactions as one-electron reduction processes.

(ii) The cell direction is given by
RH half-cell equation $-$ LH half-cell equation

(iii) The sign of the consequent e.m.f. will indicate in which direction the cell runs.

For this electrochemical cell

RH half-cell: $\quad \frac{1}{2}Br_2 + e \rightarrow Br^-$

LH half-cell: $\quad Fe^{3+} + e \rightarrow Fe^{2+}$

The overall cell is given by

RH half-cell equation $-$ LH half-cell equation, i.e.

$$\frac{1}{2}Br_2 + Fe^{2+} \rightarrow Br^- + Fe^{3+}$$

The standard e.m.f. of the cell is given by

$$E^{\ominus}_{cell} = E^{\ominus}_R - E^{\ominus}_L$$

$$= 1.065 - 0.771 = 0.294 \text{ V}$$

(b) At 298 K from the Nernst equation (equation (6.6)) the e.m.f. of the cell is given by

$$E_{cell} = E_{cell}^{\ominus} - 0.059 \log_{10}\left(\frac{\Pi(\text{activities of products})}{\Pi(\text{activities of reactants})}\right)$$

$$= E_{cell}^{\ominus} - 0.059 \log_{10}\left(\frac{a_{Fe^{3+}}\, a_{Br^-}}{(a_{Br_2})^{1/2}\, a_{Fe^{2+}}}\right)$$

Since $a_{Br_2} = 1$,

$$E_{cell} = 0.294 - 0.059 \log_{10}\left(\frac{0.05 \times 0.02}{0.01}\right) = 0.353 \text{ V}$$

6.6.3 Equilibrium Constant

In the cell

Pt | Fe^{3+} ($a = 1$), Fe^{2+} ($a = 1$) ‖ Ag^+ ($a = 1$) | Ag

the e.m.f. at 298 K for the half-cell Ag^+ | Ag is 0.80 V and for Fe^{3+}, Fe^{2+} | Pt is 0.77 V. Calculate the equilibrium constant for the cell reaction at 298 K.

Answer

As an alternative to the approach used in Worked Example 6.6.2, the principles on which Table 6.1 is based can be applied to the particular cell system, i.e. the half-cell with the more positive reduction potential will be the reduction process (see Section 6.2.3).

Hence in the above cell we have:

At −ve electrode	$Fe^{2+} \rightarrow Fe^{3+} + e$	(oxidation)
At +ve electrode	$Ag^+ + e \rightarrow Ag$	(reduction)
Overall reaction	$Ag^+ + Fe^{2+} \rightarrow Fe^{3+} + Ag$	

The overall standard e.m.f. is given by

$$E^{\ominus} = E_R^{\ominus} - E_L^{\ominus} = E_{Ag}^{\ominus} - E_{Fe^{3+}|Fe^{2+}}^{\ominus}$$

where $E_{Ag}^{\ominus}$ and $E_{Fe^{3+}|Fe^{2+}}^{\ominus}$ are the standard reduction potentials, giving

$$E^{\ominus} = 0.80 \text{ V} - 0.77 \text{ V} = 0.03 \text{ V}$$

As the cell reaction occurs, silver is deposited and the $a_{Fe^{3+}}/a_{Fe^{2+}}$ ratio increases causing the E_{cell} to fall eventually to zero. At this point no further net reaction occurs and equilibrium is established. Under such conditions, the Nernst equation becomes

$$E_{cell} = 0 = E^{\ominus} - \ln K^{\ominus}$$

where, for the above, the equilibrium constant $K^{\ominus}$ is given by

$$0.03 = \frac{RT}{F} \ln K^{\ominus} = 0.059 \log_{10} K^{\ominus}$$

giving

$$\log_{10} K^{\ominus} = \frac{0.03}{0.059} \qquad \text{and} \qquad K^{\ominus} = 3.2$$

6.6.4 Nernst Equation

Deduce the overall reaction for the cell

$$Zn \mid ZnCl_2 \, (a = 0.5) \mid AgCl(s), Ag$$

The standard electrode potentials at 298 K are $E^{\ominus}(Zn^{2+} \mid Zn) = -0.763$ V and $E^{\ominus}(Cl^- \mid AgCl(s), Ag) = 0.222$ V. Calculate the e.m.f. of the cell at 298 K.

Answer

At − ve electrode

$$Zn \rightarrow Zn^{2+} + 2e$$

At +ve electrode

$$2AgCl + 2e \rightarrow Ag + ZnCl_2$$

Overall reaction

$$Zn + 2AgCl \rightarrow 2Ag + ZnCl_2$$

$$E^{\ominus}_{cell} = E^{\ominus}_{Cl^- \mid AgCl, Ag} - E^{\ominus}_{Zn^{2+} \mid Zn}$$

$$= 0.222 - (-0.763) = 0.985 \text{ V}$$

From equation (6.6)

$$E_{cell} = E^{\ominus} - \frac{RT}{zF} \ln \left(\frac{\Pi(\text{activities of products})}{\Pi(\text{activities of reactants})} \right)$$

$$= E^{\ominus} - \frac{RT}{2F} \ln \left(\frac{a_{Ag} \, a_{ZnCl_2}}{a_{Zn} (a_{AgCl})^2} \right)$$

But since the activities of the solids can be taken as unity, at 298 K, this reduces to

$$E_{cell} = E^{\ominus} - \frac{0.059}{2} \log_{10} a_{ZnCl_2}$$

$$= 0.985 - 0.0295 \log_{10} 0.5$$

$$= 0.994 \text{ V}$$

6.6.5 Direction of Spontaneous Change

Deduce whether the reaction at 298 K

$$2Fe^{2+} + Hg_2^{2+} \rightarrow 2Hg + 2Fe^{3+}$$

will occur spontaneously in the cell

$$Pt \mid Fe^{2+} (a = 10^{-4}), Fe^{3+} (a = 1) \parallel Hg_2^{2+} (a = 1) \mid Hg$$

given that $E^{\ominus}(Fe^{3+}, Fe^{2+}) = +0.771$ V and $E^{\ominus}(Hg_2^{2+} \mid Hg) = +0.789$ V.

Answer

For the above overall reaction, the individual electrode reactions are:

At −ve electrode

$$2Fe^{2+} \rightarrow 2Fe^{3+} + 2e \qquad E = -0.771 \text{ V}$$

At +ve electrode

$$Hg_2^{2+} + 2e \rightarrow Hg \qquad E = +0.789 \text{ V}$$

The standard e.m.f. of the cell equals $0.789 - 0.771 = +0.018$ V. Hence under standard conditions, the cell reaction will occur spontaneously.

However, under the conditions given,

$$E = E^\ominus - \frac{RT}{zF} \ln\left(\frac{\Pi(\text{activities of products})}{\Pi(\text{activities of reactants})}\right)$$

$$= E^\ominus - \frac{0.059}{2} \log_{10}\left(\frac{(a_{Fe^{3+}})^2}{(a_{Fe^{2+}})^2 (a_{Hg_2^{2+}})}\right)$$

$$= 0.018 - \frac{0.059}{2} \log_{10}\left(\frac{1}{10^{-8} \times 1}\right)$$

$$= -0.218 \text{ V}$$

Therefore, under these cell conditions, the reaction is not spontaneous and it is the following reverse reaction that will occur spontaneously:

$$2Hg + 2Fe^{3+} \rightarrow 2Fe^{2+} + Hg_2^{2+}$$

6.6.6 Equilibrium Ratio

At 298 K, the standard electrode potentials for $Sn^{2+}|Sn$ and $Pb^{2+}|Pb$ are -0.140 V and -0.126 V, respectively. For the cell

$$Sn \,|\, Sn^{2+}(aq) \,\|\, Pb^{2+}(aq) \,|\, Pb$$

calculate
(a) the standard e.m.f. for the cell, and
(b) the ratio $[Sn^{2+}]/[Pb^{2+}]$ when the cell reaction has attained equilibrium.

(Liverpool Polytechnic, BSc, 1st year)

Answer

(a) The standard e.m.f. of the cell is given by

$$E_{cell} = E_{right} - E_{left}$$

$$= -0.126 \text{ V} - (-0.140 \text{ V}) = +0.014 \text{ V}$$

(b) The positive e.m.f. shows that the Pb is the positive electrode and accepts electrons supplied by the Sn electrode. Therefore the electrode reactions are

$$Pb^{2+} + 2e \rightarrow Pb$$

$$Sn \rightarrow Sn^{2+} + 2e$$

Overall reaction

$$Pb^{2+} + Sn \rightarrow Pb + Sn^{2+}$$

For this cell reaction, the Nernst equation is

$$E = E^\ominus - \frac{RT}{zF} \ln\left(\frac{a_{Pb}\, a_{Sn^{2+}}}{a_{Pb^{2+}}\, a_{Sn}}\right)$$

Assuming the activities of the solids can be taken as unity, at 298 K

$$E = 0.014 - \frac{0.059}{2} \log_{10}\left(\frac{a_{Sn^{2+}}}{a_{Pb^{2+}}}\right)$$

But at equilibrium, $E_{cell} = 0$, so that

$$0 = 0.014 - 0.0295 \log_{10}\left(\frac{a_{Sn^{2+}}}{a_{Pb^{2+}}}\right)$$

giving

$$a_{Sn^{2+}}/a_{Pb^{2+}} = 2.98$$

6.6.7 Solubility Product

The standard electrode potentials of $Ag^+(aq) \mid Ag$ and $SO_4^{2-}(aq) \mid Ag_2SO_4(s)$, Ag at 298 K are +0.799 V and +0.652 V, respectively. Determine the solubility product of silver sulphate at this temperature.

Answer

$$E_{Ag_2SO_4} = E_{Ag}^{\ominus} + (RT/F) \ln a_{Ag^+}$$

$$K_s = (a_{Ag^+})^2 a_{SO_4^{2-}}$$

Therefore

$$E_{Ag_2SO_4} = E_{Ag}^{\ominus} + \frac{RT}{F} \ln \left(\frac{K_s}{a_{SO_4^{2-}}}\right)^{1/2}$$

$$= E_{Ag}^{\ominus} + \frac{RT}{2F} \ln K_s - \frac{RT}{2F} \ln a_{SO_4^{2-}}$$

Putting $a_{SO_4^{2-}}$ equal to unity makes $E_{Ag_2SO_4}$ the standard potential, $E_{Ag_2SO_4}^{\ominus}$. Therefore

$$E_{Ag_2SO_4}^{\ominus} = E_{Ag}^{\ominus} + (RT/2F) \ln K_s$$

from which

$$\log_{10} K_s = \frac{0.652 - 0.799}{0.5 \times 0.05916} = -4.970$$

and

$$K_s = 1.1 \times 10^{-5}$$

6.6.8 Temperature Coefficient of e.m.f.

What are the electrode reactions occurring in the cell

Pt, H_2 (g) $\mid$ HCl(aq) $\mid$ AgCl(s), Ag

Calculate the standard e.m.f. of the cell and the temperature coefficient of the cell from the following thermodynamic data at 298 K:

	$-\Delta_f H^{\ominus}/kJ\ mol^{-1}$	$-\Delta_f G^{\ominus}/kJ\ mol^{-1}$
AgCl(s)	128.0	109.7
HCl(aq)	165.5	131.2

Answer

At −ve electrode

$\frac{1}{2}H_2 \rightarrow H^+ + e$

At +ve electrode

$AgCl(s) + e \rightarrow Ag(s) + Cl^- (aq)$

Therefore the overall cell reaction is

$\frac{1}{2}H_2 + AgCl(s) \rightarrow Ag(s) + HCl(aq)$

The e.m.f. of the cell under standard conditions is given by

$\Delta G^{\ominus} = -zE^{\ominus}F = -(131.2 - 109.7) \times 10^3 \text{ J mol}^{-1}$

$\qquad = -21\,500 \text{ J mol}^{-1}$

giving

$E^{\ominus} = \dfrac{21.5 \times 10^3}{96\,500} \text{ V} = 0.223 \text{ V}$

For the cell reaction,

$\Delta H^{\ominus} = -(165.5 - 128.0) \times 10^3 \text{ J mol}^{-1}$

$\qquad = -37\,500 \text{ J mol}^{-1}$

From the Gibbs–Helmholtz equation,

$\Delta H^{\ominus} = \Delta G^{\ominus} + zFT \left(\dfrac{\partial E^{\ominus}}{\partial T} \right)_p$

Therefore

$\left(\dfrac{\partial E^{\ominus}}{\partial T} \right)_p = \dfrac{\Delta H^{\ominus} - \Delta G^{\ominus}}{zFT}$

$\qquad = \dfrac{-37\,500 - (-21\,500)}{1 \times 96\,500 \times 298} \text{ V K}^{-1}$

$\qquad = -5.56 \times 10^{-4} \text{ V K}^{-1}$

6.6.9 Thermodynamics of Cells

For the cell

$Zn, Hg \mid ZnCl_2 (aq, 0.5 \text{ mol dm}^{-3}) \mid AgCl(s) \mid Ag$

the e.m.f. varies with temperature, as follows:

E/V	1.0352	1.0335	1.0330	1.0317	1.0304	1.0280
T/K	295.0	300.5	303.5	307.9	313.9	322.6

Determine the values of ΔG, ΔH and ΔS for the cell reaction.

Answer

The cell reaction is

$Zn + 2AgCl(s) \rightarrow 2Ag + Zn^{2+} + 2Cl^-$

so that $z = 2$. From a plot of e.m.f. versus T (Fig. 6.8), $E_{298\,K} = 1.0344$ V and from the slope

$$\left(\frac{\partial E}{\partial T}\right)_p = -2.54 \times 10^{-4} \text{ V K}^{-1}$$

From equations (6.1), (6.3) and (6.4)

$$\Delta G = -zFE = -(2 \times 1.0344 \times 96\,500) \text{ J mol}^{-1}$$

$$= -199.6 \text{ kJ mol}^{-1}$$

$$\Delta S = zF\left(\frac{\partial E}{\partial T}\right)_p$$

$$= [2 \times 96\,500 \times (-2.54 \times 10^{-4})] \text{ J K}^{-1} \text{ mol}^{-1}$$

$$= -49.0 \text{ J K}^{-1} \text{ mol}^{-1}$$

$$\Delta H = \Delta G + T\Delta S$$

$$= [-199\,600 + 298 \times (-49.0)] \text{ J mol}^{-1}$$

$$= -214.2 \text{ kJ mol}^{-1}$$

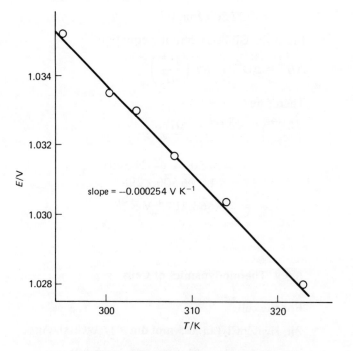

Figure 6.8   Plot of e.m.f. versus T.

6.6.10 Concentration Cells

Calculate the e.m.f. at 298 K of the following concentration cells:
(a) $Ag \mid AgNO_3 (a = 0.01) \parallel AgNO_3 (a = 0.1) \mid Ag$
(b) $Ag \mid AgNO_3 (a = 0.01) \vdots AgNO_3 (a = 0.1) \mid Ag$
given that $t_{Ag^+} = 0.465$ (independent of $AgNO_3$ concentration).

Answer

(a) $E_{cell} = (RT/F) \ln (a_2/a_1)$

$$= 0.059 \log_{10} (0.1/0.01) \text{ V} = 0.059 \text{ V}$$

(b) In this case the e.m.f. depends on the transport number of the nitrate ions,

$$E = 2t_{NO_3^-} \frac{RT}{F} \ln\left(\frac{a_2}{a_1}\right)$$

where

$$t_{NO_3^-} = 1 - t_{Ag^+} = 1 - 0.465 = 0.535$$

giving

$$E = 2 \times 0.535 \times 0.059 \log_{10} (0.1/0.01) \text{ V}$$

$$= 0.063 \text{ V}$$

6.6.11 Effect of Activity Coefficients on Cell e.m.f.

Calculate the e.m.f. at 298 K of the cell

Zn | ZnSO$_4$ ($m = 0.05$ mol kg^{-1}) ‖ KCl(saturated), Hg$_2$Cl$_2$ (s), Hg

At 298 K the standard electrode potential of the zinc electrode is -0.763 V, the mean ionic activity coefficient $\gamma_\pm$ of 0.05 mol kg^{-1} ZnSO$_4$ is 0.225 and the potential of the saturated calomel electrode is $+0.242$ V.

Answer

The e.m.f. of the cell is given by

$$E_{cell} = E_{right} - E_{left}$$

The potential of the zinc electrode is given by

$$E_{left} = E^{\ominus} + \frac{RT}{zF} \ln a_{Zn^{2+}}$$

Assuming that $\gamma_{Zn^{2+}} = \gamma_{SO_4^{2-}}$, then $a_{Zn^{2+}} = 0.05 \times 0.225 = 0.01125$ and since $z = 2$

$$E_{left} = -0.763 + \frac{0.05916}{2} \log_{10} 0.01125$$

$$= -0.821 \text{ V}$$

giving

$$E_{cell} = 0.242 \text{ V} - (-0.821 \text{ V}) = 1.063 \text{ V}$$

6.6.12 Standard e.m.f. and Activity Coefficient

For the cell

Pt, H$_2$ (1 atm) | HCl(aq, m) | AgCl(s), Ag

the values of the e.m.f. E as a function of the molality m of the hydrochloric acid is as follows:

m/mol kg^{-1}	0.004488	0.011195	0.01710	0.02563	0.05391
E/V	0.50384	0.45861	0.43783	0.41824	0.38222

Determine the standard e.m.f. of the cell by a graphical method and the mean activity coefficient at the lowest molality reading in the above table.

Answer

For the above cell, the e.m.f. is given by

$$E = E^{\ominus} - \frac{2RT}{F} \ln m_{\pm} - \frac{2RT}{F} \ln \gamma_{\pm}$$

where $\gamma_{\pm}$ is the mean ionic activity coefficient and $m_{\pm}$ is the mean molality, in this case equal to m (see Section 6.5.2). Rearranging therefore gives

$$E + \frac{2RT}{F} \ln m = E^{\ominus} - \frac{2RT}{F} \ln \gamma_{\pm}$$

Since $\gamma_{\pm}$ is proportional to $\sqrt{m}$ (from the Debye–Hückel limiting law), a plot of $E + (2RT/F) \ln m$ against $\sqrt{m}$ should be approximately linear.

E/V	0.50384	0.45861	0.43783	0.41824	0.38222
$m/\text{mol kg}^{-1}$	0.004488	0.011195	0.01710	0.02563	0.05391
$[E + (2RT/F) \ln m]/\text{V}$	0.22604	0.22781	0.22883	0.23004	0.23222
$\sqrt{m}/(\text{mol kg}^{-1})^{1/2}$	0.06700	0.1058	0.1308	0.1601	0.2322

From the graph (Fig. 6.9), extrapolation to zero m gives the standard electrode potential of $Cl^{-}(\text{aq}) \mid AgCl(\text{s}), Ag$ as

$$E^{\ominus} = 0.2224 \text{ V}$$

At $m = 0.004\,488 \text{ mol kg}^{-1}$

$$0.22604 = 0.2224 - \frac{2RT}{F} \ln \gamma_{\pm} = 0.2224 - 0.1183 \log_{10} \gamma_{\pm}$$

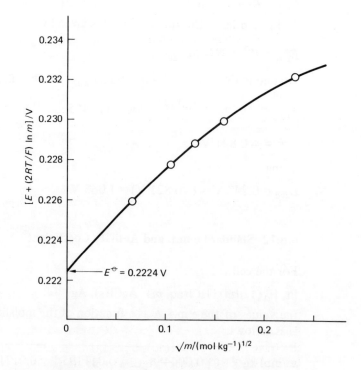

Figure 6.9 Plot of $E + (2RT/F) \ln m$ against $\sqrt{m}$.

Therefore

$$\log_{10} \gamma_\pm = -\frac{0.00364}{0.1183} = -0.03077$$

giving

$$\gamma_\pm = 0.932$$

6.7 Unworked Examples

6.7.1
For the cell

Ag, AgCl(s) | HCl($a = 1$) | Cl$^-$ (1 atm), Pt

determine the e.m.f., given that the standard electrode potential of the silver-silver chloride electrode is 0.2225 V and that of the chlorine electrode is 1.3595 V.

6.7.2
Inert electrodes are immersed in an aqueous solution at 298 K containing Ag$^+$ (0.01 mol dm^{-3}) and Cu^{2+} (1 mol dm^{-3}) ions. What electrolysis reaction would you expect to take place first at the cathode if the applied potential is gradually increased. The standard electrode potentials are $E^\ominus$(Ag$^+$ | Ag) = 0.80 V and $E^\ominus$(Cu^{2+} | Cu) = 0.34 V.

6.7.3
Determine the reaction for the cell

Zn | Zn^{2+}(aq, $a_{\text{Zn}^{2+}} = 0.1$) ‖ Cl$^-$ (aq, $a_{\text{Cl}^-} = 0.2$) | Hg$_2$Cl$_2$ (s), Hg(l)

If the standard electrode potential of the zinc electrode is –0.763 V and that of the calomel electrode is 0.268 V, what is the e.m.f. of the cell?

6.7.4
At 298 K the standard potentials of the electrodes Co^{3+}, Co^{2+} | Pt and Fe^{3+}, Fe^{2+} | Pt are 1.82 V and 0.77 V, respectively. What conclusions can be drawn?

6.7.5
Calculate the e.m.f. at 298 K of the cell

Pt, H$_2$ (1 atm) | H$^+$(aq, 0.1 mol dm^{-3}) ‖ H$^+$(aq, 0.2 mol dm^{-3}) | H$_2$ (10 atm), Pt

(Liverpool Polytechnic, BSc, 1st year)

6.7.6
Devise cells in which the following overall reactions can occur:
(a) Zn + Ni^{2+} → Zn^{2+} + Ni
(b) H$_2$ (g) + 2AgCl(s) → 2Ag(s) + 2HCl(aq)
(c) Cu(s) + Cl$_2$ (g) → Cu^{2+}(aq) + 2Cl$^-$ (aq)
(d) Na + H$_2$O → NaOH(aq) + $\frac{1}{2}$H$_2$ (g)
(e) AgBr(s) + Cl$^-$ (aq) → AgCl(s) + Br$^-$ (aq)
(f) Pb(s) + PbO$_2$ (s) + 2H$_2$SO$_4$(aq) → 2PbSO$_4$ (s) + 2H$_2$O

6.7.7

The e.m.f. of the following cell was found to be 0.450 V at 298 K:

Ag | sat AgCl in KCl(aq, 0.1 mol dm^{-3}) ‖ AgNO$_3$(aq, 0.1 mol dm^{-3}) | Ag

What is the solubility product and the solubility of silver chloride in water at 298 K?

6.7.8

Given that the solubility product of zinc hydroxide is 7.68×10^{-17} at 298 K, determine the standard electrode potential of the reaction

$$Zn(OH)_2(s) + 2e \rightarrow Zn(s) + 2OH^-(aq)$$

6.7.9

The e.m.f. of the cell

Zn | ZnCl$_2$(aq, 0.05 mol dm^{-3}) | AgCl(s), Ag

is 1.015 V at 298 K and the temperature coefficient of its e.m.f. is $-0.000\,493$ V K^{-1}. Write down the equation for the reaction occurring when the cell is allowed to discharge and calculate the changes in (a) free energy, (b) entropy and (c) enthalpy attending this reaction at 298 K.

(GRSC, Part I)

6.7.10

At 293 K, $E(Cl^- | AgCl, Ag) = 0.2256$ V and at 303 K it is 0.2191 V. Find the values of ΔS, ΔG and ΔH for the electrode reaction.

6.7.11

Calculate the e.m.f. of the following cell at 298 K:

Ag, AgCl(s) | LiCl(aq, 0.01 mol kg^{-1}) ¦ LiCl(aq, 0.001 mol kg^{-1}) | AgCl(s), Ag

given that the mean activity coefficients of the lithium chloride in 0.01 mol kg^{-1} and 0.001 mol kg^{-1} are 0.90 and 0.97, respectively, and the transport number of the Li^{2+} ions in LiCl (assumed concentration-independent) is 0.329.

6.7.12

At 298 K the e.m.f. of the following cell is 0.7585 V:

Cd-Hg | CdCl$_2$(aq, 0.01 mol kg^{-1}) | AgCl(s), Ag

The standard e.m.f. of the cell is 0.5732 V. Calculate
(a) the stoichiometric mean ion activity coefficient of cadmium chloride in 0.01 mol kg^{-1} solution, and
(b) compare it to the value calculated from the Debye–Hückel limiting law.

(GRSC, Part II)

6.7.13

The mean ionic activity coefficient of hydrochloric acid in a solution of concentration 9.14×10^{-3} mol dm^{-3} is 0.906. If the standard electrode potential, $E^{\ominus}(Cl^-(aq) | AgCl(s), Ag) = 0.2223$ V at 298 K, what is the e.m.f. of the following cell:

Pt, H$_2$(g) | HCl(aq, 9.14×10^{-3} mol dm^{-3}) | AgCl(s), Ag

6.7.14

The cell

$$H_2 \, (1 \text{ atm}), \text{Pt} \mid HCl(m) \mid Hg_2 Cl_2 , Hg$$

has, at 298 K, the following values of e.m.f. E for the given molalities m of hydrochloric acid:

$m/\text{mol kg}^{-1}$	0.07508	0.03769	0.01887	0.00504
E/V	0.4119	0.4452	0.4787	0.5437

By a simple graphical method determine the standard e.m.f. of this cell and calculate the activity coefficient of hydrochloric acid in the most concentrated of the four solutions mentioned.

(GRSC, Part II)

7 Surface Chemistry and Colloids

7.1 Introduction

The range of systems and processes where surface characteristics are of primary importance is vast. Adhesion, ore flotation, detergency, heterogeneous catalysis, wetting, lubrication, emulsions and foams are just a few subject areas where surface science is of central importance. Most biological processes take place at surfaces.

This chapter offers a concise account of the more important areas of this subject which are likely to feature in non-specialised undergraduate teaching.

7.2 The Solid–Gas Interface

The extent to which gas (the adsorbate) adsorbs on, or is otherwise taken up by, a solid (the adsorbent) depends on the following factors:

(a) the physical and chemical nature of the gas,
(b) the physical and chemical nature of the solid (the important physical features being the specific surface area and the pore size distribution),
(c) temperature,
(d) pressure.

Finely divided and porous solids can have specific surface areas up to ~ 1000 m^2 g^{-1}. The pores in a porous solid are classified as

- **micropores** – pore diameter up to 2 nm,
- **mesopores** – pore diameter 2 to 50 nm,
- **macropores** – pore diameter greater than 50 nm.

At a given temperature, the relationship between the equilibrium amount of gas adsorbed and the pressure of the gas is known as the adsorption isotherm. The adsorption isotherm is an important means of characterising gas adsorption and examples are discussed later in this section.

Gas adsorption is a spontaneous process, i.e. ΔG is negative. It involves a loss of translational freedom; therefore, ΔS is negative. It follows, from $\Delta H = \Delta G + T\Delta S$, that ΔH must be negative, i.e. gas adsorption is an exothermic process.

Increasing the temperature means an increase in the kinetic energy of gas molecules, which favours desorption. The equilibrium amount of gas adsorbed on a solid, therefore, decreases with increasing temperature.

7.2.1 Physical Adsorption and Chemisorption

The adsorption of gases or vapours on solids will always involve van der Waals' forces (physical adsorption) and may involve chemical reaction (chemisorption). The main features of physical adsorption and chemisorption are as follows.

(a) *Physical Adsorption*

The adsorbed gas is held to the solid surface by weak, non-specific van der Waals' forces, similar to those found in liquefaction. Any gas will physically adsorb on any solid surface to some extent.

Adsorption equilibrium is attained rapidly and the process is easily reversible. The activation energy of physical adsorption is zero. Physical adsorption is, therefore, most prominent at low temperature.

The enthalpy of adsorption is low, typically of the order of magnitude of -10 kJ mol^{-1} (comparable with the enthalpy of condensation to bulk liquid). Because of this, the adsorbed gas may have some two-dimensional freedom.

Multilayer adsorption can take place.

(b) *Chemisorption*

The adsorbed gas is held to the solid surface by strong, specific chemical bonding.

Adsorption equilibrium is established only slowly, owing to the high activation energy that is usually involved (as with other chemical reactions). Chemisorption is, therefore, most prominent at high temperatures.

The enthalpy of adsorption is high, typically of the order of magnitude of -10^2 kJ mol^{-1} (comparable with ΔH for chemical reactions in general). Adsorption will tend to be localised.

Only monolayer adsorption is possible.

The nature of physical adsorption and chemisorption is illustrated in Fig. 7.1 for the adsorption of a diatomic gas X_2 on a metal M. Curve P represents the physical adsorption process, $M + X_2 \rightarrow M - - - - X_2$. Curve C is a Morse curve representing chemisorption by the process, $M + X \rightarrow MX$. Formation of atoms of X in the gas phase prior to chemisorption does not represent a realistic mechanism, however, since the activation energy (the dissociation energy of X_2) would be far too high. Instead, chemisorption is preceded by physical adsorption and transfers to chemisorption at the intersection of curves P and C with a much reduced activation energy.

7.2.2 Adsorption Isotherms

Adsorption isotherms exhibit considerable variety. Two important characteristic shapes are illustrated in Fig. 7.2. Type I isotherms show a fairly rapid initial rise in the amount of adsorption with increasing pressure followed by a levelling off to a limiting value. It is often referred to as a Langmuir-type isotherm and is obtained when gas adsorption is restricted to a monomolecular layer. Chemisorption isotherms, therefore, approximate this shape.

Type II isotherms (e.g. nitrogen on silica gel at 77 K) represent multilayer physical adsorption. Point B represents the formation of an adsorbed monolayer. Often, as illustrated, there is fairly rapid uptake of gas into the first monolayer before significant multilayer adsorption takes place, thus giving the characteristic shape of a Type II isotherm. Isotherms for water vapour adsorption tend not to

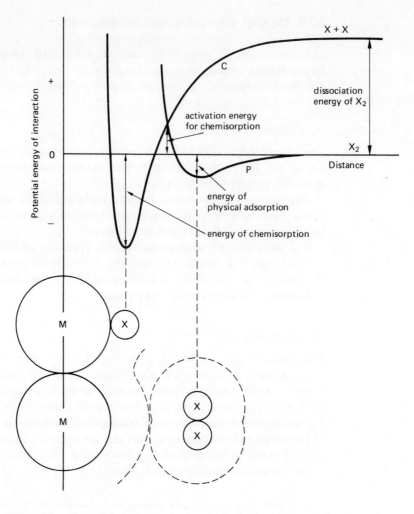

Figure 7.1 Potential-energy curves for physical adsorption and chemisorption.

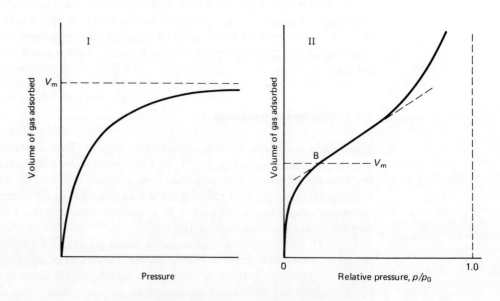

Figure 7.2 Types I and II adsorption isotherms.

show the same rapid initial uptake, because adsorption into the first monolayer is, if anything, weaker than multilayer adsorption where hydrogen bonding prevails.

Condensation of vapour can take place in porous solids at pressures p_r that are less than the saturation vapour pressure p_0. For a cylindrical pore, p_r/p_0 is given by the Kelvin equation,

$$RT \ln\left(\frac{p_r}{p_0}\right) = - \frac{2\gamma V_m \cos\theta}{r} \tag{7.1}$$

where r is the radius of the capillary, V_m the molar volume of the condensed liquid and θ the contact angle between the condensed liquid and the capillary wall. The adsorption isotherms of porous solids are characterised by a limit in the uptake of vapour which represents the total pore volume. They usually exhibit hysteresis. Capillary condensation into mesopores takes place at pressures slightly less than the saturation vapour pressure, but condensation into micropores can take place at much lower pressures. Macropores manifest themselves in terms of gas adsorption simply in terms of their contribution to the overall surface area of the solid; but their existence as pores can be detected by the technique of mercury porosimetry, where pore size distribution and capacity is investigated by measuring the amount of mercury that enters a porous solid as a function of applied pressure.

7.2.3 Langmuir Adsorption Isotherm

This describes Type I isotherms and is based on the following model:
(a) adsorption is restricted to a monomolecular layer,
(b) adsorption is localised,
(c) the enthalpy of adsorption is independent of surface coverage.

In practice, solid surfaces are heterogeneous with respect to both geometry and chemical activity. The first molecules to adsorb will tend to seek out the sites for which ΔH is most negative. As monolayer completion is approached, adsorption may become easier (i.e. more negative ΔH) because of lateral interactions; or (in chemisorption) it may become more difficult (i.e. less negative ΔH) owing to the adsorbed layer being dipolar.

Let V be the equilibrium volume of gas adsorbed at pressure p and V_m the volume of gas required to cover the solid with a complete monolayer. At adsorption equilibrium, the rate of adsorption will equal the rate of desorption. The rate of adsorption depends on (i) the rate at which gas molecules collide with the solid surface, which is proportional to the pressure, (ii) the probability of striking a vacant site $(1 - V/V_m)$, and (iii) an Arrhenius factor, $\exp(-E_{ads}/RT)$, where E_{ads} is the activation energy for adsorption. The rate of desorption depends on (i) the fraction of the surface covered (V/V_m), and (ii) an Arrhenius factor, $\exp(-E_{des}/RT)$, where E_{des} is the activation energy for desorption. Equating these rates,

$$p(1 - V/V_m) \exp(-E_{ads}/RT) = k(V/V_m) \exp(-E_{des}/RT)$$

where k is a proportionality constant. Therefore,

$$p = k \exp(\Delta H_{ads}/RT) \frac{V/V_m}{(1 - V/V_m)}$$

where

$$\Delta H_{ads} = E_{ads} - E_{des}.$$

Assuming ΔH_{ads} to be independent of surface coverage,

$$k \exp(\Delta H_{ads}/RT) = 1/b$$

where b is a constant depending on the temperature, but independent of the surface coverage. Therefore,

$$bp = \frac{V/V_m}{(1 - V/V_m)} \tag{7.2}$$

or

$$V = \frac{V_m \, bp}{1 + bp} \tag{7.3}$$

At low pressure, $bp \ll 1$, and equation (7.3) reduces to $V = V_m \, bp$; and at high pressure, $bp \gg 1$, and equation (7.3) reduces to $V = V_m$; thus describing a Type I isotherm.

Inverting equation (7.2) and multiplying throughout by p gives

$$\frac{p}{V} = \frac{1}{bV_m} + \frac{p}{V_m} \tag{7.4}$$

The fit of adsorption data to the Langmuir equation can, therefore, be tested by plotting p/V versus p, which should give a straight line of slope $1/V_m$.

7.2.4 Brunauer, Emmett and Teller (B.E.T.) Adsorption Isotherm, Surface Areas

This is an extension of the Langmuir treatment to allow for multilayer adsorption. It is derived by balancing the rates of adsorption and desorption for each molecular layer of adsorbate and is based on the simplifying assumption that a characteristic enthalpy of adsorption, ΔH_1, applies to the first monolayer whilst the enthalpy of liquefaction, ΔH_L, of the adsorbate applies to adsorption in the second and subsequent molecular layers. The equation is usually expressed in the form

$$\frac{p}{V(p_0 - p)} = \frac{1}{V_m c} + \frac{(c-1)}{V_m c} \cdot \frac{p}{p_0} \tag{7.5}$$

where p_0 is the saturation vapour pressure of the adsorbate, V_m is the monolayer capacity and $c \approx \exp[(\Delta H_L - \Delta H_1)/RT]$. According to the B.E.T. equation, a plot of $p/V(p_0 - p)$ versus p/p_0 should give a straight line of slope $(c-1)/V_m c$, and an intercept $1/V_m c$, from which V_m is given by

$$V_m = \frac{1}{\text{slope} + \text{intercept}} \tag{7.6}$$

V_m is a parameter of particular interest, since it can be used for calculating the surface area of an adsorbent if the effective area occupied by each adsorbate molecule is known. The B.E.T. equation fits many experimental adsorption isotherms particularly well in the pressure range $0.05p_0$ to $0.35p_0$ (within which range V_m is usually reached). With only a small loss of accuracy a B.E.T. plot can be assumed to pass through the origin and V_m can be calculated on the basis of a single gas adsorption measurement.

The adsorbate most commonly used for B.E.T. surface area determination is nitrogen at 77 K. The effective area occupied by each adsorbed nitrogen molecule at monolayer capacity is taken as $16.2 \times 10^{-20} \text{ m}^2$. Since nitrogen adsorption tends to be non-localised, this area applies to most adsorbents. With other adsorbates, the adsorption tends to be more localised and the effective molecular area varies depending on the nature of the adsorbent.

7.2.5 Freundlich Adsorption Isotherm

Over a limited range, adsorption data often fit the empirical relationship

$$V = kp^{1/n} \tag{7.7}$$

where k and n are constants.

Adsorption from solution data, in particular, can often be fitted to this equation, in the form

$$x/m = kc^{1/n} \tag{7.8}$$

where x is the apparent amount of solute adsorbed by a mass m of solid and c is the solute concentration.

Taking logarithms,

$$\log(x/m) = \log k + (1/n) \log c \tag{7.9}$$

The fit of adsorption data to the Freundlich equation can, therefore, be tested in terms of the linearity of a $\log x$ versus $\log c$ plot.

7.3 Liquid–Gas and Liquid–Liquid Interfaces

7.3.1 Surface and Interfacial Tensions

The existence of the liquid state is due to short-range van der Waals' attractive forces, and aided, in some cases, by other cohesive forces, such as hydrogen bonding. The molecules in the bulk of a liquid are subjected, on average, to equal attractive forces in all directions. Those located at the liquid surface, however, experience unbalanced attractive forces and a net inward pull, as illustrated in Fig. 7.3. There is, therefore, a spontaneous tendency (negative ΔG) for molecules to migrate from the surface to the bulk of the liquid and for the surface area of the liquid to decrease. For this reason, droplets of liquid and gas bubbles tend to attain a spherical shape.

The surface free energy ΔG_s is the free-energy increase accompanying unit increase of surface area (isothermally and reversibly). An equivalent quantity is the surface tension, which is usually defined as the force acting at right angles to any line of unit length in the surface. This definition is somewhat misleading, since (as illustrated in Fig. 7.3) there is no tangential force as such at a liquid surface. It does, however, relate to detachment methods for measuring surface tension and to certain experiments on thin films.

There is no fundamental difference between the terms 'surface' and 'interface', although it is sometimes practice to describe the boundary between two surfaces, one of which is gaseous, as a surface, and the boundary between two non-gaseous phases as an interface.

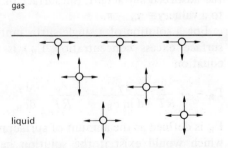

Figure 7.3   Attractive forces between molecules in bulk liquid and at the liquid–gas interface.

7.3.2 Surface Activity

Surface-active agents (or surfactants) make up a very important class of molecules. They are characterised by having polar (hydrophilic) and non-polar (hydrophobic) parts, i.e. they are amphiphilic. They may be ionic or non-ionic, as illustrated by the following examples.

- **Anionic:** sodium octadecanoate, $C_{17}H_{35}COO^- Na^+$
  sodium dodecylsulphate, $C_{12}H_{25}SO_4^- Na^+$
- **Cationic:** hexadecyltrimethylammonium bromide, $C_{16}H_{33}N(CH_3)_3^+ Br^-$
- **Non-ionic:** poly(ethene oxide) derivatives, e.g. $C_6H_{13}(OCH_2CH_2)_8OH$ (C_6E_8)

In an oil–water system the hydrophilic and hydrophobic nature of the different parts of the surfactant molecule can be satisfied simultaneously if the surfactant adsorbs and orientates in a monomolecular layer at the interface, as illustrated in Fig. 7.4a. Adsorption will also take place at an air–water interface (Fig. 7.4b), but in this case the hydrophobic part of the surfactant will be attracted by and lie on the water surface. A common misconception is that oil and water do not mix because they repel one another. This is not true; indeed, the van der Waals' attraction between oil and water is generally as strong as between oil and oil.

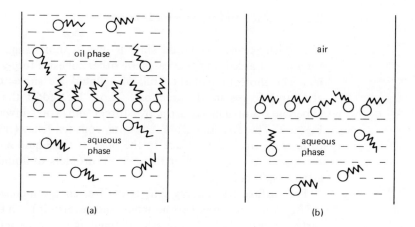

Figure 7.4 Adsorption of surfactant at (a) oil–water and (b) air–water interfaces.

The reason why oil and water do not mix is because water attracts itself so strongly by hydrogen bonding and mixing with oil would prevent this.

The tendency for surfactant molecules to pack into an interface favours an expansion of the interface and so acts opposite to the contracting tendency under normal surface tension forces. If π is the expanding force (or surface pressure) of the adsorbed surfactant, the surface or interfacial tension will be lowered from γ_0 to a value $\gamma = \gamma_0 - \pi$.

For a solution of a single surfactant, the extent of adsorption (expressed as a surface excess concentration Γ_B) is related to surface tension by the Gibbs equation

$$\Gamma_B = -\frac{1}{RT}\frac{d\gamma}{d\ln c_B} = -\frac{c_B}{RT}\frac{d\gamma}{dc_B} \tag{7.10}$$

Γ_B is defined as the amount of surfactant per unit area of surface in excess of that which would exist if the solution had uniform concentration right up to the surface. Its magnitude depends on the location of the surface, which is arbitrarily chosen as the plane at which the surface excess concentration of the solvent, Γ_A, is zero. In reality, the surface is not a mathematical plane, but a three-dimensional region of rapidly changing composition.

7.3.3 Micelles

Solutions of highly surface-active materials often exhibit unusual physical properties. In dilute solution, the surfactant acts as a normal solute, but at a fairly well defined concentration, abrupt changes in various physical properties are observed, as illustrated in Fig. 7.5.

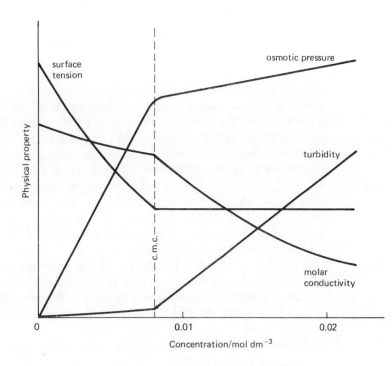

Figure 7.5 Physical properties of sodium dodecylsulphate solutions at 25°C.

This is explained in terms of the formation of micelles, which are aggregates of typically 10 to 100 surfactant molecules with the hydrophobic parts orientated towards the interior and the polar groups on the outside in contact with the aqueous medium, as illustrated in Fig. 7.6. These aggregates are called micelles. They are usually of spherical shape. Micellisation is, therefore, an alternative mechanism by which the interfacial energy of a surfactant solution might decrease.

Osmotic pressure is a colligative property; therefore, the abrupt slowing down of the rate of increase of osmotic pressure with concentration reflects fewer units for a given amount of material, i.e. aggregation. The sharp increase in turbidity reflects the fact that the amount of light scattered is approximately proportional to nm^2, where n is the number of scattering units and m their mass. The surface tension ceases to drop and remains approximately constant because micellisation is a bulk phenomenon. The sharp drop in molar conductivity mainly reflects the fact that small counter-ions bind to the highly charged ionic micelle, and this reduces the number of counter-ions available for carrying the current as well as lowering the net charge on the micelle.

221

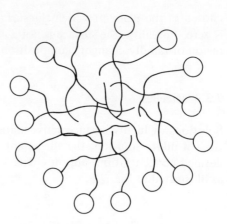

Figure 7.6   A spherical micelle.

The concentration at which these discontinuities in physical properties occur is called the critical micelle concentration (c.m.c.). Below the c.m.c. virtually all of the dissolved surfactant exists in monomer form. Above the c.m.c., the surfactant that is in excess of the c.m.c. exists in micellar form.

The abruptness with which micellisation takes place above the c.m.c. has been interpreted in terms of the law of mass action (the reaction, at its simplest, is $mX = X_m$, where m is large). An alternative approach is to treat micelles as an extra phase. Monomer surfactant has a certain saturation solubility (the c.m.c.); any surfactant in excess of this must, therefore, exist in another phase, but instead of existing as undissolved solid, which would be the alternative for most solutes, the micellar phase is available.

In general, micellisation is favoured by the following factors.
(a) Increasing the hydrophobic part of the surfactant. For ionic surfactants, the c.m.c. is approximately halved by each additional CH_2 group, but above the C_{18} homologue the c.m.c. changes little since the hydrocarbon chain can coil up on itself.
(b) Lowering the temperature. This reduces the thermal energy available for breaking up the micelle.
(c) Addition of electrolyte. This screens and reduces the repulsion between charged head groups at the micelle surface.

Surfactant solutions above the c.m.c. can solubilise otherwise insoluble organic material by incorporating it into the interior of the micelles.

The solubility of micelle-forming surfactants often shows a marked discontinuity at a particular temperature, known as the Krafft temperature. This is because the normal solubility is less than the c.m.c. one side of the Krafft temperature and so of limited magnitude; but it exceeds the c.m.c. on the other side of the Krafft temperature, thus allowing a large quantity of surfactant to be 'dissolved', either as monomer or as micelles.

7.4   The Solid–Liquid Interface

7.4.1 Contact Angles and Wetting

When a drop of liquid is placed on a flat solid surface it may spread completely over the surface, or it may remain as a drop having a definite angle of contact with the solid surface.

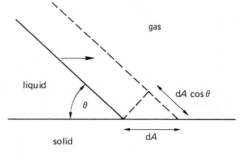

Figure 7.7

Consider a liquid making an equilibrium contact angle θ to spread an infinitesimal amount further so as to cover an extra area dA of the solid surface. The increase in liquid–gas interfacial area is $dA \cos \theta$ (Fig. 7.7) and the increase in the free energy of the system is given by

$$dG = \gamma_{SL}\ dA - \gamma_{SG}\ dA + \gamma_{LG}\ dA \cos \theta$$

At equilibrium, $dG = 0$. Therefore, dividing throughout by dA,

$$\gamma_{SL} + \gamma_{LG} \cos \theta - \gamma_{SG} = 0 \tag{7.11}$$

which is known as Young's equation.

Zero contact angle ($\cos \theta = 1$) will be obtained when $\gamma_{SL} + \gamma_{LG} - \gamma_{SG}$ is zero. The negative of this quantity is called the spreading coefficient, i.e.

$$S = \gamma_{SG} - \gamma_{SL} - \gamma_{LG} \tag{7.12}$$

Liquid spreads spontaneously when S is positive or zero and remains as a drop on the solid surface when S is negative.

The work of adhesion of a liquid to a solid is the work required to separate unit area of the liquid–solid interface and form unit area of liquid–gas and solid–gas interfaces (Fig. 7.8), i.e.

$$W_a = \gamma_{SG} + \gamma_{LG} - \gamma_{SL} \tag{7.13}$$

which is known as the Dupré equation.

Combining (7.11) and (7.13) gives the Young–Dupré equation

$$W_a = \gamma_{LG}\ (1 + \cos \theta) \tag{7.14}$$

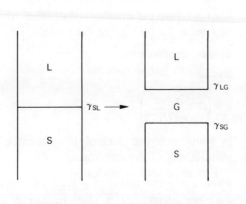

Figure 7.8   Work of adhesion.

Consider a drop of water on a waxy surface. Added surfactant adsorbs at the water–air interface and lowers γ_{LG}. It also adsorbs at the solid–water interface, thus making the solid surface more hydrophilic and so increasing W_a. The contact angle is, therefore, decreased on two counts.

On the other hand, the contact angle between water and glass is increased considerably by a fraction of a monolayer of greasy material, such as fatty acid. W_a is decreased, since some of the glass–water interface is replaced by hydrocarbon–water interface and θ, therefore, increases.

Manipulation and control of wetting characteristics is of central importance in processes such as ore flotation, detergency and the application of herbicides and insecticides. In detergency, the surfactant (in particular) plus other components in the formulation have three major roles: (a) the creation of good wetting characteristics, (b) reduction of the work of adhesion between dirt and substrate to facilitate dirt removal by mechanical action, and (c) stabilisation of removed dirt against redeposition.

7.5 Charged Interfaces

7.5.1 The Electric Double Layer

Most substances acquire a surface electric charge when brought into contact with a polar (e.g. aqueous) medium, possible charging mechanisms being ionisation, unequal ion adsorption and unequal ion dissolution. Ions of opposite charge (counter-ions) are attracted towards the surface and (less importantly) ions of like charge (co-ions) are repelled away from the surface. This, together with the mixing tendency of thermal motion, leads to the formation of an electric double layer made up of the charged surface and an excess of counter-ions over co-ions distributed in a diffuse manner in the polar medium, as illustrated in Fig. 7.9.

Quantitative treatment of the electric double layer is extremely complicated. A basic model is that considered by Gouy and Chapman. It is largely a one-dimensional version of the Debye–Hückel model of strong electrolytes mentioned in Chapter 5. The following simplifying assumptions are made:
(a) the surface is flat and uniformly charged,
(b) the ions in the diffuse part are point charges distributed according to the Boltzmann distribution,
(c) the liquid influences the double layer only through its permittivity (see Section 1.4),
(d) a symmetrical electrolyte is assumed.

The derived equation for even this model is very complicated; however, in the limit of low potentials it simplifies to an exponential decay of potential with increasing distance from the surface, i.e.

$$\psi = \psi_0 \exp(-\kappa x) \tag{7.15}$$

where

$$\kappa = \left(\frac{2e^2 N_A c z^2}{\epsilon k T} \right)^{1/2} \tag{7.16}$$

in which c is the electrolyte concentration, z the counter-ion valency and ϵ the permittivity of the solution.

For an aqueous solution at 25°C,

$$\kappa = 0.33 \times 10^{10} \left(\frac{c z^2}{\text{mol dm}^{-3}} \right)^{1/2} \text{m}^{-1} \tag{7.17}$$

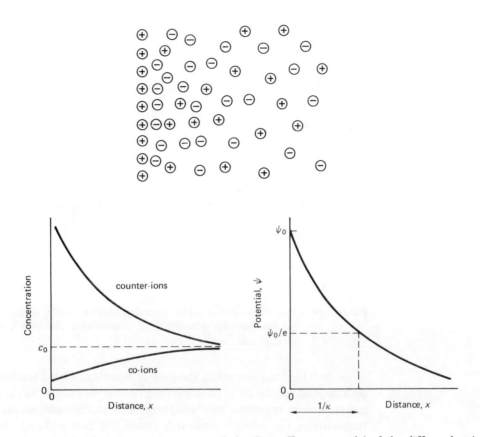

Figure 7.9 Schematic representation of the Gouy–Chapman model of the diffuse electric double layer.

$1/\kappa$ is the distance over which the potential decays by a factor of e, and is often referred to as the 'thickness' of the electric double layer. Thus, for a 1–1 electrolyte, the double-layer thickness is approximately 10^{-9} m for a 0.1 mol dm^{-3} solution and 10^{-8} m for a 0.001 mol dm^{-3} solution.

The Stern model of the electric double layer allows for the finite size of the ions in solution and for the possibility of specific adsorption of ions at the solid surface. The double layer is divided into an inner part and an outer part. Specifically, adsorbed ions have their centres in the inner part and free ions have their centres in the outer part. The potential decays from ψ_0 to ψ_d (the Stern potential) in the inner part and then exponentially to zero (as in the Gouy–Chapman model) in the outer part (Fig. 7.10a). Sometimes the specific adsorption of counter-ions (especially if polyvalent and/or surface-active) is so strong that reversal of charge takes place in the inner part of the double layer (Fig. 7.10b).

7.5.2 Electrokinetic Phenomena, Zeta Potential

If an electric field is applied tangentially along a charged solid surface, a force is exerted on both parts of the electric double layer. The charged solid plus attached material tends to move one way and the mobile part of the double layer tends to move in the opposite direction.

In electrophoresis, the experimental arrangement is such that the movement of charged particles due to an applied electric field relative to stationary liquid is

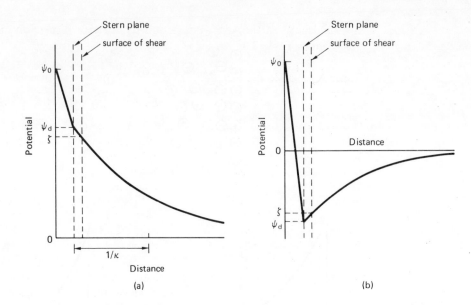

Figure 7.10 Potential–distance curves according to Stern model of the electric double layer; (a) low specific adsorption of counter-ions; (b) high specific adsorption of counter-ions causing charge reversal.

measured. In electro-osmosis, the flow of liquid through a (stationary) capillary or porous plug due to an applied electric field is measured. Streaming potential and sedimentation potential are the opposites of electro-osmosis and electrophoresis, respectively, i.e. relative motion between the two parts of the double layer is imposed mechanically and the resulting electric field is measured.

All of these so-called electrokinetic phenomena yield information concerning the surface of shear, i.e. the kinetic dividing 'plane'. The electric potential at the surface of shear is called the zeta potential (ζ).

Electrophoresis is, in principle, no different from ion migration, discussed in Chapter 5. The practical difference is one of scale. The motion of a charged colloidal particle can often be measured directly with the aid of a microscope. Both the electric driving force and the liquid viscous drag on a migrating charged colloidal particle will be greater than those on a small ion, but the ratio of these forces will be similar. Electrophoretic mobilities of colloidal particles and small-ion mobilities, therefore, tend to be of similar magnitude (of the order of 10^{-8} m^2 s^{-1} V^{-1}).

The conversion of an electrophoretic mobility into a zeta potential is complicated. However, a simple expression, the Smoluchowski equation, applies when the radius of curvature of the particle surface is large compared with the double-layer thickness (i.e. κa is large ($> c.$ 200)),

$$\zeta = u_E \eta / \epsilon \tag{7.18}$$

where u_E is the electrophoretic mobility and η the coefficient of viscosity of the dispersion medium. If the above condition is not met, ζ is likely to be underestimated when using the Smoluchowski equation.

7.6 Colloidal Dispersions

7.6.1 Classification

Simple colloidal dispersions are two-phase systems in which one of the phases has at least one dimension within the range of about 1 nm to 1 μm. The phases are

226

distinguished by the terms 'dispersed phase' and 'dispersion medium'. Examples are given in Table 7.1.

Table 7.1 Colloidal dispersions

Dispersed phase	Dispersion medium	Name	Examples
Liquid	Gas	Liquid aerosol	Fog, liquid sprays
Solid	Gas	Solid aerosol	Smoke, dust
Gas	Liquid	Foam	Foam from soap solution
Liquid	Liquid	Emulsion	Milk, crude oil
Solid	Liquid	Sol	AgI sol, pastes
Gas	Solid	Solid foam	Expanded polystyrene
Liquid	Solid	Solid emulsion	Opal, pearl
Solid	Solid	Solid suspension	Pigmented plastics

The physical nature of a dispersion depends on the respective roles of the constituent phases; for example, an oil-in-water (O/W) emulsion and a water-in-oil (W/O) emulsion could have similar overall composition, but their physical properties would be very different.

The physical properties of dispersions depend mostly on the nature of the interface between dispersed phase and dispersion medium. Despite the existence of a large area-to-volume ratio, the amount of material required to give significant molecular coverage and modification of the interface in a typical dispersion can be quite small. The addition of small quantities of suitable additives (particularly surfactants, polymers, polyvalent counter-ions) can, therefore, cause substantial modification of the bulk properties of a colloidal dispersion. For example, pronounced changes in the consistency of clay suspensions can be effected by the addition of small amounts of calcium ions (thickening) or phosphate ions (thinning). Surface science is, therefore, closely linked with colloid science.

The terms 'lyophilic' (liquid–loving) and 'lyophobic' (liquid-hating) are frequently used to describe the tendency of a surface or functional group to become wetted or solvated. If the liquid is aqueous, the terms 'hydrophilic' and 'hydrophobic' can be used. These terms, however, are used rather loosely in describing colloidal systems. Lyophobic dispersions are those produced by mechanical or chemical action (e.g. silver iodide, silica and polystyrene latex dispersions). There is, however, always some (often considerable) affinity between the particle surfaces and the dispersion medium (otherwise the surface would not be wetted and no dispersion could be formed); so, the particles of these 'lyophobic' dispersions have 'lyophilic' surfaces! 'Lyophilic' traditionally describes soluble macromolecular material (even though lyophobic regions may be present, e.g. in proteins). It is more satisfactory to classify colloidal systems thermodynamically as reversible or irreversible, according to whether or not they form spontaneously when their components are mixed.

7.6.2 Colloid Stability

Probably the most important physical property of a colloidal dispersion is the tendency of the particles to aggregate. **Coagulation** refers to strong aggregation, and **flocculation** refers to weak, easily reversed, aggregation. **Peptisation** is a process in which dispersion is achieved (with little or no agitation) by changing the composition of the dispersion medium.

Colloid stability is a complex subject. A universal cause of aggregation is the van der Waals' attractive forces between the particles, whereas stability against aggregation is given by the overlap of like-charged electric double layers and by particle solvation. The adsorption of polymer on to the particle surfaces may promote stability or may induce aggregation depending on a number of factors, including the enthalpy and entropy changes that take place when the polymer chains around different particles overlap.

The stability of lyophobic sols can be simplified to a consideration of van der Waals' attractive energy and electric double-layer repulsive energy. Derjaguin, Landau, Verwey and Overbeek (D.L.V.O.) developed a theory which involves estimates of these energies and their summation to give the total interaction energy in terms of interparticle distance. Stability is then interpreted in terms of the nature of this interaction energy–distance curve. The interaction between identical spherical colloidal particles is considered.

The repulsion energy V_R due to the overlapping of the diffuse parts of the electric double layers around the particles depends on several factors, the particle radius a, the nature of the electrolyte, κ and ϵ, and the Stern potential ψ_d. Since Stern and shear planes are likely to have similar locations, Stern and zeta potentials are taken as equal. The analysis of this situation is complex, a relatively simple and approximated expression for V_R being

$$V_R = 2\pi\epsilon a\zeta^2 \exp(-\kappa H) \tag{7.19}$$

where H is the distance of closest approach between the particles. The important features in this expression are the dependence of V_R on ζ, the exponential decay of V_R with increasing H and the dependence of the rate of this decay on κ.

The London–van der Waals' dispersion energy between two atoms is very short-range, varying inversely with the sixth power of the interatomic distance. For an assembly of atoms, dispersion forces are additive and the attraction energy V_A between two colloidal particles can be computed by summing the attractions between all interparticle atom pairs. The analysis of this situation is also complex, but a very simple approximated expression can be derived as

$$V_A = -aA/12H \tag{7.20}$$

where A is a constant, known as the Hamaker constant, which depends on the nature of the particles and of the dispersion medium. A is largest when particles and dispersion medium are chemically dissimilar. The important feature of this equation is that V_A varies approximately as $1/H$.

The total interaction energy is obtained as $V = V_R + V_A$. Figure 7.11 illustrates possible results of this summation. A single V_A curve is summed in turn with double-layer repulsion curves $V_R(1)$ (low κ) and $V_R(2)$ (high κ) to give total potential-energy curves $V(1)$ and $V(2)$, respectively. Curve $V(1)$ shows an energy barrier (rather like the activation-energy barrier to a chemical reaction) and the rate of coagulation will be correspondingly slow. If the height of the barrier is more than $\sim 20kT$, the rate of coagulation is so slow that the dispersion can be regarded as stable in the practical sense. Curve $V(2)$ shows no potential-energy barrier by virtue of the shorter range of the double-layer overlap.

Transition from curve $V(1)$ to curve $V(2)$ is effected by the addition of electrolyte. The extra electrolyte required to change the curve from one having a maximum of $\sim 20kT$ to one having no maximum is relatively small. A critical coagulation concentration can, therefore, be measured.

The critical coagulation concentration (c.c.c.) of an inert electrolyte (i.e. the concentration of the electrolyte which is just sufficient to coagulate a lyophobic sol to an arbitrarily defined extent in an arbitrarily chosen time) shows considerable dependence on counter-ion valency, moderate dependence on the nature of the sol and relatively little dependence on which counter-ion of a given valency is

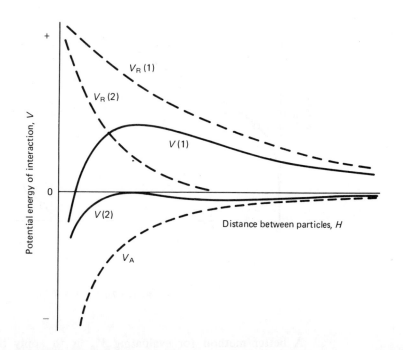

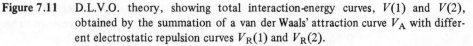

Figure 7.11   D.L.V.O. theory, showing total interaction-energy curves, $V(1)$ and $V(2)$, obtained by the summation of a van der Waals' attraction curve V_A with different electrostatic repulsion curves $V_R(1)$ and $V_R(2)$.

involved, the co-ion valency or the concentration of the sol. These generalisations are known as the Schulze–Hardy rule.

If counter-ions, or any other material, bring about aggregation by virtue of specific adsorption, then the amount of additive required will relate to the total surface area of the particles.

7.7   Worked Examples

7.7.1 B.E.T. Nitrogen Surface Area

The following data refer to the adsorption of nitrogen at 77 K on a 0.85 g sample of silica gel:

p/kPa	2.7	7.3	13.6	21.4	30.0	38.8	48.5
V/cm^3 (s.t.p.)*	71	88	104	119	134	152	173
$p_0 = 101.3$ kPa							

Calculate the monolayer capacity V_m by 'point B' and B.E.T. methods. Use the B.E.T. value to calculate a specific surface area for the silica gel sample, taking the molecular area of nitrogen as 16.2×10^{-20} m^2.

Answer

The adsorption isotherm (Fig. 7.12a) is a typical 'Type II' isotherm, reflecting multilayer adsorption. Point B on the isotherm corresponds to the monolayer capacity V_m, and its value is noted to be about 100 to 105 cm^3 (s.t.p.).

*s.t.p. indicates standard temperature and pressure (0°C and 1 atm) − 1 mole of gas occupies 22 400 cm^3 at s.t.p.

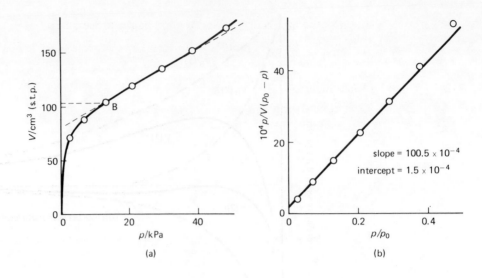

Figure 7.12 B.E.T. plots.

A better method for evaluating V_m is to apply the B.E.T. equation (7.5), which predicts a straight-line plot of $p/V(p_0 - p)$ versus p/p_0 (Fig. 7.12b). The straight line is drawn through the points in the pressure range of about $0.05p_0$ to $0.35p_0$, where the B.E.T. equation is most applicable.

Using equation (7.6),

$$V_m = \frac{1}{\text{slope} + \text{intercept}} = \frac{1}{(100.5 + 1.5) \times 10^{-4}} = 98.0 \text{ cm}^3 \text{ (s.t.p.)}$$

Assuming perfect-gas behaviour, one mole of nitrogen (i.e. 6.02×10^{23} molecules) occupies $22\,400 \text{ cm}^3$ at s.t.p. Therefore, 98.0 cm^3 of nitrogen at s.t.p. contains $6.02 \times 10^{23} \times 98.0/22\,400$ molecules. Since the effective area occupied by each adsorbed nitrogen molecule is $16.2 \times 10^{-20} \text{ m}^2$, the surface area of the silica gel sample is

$$\frac{6.02 \times 10^{23} \times 98.0 \times 16.2 \times 10^{-20}}{22\,400} = 427 \text{ m}^2$$

and the specific surface area is

$$427 \text{ m}^2 /0.85 \text{ g} = 502 \text{ m}^2 \text{ g}^{-1}$$

7.7.2 Enthalpy of Adsorption

The pressures of nitrogen required to cause the adsorption of 1 mg of gas on a 1 g sample of graphitised carbon black are 50 Pa at 77 K and 500 Pa at 90 K. Calculate an isosteric enthalpy of adsorption for this surface coverage.

Answer

Isosteric (constant adsorption) enthalpies of adsorption can be measured directly by accurate calorimetry, or calculated from adsorption isotherms using the Clausius–Clapeyron equation

$$\left(\frac{\partial \ln p}{\partial T} \right)_V = - \frac{\Delta H_{ads}}{RT^2}$$

(the negative sign reflects the direction of the process). So

$$\ln\left(\frac{500}{50}\right) = \frac{\Delta H_{ads}/\text{J mol}^{-1}}{R}\left(\frac{1}{90} - \frac{1}{77}\right)$$

from which

$$\Delta H_{ads} = -\,10\,200\ \text{J mol}^{-1} = -\,10.2\ \text{kJ mol}^{-1}$$

7.7.3 Particle Electrophoresis

Spherical particles of diameter 1.0 μm suspended in KCl (aq, 0.01 mol dm^{-3}) have an average electrophoretic mobility of 2.5×10^{-8} m^2 s^{-1} V^{-1} at 25°C. Calculate an approximate value for the zeta potential. Briefly mention any systematic error involved in this calculation. ($\eta = 8.9 \times 10^{-4}$ kg m^{-1} s^{-1}, $\epsilon/\epsilon_0 = 78.5$).

Answer

To estimate the zeta potential, it is first necessary to calculate κa (the ratio of particle radius to double-layer thickness). Using equation (7.17),

$$\kappa a = 0.33 \times 10^{10} \times (0.01)^{1/2}\ \text{m}^{-1} \times 0.5 \times 10^{-6}\ \text{m}$$

$$= 165$$

This value of κa is sufficiently large to justify using the Smoluchowski equation, but it is not large enough to avoid a small underestimate of ζ on this account. Surface conductance and relaxation will also cause a small, but significant, underestimation of ζ.

$$\zeta = \eta u_E/\epsilon$$

$$= \frac{8.9 \times 10^{-4}\ \text{kg m}^{-1}\ \text{s}^{-1} \times 2.5 \times 10^{-8}\ \text{m}^2\ \text{s}^{-1}\ \text{V}^{-1}}{78.5 \times 8.85 \times 10^{-12}\ \text{kg}^{-1}\ \text{m}^{-3}\ \text{s}^4\ \text{A}^2}$$

$$= 0.032\ \text{V} = 32\ \text{mV}$$

7.8 Unworked Examples

7.8.1

The volume of butane adsorbed on a one gram sample of activated carbon at 0°C varies with pressure, as follows:

p/kPa	14.0	28.6	42.6	57.2	73.1	94.4
V/cm^3 (s.t.p.)	15.4	19.6	21.0	21.9	22.7	23.2

Show that the data fit the Langmuir equation and evaluate the constants.

7.8.2

The following data refer to the adsorption of hexadecanol from methylbenzene solutions at 25°C by a sample of carbon black, the B.E.T. nitrogen adsorption area of which is 145 m^2 g^{-1}:

Equilibrium concentration/ mol dm^{-3}	0.012	0.026	0.047	0.070	0.101	0.126
Amount adsorbed/μmol g^{-1}	29.4	49.8	67.1	79.4	90.0	95.9

Show that the data fit a Langmuir adsorption isotherm and calculate the area occupied by each adsorbed hexadecanol molecule at limiting adsorption.

7.8.3

At a relative pressure (p/p_0) of 0.20 a 1.25 g sample of alumina adsorbs 52.5 cm^3 (corrected to s.t.p.) of nitrogen at 77 K. Assuming the B.E.T. equation to be valid and taking the molecular area of nitrogen to be 16.2×10^{-20} m^2, calculate the specific surface area of the alumina.

7.8.4

The following data refer to the adsorption of butane at 0°C by a sample of tungsten powder which has a specific surface area (as determined from nitrogen adsorption measurements at 77 K) of 16.7 m^2 g^{-1}.

Relative pressure, p/p_0	0.06	0.12	0.17	0.23	0.30	0.37
Volume adsorbed/cm^3 (s.t.p.) g^{-1}	1.10	1.34	1.48	1.66	1.85	2.05

Calculate a molecular area for the adsorbed butane at monolayer coverage and compare it with the value of 32×10^{-20} m^2 estimated from the density of liquid butane.

7.8.5

The following results refer to the adsorption of nitrogen on a graphitised sample of carbon black, and give the ratio of the nitrogen pressures for temperatures of 90 K and 77 K which are required to achieve a given amount of adsorption:

V/V_m	0.25	0.75	1.25
p (90 K)/p (77 K)	11.5	14.3	5.3

Calculate the isosteric enthalpy of adsorption for each value of V/V_m.

7.8.6

Use the Kelvin equation to calculate the pore radius corresponding to capillary condensation of nitrogen at 77 K and a relative pressure of 0.5. Make a correction for the multilayer adsorption on the pore wall by taking the thickness of the adsorbed layer on a non-porous solid as 0.65 nm at this relative pressure. State any assumptions that are made in the calculation. The surface tension and molar volume of nitrogen at 77 K are 8.85 mN m^{-1} and 34.7 cm^3 mol^{-1}, respectively.

(Liverpool Polytechnic, BSc, Hons)

7.8.7

The following surface tensions were measured for aqueous solutions of the non-ionic surfactant, $C_{10}E_5$, at 25°C:

$c/10^{-4}$ mol dm^{-3}	0.1	0.3	1.0	2.0	5.0	8.0	10.0	20.0	30.0
γ/mN m^{-1}	63.9	56.2	47.2	41.6	34.0	30.3	29.8	29.6	29.5

Determine the critical micelle concentration and calculate the area occupied by each adsorbed surfactant molecule at the critical micelle concentration.

7.8.8

The surface tension of water at 25°C is 72 mN m^{-1} and the contact angle of a drop of water on a paraffin wax surface is 105°. Calculate the work of adhesion of water to paraffin wax and compare it with the work of cohesion of water (i.e. the work of adhesion of water to itself).

7.8.9

Spherical particles of radius 0.2 μm suspended in NaCl (aq, 0.1 mol dm^{-3}) are observed to have an average electrophoretic velocity of 1.0×10^{-3} cm s^{-1} in an electric field of 5.0 V cm^{-1} at 25°C. Calculate an approximate value for the zeta potential. ($\eta = 8.9 \times 10^{-4}$ kg m^{-1} s^{-1}, $\epsilon/\epsilon_0 = 78.5$).

8 Molecular Structure and Spectroscopy

8.1 Introduction

This chapter introduces the topic of molecular spectroscopy by considering the nature of electromagnetic radiation and its interaction with molecules. The basic principles of quantum chemistry are introduced to assist in the understanding of electronic, vibrational and rotational transitions of energy within molecules. The application of molecular spectroscopy in the study of the structure of simple molecules is illustrated with a number of worked examples and questions.

The topic of molecular spectroscopy constitutes an important part of the physical chemistry syllabus in all degree courses, though the timetabling of the topic varies from course to course. Sometimes it is given a single in-depth treatment in the final year, but more often the subject is introduced in the first or second year of the course. Some students may, therefore, find certain topics in this chapter are not covered in the early stages of their particular course. Nevertheless, it is essential that the basic principles outlined in this chapter be grasped from the outset.

8.2 Spectroscopic Techniques

When a beam of electromagnetic radiation is passed through a chemical substance, it is found that some of the radiation can be absorbed while the balance is either scattered or transmitted. Spectrophotometric techniques rely on measuring the fraction of the radiation transmitted as a function of its wavelength. A typical spectrophotometer consists of a source of radiation which illuminates the sample. The transmitted beam passes through a dispersion prism or grating and a photoelectric detector connected to a recorder measures the intensity of transmitted light over a range of frequencies at which absorption occurs. This is illustrated in block diagram form in Fig. 8.1.

mbert–Beer Law

This law states that when monochromatic radiation passes through a medium of thickness l, the intensity of the transmitted light I_t is related to the intensity of the incident light I_0 by

$$I_t = I_0 \exp(-\kappa c l) \tag{8.1}$$

where κ is the molar Napierian absorption coefficient and c is the concentration of the absorbing medium. The transmittance T is defined as the fraction of the light transmitted. Therefore,

Figure 8.1 Block diagram for a typical experimental measurement of adsorption of radiation.

$$T = I_t/I_0 = \exp(-\kappa cl) \tag{8.2}$$

In practice, it is more usual to consider absorbance in decadic terms. The decadic absorbance A is given by

$$A = \log_{10}\left(\frac{1}{T}\right) = \log_{10}\left(\frac{I_0}{I_t}\right) = \frac{\kappa cl}{2.303} = \epsilon cl \tag{8.3}$$

where ϵ is the molar decadic absorption coefficient (sometimes called the extinction coefficient).

Therefore, if the Lambert–Beer law is obeyed, a plot of A versus c will be linear with slope equal to ϵl (see Unworked Example 8.14.2).

Example 8.1

A 0.02 mol dm^{-3} solution absorbs 25% of the incident light of a certain wavelength in a cell of 1 cm path-length. What concentration of the same solution would be required to absorb 50% of the light in a cell of 5 cm path-length?

The absorbance A is given by

$$A = \log_{10}\left(\frac{I_0}{I_t}\right) = \epsilon cl$$

Therefore, for 25% absorbance in the cell

$$A = \log_{10}\left(\frac{100}{75}\right) = \epsilon cl = \epsilon \times 0.02 \text{ mol dm}^{-3} \times 0.1 \text{ dm}$$

giving

$$\epsilon = 62.47 \text{ dm}^2 \text{ mol}^{-1}$$

Therefore for 50% absorbance in the 5 cm cell,

$$\log_{10}\left(\frac{100}{50}\right) = 62.47 \text{ dm}^2 \text{ mol}^{-1} \times c \times 0.5 \text{ dm}$$

giving

$$c = 9.64 \times 10^{-3} \text{ mol dm}^{-3} \qquad \blacksquare$$

8.4 Electromagnetic Radiation

8.4.1 Wavelength, Frequency, Wavenumber

An electromagnetic wave consists of oscillating electric and magnetic fields perpendicular to each other and to the direction of propagation. It is characterised by its wavelength, frequency or wavenumber:

- **Wavelength** (λ) is the distance between each complete oscillation.
- **Frequency** (ν) is the number of cycles of radiation per unit time. If the speed of propagation in a vacuum is c, the frequency ν is given by

$$\nu = c/\lambda \qquad (8.4)$$

The speed of light in a vacuum is equal to 2.998×10^8 m s^{-1}.

● **Wavenumber** ($\overline{\nu}$) is the number of cycles per unit distance, and is given by

$$\overline{\nu} = 1/\lambda = \nu/c \qquad (8.5)$$

Both frequency and wavenumber are proportional to energy and are therefore more widely used than wavelength.

Example 8.2

What is the frequency and wavenumber of light of wavelength 400 nm?

The speed of light in a vacuum is 2.998×10^8 m s^{-1} so the frequency and wavenumber are given by

$$\nu = \frac{2.998 \times 10^8 \text{ m s}^{-1}}{400 \times 10^{-9} \text{ m}} = 7.5 \times 10^{14} \text{ s}^{-1} = 7.5 \times 10^{14} \text{ Hz}$$

$$\overline{\nu} = \frac{1}{\lambda} = \frac{1}{400 \times 10^{-9}} \text{ m}^{-1} = 2.5 \times 10^6 \text{ m}^{-1}$$

Note that the unit of frequency is the hertz (Hz), i.e. 1 cycle per second.　■

8.4.2 Electromagnetic Spectrum

Visible light is only one possible form of electromagnetic radiation. Other forms include x-rays, ultraviolet, infrared, microwave and radiowave radiation. Each type is associated with a range of frequency, wavelength and wavenumber, as illustrated in Fig. 8.2.

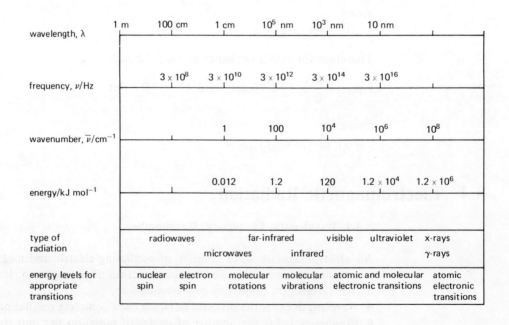

Figure 8.2　Electromagnetic spectrum.

8.5 Energy Within Molecules

8.5.1 Quantised Energy Levels

In investigating the intensity I of radiation from a black-body or a cavity, Planck found that I was proportional to T^4 and was able to show that the solids could neither emit nor absorb radiation continuously, but could only do so in multiples of $h\nu$, where h is a constant later termed Planck's constant and ν is the frequency. This observation provided the basis for quantum theory. The energy of a microscopic system such as an atom or molecule is quantised, that is only certain definite energies are allowed. These systems can only radiate or absorb energy in quanta of size $h\nu$ where h is 6.626×10^{-34} J s. However, since h is so small, it is only at high frequencies that the differences between the energies of $1h\nu$, $2h\nu$, $3h\nu$, etc., become significant.

8.5.2 Types of Energy Within Molecules

The four main types of energy within a molecule are summarised in Table 8.1. The electronic energy levels (arising from the orbitals that are occupied by electrons), although quantised, are widely separated in terms of difference in energy. The vibrational energy levels (arising from the vibration of the atoms relative to one another) are also quantised and therefore only discrete frequencies of vibration are allowed. Rotational energy levels (arising from the rotation of the molecules about different axes) are quantised, but the energy levels are fairly close together. Translational energy levels are, in theory, quantised, but the energy separation between levels is so small that in spectroscopic terms they can be considered continuous.

Table 8.1

Type of energy	Typical energy separation	
	per molecule	per mole
Electronic	10^{-18} J	600 kJ mol^{-1}
Vibrational	10^{-19} J	60 kJ mol^{-1}
Rotational	10^{-22} J	60 J mol^{-1}
Translational[a]	10^{-39} J	6×10^{-16} J mol^{-1}

[a] $h\nu$ is so small as to be considered continuous.

A further type of energy change can occur when there is interaction with an applied magnetic field. Transitions between energy levels due to the orientation of the spinning atomic nuclei give rise to nuclear magnetic resonance (n.m.r.); transitions due to the electron orientation in substances with unpaired electrons give rise to electron spin resonance (e.s.r.). In both cases, the differences in energy are smaller than those for rotational energy changes (see Fig. 8.2). However, a detailed consideration of magnetic resonance spectroscopy is beyond the scope of this chapter.

A typical energy-level diagram for a molecule with two electronic energy states is illustrated in Fig. 8.3. Each electronic energy level has a number of vibrational levels (distinguished by their vibrational quantum number, v). Each vibrational level has a number of rotational levels associated with it.

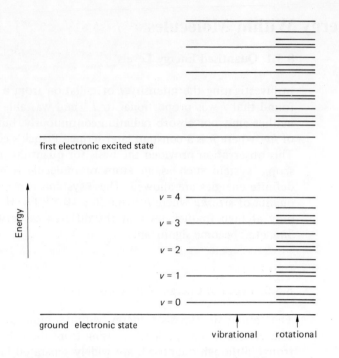

first electronic excited state

Energy

$v = 4$

$v = 3$

$v = 2$

$v = 1$

$v = 0$

ground electronic state

vibrational   rotational

Figure 8.3   A schematic energy-level diagram for a molecule with spacing between levels of the order given in Table 8.1.

8.5.3 Transitions Between Energy Levels

When an atom or molecule emits radiation, the system drops from one discrete energy level E_2 to a lower energy E_1. The frequency or wavenumber of the emitted light associated with this energy transition is given by

$$\Delta E = E_2 - E_1 = h\nu = hc\bar{\nu} = hc/\lambda \qquad (8.6)$$

This basic equation is fundamental to our understanding of spectroscopy. It applies equally if radiation is absorbed and the system rises to a higher energy level.

For example, if a molecule drops from one rotational state to a lower one (i.e. it rotates more slowly) and the separation between the energy levels is 0.01 kJ mol^{-1}, then the frequency of the emitted radiation is 15×10^{10} Hz or has a wavenumber of 5 cm^{-1}. From Fig. 8.2, it can be seen that this will occur in the microwave region of the spectrum. Vibrational transitions are observed in the infrared region, while electronic transitions occur in the visible and ultraviolet regions.

Example 8.3

What is the energy of a single quantum of radiation per mole in the following cases?
(a) ultraviolet radiation at a wavelength of 254 nm,
(b) infrared radiation at a frequency of 4.3×10^{13} Hz,
(c) microwave radiation at a wavenumber of 5 cm^{-1}.

(a) $E = \dfrac{N_A hc}{\lambda} = \dfrac{(6.023 \times 10^{23}) \times (6.626 \times 10^{-34}) \times (2.998 \times 10^8)}{254 \times 10^{-9}}$ J mol^{-1}

$= 4.71 \times 10^5$ J mol^{-1} = 471 kJ mol^{-1}

(b) $E = N_A h\nu = (6.023 \times 10^{23}) \times (6.626 \times 10^{-34}) \times (4.3 \times 10^{13})$ J mol^{-1}

$= 1.716 \times 10^4$ J mol^{-1} = 17.2 kJ mol^{-1}

(c) $E = N_A hc\bar{\nu}$

$= (6.023 \times 10^{23}) \times (6.626 \times 10^{-34}) \times (2.998 \times 10^8) \times (5 \times 10^2)$ J mol^{-1}

$= 59.8$ J mol^{-1} ∎

8.5.4 Population of Energy Levels

As illustrated in Fig. 8.3, a molecule usually has a large number of energy levels associated with it. The distribution of the molecules among the various energy levels is temperature-dependent. The Boltzmann distribution (see Section 4.7.1) applies, so the population of energy level E is proportional to $\exp(-E/kT)$. This aspect is described and illustrated later in the chapter.

8.5.5 De Broglie Relationships

De Broglie showed that the dual nature of light (e.g. diffraction can be explained by waves, and photoelectric emission explained by particles) could be reconciled by the approach that **the energy in a radiation field occurs only in multiples of $h\nu$ or photons** related by equation (8.6), i.e.

$E = h\nu = hc/\lambda$

Also a photon's momentum p can be calculated from Einstein's equation $E = mc^2$ as follows (although a photon has no mass)

$p = mc = E/c$

From the combination of these expressions, de Broglie was able to postulate that a particle with momentum p has wave properties, i.e.

$p = mu = h/\lambda$

where u is the velocity of the particle.

8.6   Heisenberg Uncertainty Principle

This basic principle highlights another distinctive feature of quantum theory. It states that the energy of a state is only precisely defined if the lifetime is infinite. If the lifetime of the state is finite, there is a corresponding uncertainty about its energy. It is, therefore, meaningless to ask about the exact position and velocity of an electron in an atom. It is not a question of 'experimental error' (as one experiences with macroscopic measurements in a laboratory) but a basic law that applies when dealing with electrons, atoms and molecules. Heisenberg expressed it by the following relations:

$\Delta q\, \Delta p \geqslant h/4\pi$

$\Delta E\, \Delta t \geqslant h/4\pi$

The above states that Δq, the root-mean-square uncertainty in position, and Δp, the root-mean-square uncertainty in momentum, are related, i.e. the more you seek to define the position of an electron, the greater will be the uncertainty about its momentum. Similarly, the more closely you define ΔE, the root-mean-square uncertainty in energy, the greater the difficulty you will have in determining the root-mean-square uncertainty in time. The small value of h explains why this uncertainty is not observed at the macroscopic level.

For example, in the simple harmonic oscillator model of a vibrating molecule (see Section 8.11), the molecule never has zero energy. If it did, both its momentum p and its position (the symbol q above) would each be zero and this would be in violation of the uncertainty principle.

8.7 Schrödinger Equation

This is the basic equation of quantum mechanics, and such is the mathematical complexity of the various forms of this equation that most introductory courses in physical chemistry confine detailed consideration of the Schrödinger equation to the simplest possible model, namely that of the one-dimensional motion of a particle of mass m in a potential V, which as a function of x is expressed as

$$\frac{d^2 \psi}{dx^2} + \frac{2m}{\hbar^2} (E - V) \psi = 0 \tag{8.7}$$

where $\hbar = h/2\pi$. The solution ψ of this equation is called the **wavefunction** and expresses all that can be known about the properties of the system when it is in a steady state that is not changing with time.

The above is a simple example, but quantum theory enables every atom or molecule to have a quantum-mechanical wavefunction which describes its state. Although the wavefunction itself does not have any physical meaning, it is mathematically connected to the **probability density** ρ associated with the particle or particles. This is defined as the probability that a particle is located in a particular small volume.

8.7.1 Energy of a System

The classical mechanical definition of the energy of a system in terms of momenta and positions is given by the 'Hamiltonian' function H, where

$H = T + V$

with V being the potential energy (dependent on position) and T the kinetic energy. In classical mechanics

$$H = \frac{p_x^2}{2m} + V$$

while in quantum theory the Hamiltonian operator* $\mathcal{H}$ is given by

$$\mathcal{H} = -\frac{\hbar^2}{2m} \frac{\partial^2}{\partial x^2} + V$$

It is postulated that

$\mathcal{H}\psi = E\psi$

---

*An **operator** is a description of a mathematical operation to be applied to a function to obtain a new function, e.g. $\times$ (multiplication), d/dx (differentiation with respect to x). In quantum mechanics, each observable quantity (e.g. energy, momentum, x direction) has a corresponding operator.

giving the Schrödinger equation for this simple system as

$$-\frac{\hbar^2}{2m}\frac{\partial^2\psi}{\partial x^2} + V\psi = E\psi$$

Extending this to a particle moving in three dimensions gives

$$\nabla^2\psi + \frac{2m}{\hbar^2}(E-V)\psi = 0 \tag{8.8}$$

where

$$\nabla^2 = \frac{\partial^2}{\partial x^2} + \frac{\partial^2}{\partial y^2} + \frac{\partial^2}{\partial z^2}$$

These values of E are called **eigenvalues** and the corresponding wavefunctions are called **eigenfunctions**. The eigenvalues can be thought of as those certain values of E that exist for this system. Therefore reference to eigenvalues of energy will merely mean the discrete values of energy that the system can have.

8.7.2 Applications of the Schrödinger Equation

The following sections consider some simple systems for which the solution of the Schrödinger equation proves useful. However, for details of these solutions, the reader will need to refer to an appropriate textbook. Most of these texts illustrate the approach by first considering a simple but artificial system, that of a particle confined to a one-dimensional box. Next, application of the Schrödinger equation to the simplest real atomic system, the hydrogen atom, shows that its predictions can be tested from a study of the atomic spectrum of hydrogen. However, two further models, namely that of the **rigid rotor** and that of the **simple harmonic oscillator** provide a basis for the study of molecular structure by spectroscopic methods. Solutions of the Schrödinger equation for these models enable the discrete values of the rotational energy and vibrational energy, respectively, of the molecule to be derived and provide the link between quantum theory and molecular spectroscopy. In all cases the models illustrate how quantum-theoretical predictions differ from those of classical mechanics.

8.8 Particle in a One-Dimensional Box and Zero-Point Energy

One of the simplest systems to which the Schrödinger equation can be applied is a particle in a one-dimensional box. Applying the Schrödinger equation to the above and defining $V = 0$ within a length a in the direction x, it can be shown that the energy of a particle in the box is given by

$$E = \frac{h^2 n^2}{8ma^2} \qquad n = 1, 2, 3, \text{ etc.} \tag{8.9}$$

where n is a non-zero, positive integer. This solution enables the lowest-energy state of a system to be defined. Whereas a free particle can have any energy, quantum theory predicts that a particle moving between two points on a line can only have energies given by the above equation, for which n must be a non-zero integer. The consequences are as follows:

(a) The particle can only have discrete values of energy given by the above.

(b) The lowest energy level must be given by the value when $n = 1$, i.e. the particle has a **zero-point energy** given by

$$E = \frac{h^2}{8ma^2} \qquad\qquad (8.10)$$

Note that, in contrast to classical mechanics, the above predicts that the lowest energy is *not* zero.

Example 8.4

Using the 'particle in a box' approach, calculate the order of magnitude of the energy differences for the first two levels ($n = 1$ and 2), when

(a) the particle is a molecule of mass 10^{-26} kg and the box is an experimental container of 0.1 m length;

(b) the particle is an electron of mass 10^{-30} kg and the box is an orbital of length 4×10^{-10} m (the typical order of magnitude of an atomic diameter).

What conclusions can be drawn from the answers?

(a) The energy difference is obtained by putting values of $n = 2$ and $n = 1$ into equation (8.9), giving

$$\Delta E = E_2 - E_1 = \frac{h^2}{8ma^2}(n_2^2 - n_1^2)$$

$$= \frac{(6.6 \times 10^{-34})^2 \times 3}{8 \times 10^{-26} \times (0.1)^2} \text{ J}$$

$$= 1.6 \times 10^{-39} \text{ J}$$

Therefore the spacing between energy levels is very small and corresponds to that for translational energy levels.

(b) Substitution of the data in equation (8.9) gives, for an electron,

$$\Delta E = \frac{(6.6 \times 10^{-34})^2 \times 3}{8 \times 10^{-30} \times (4 \times 10^{-10})^2} \text{ J}$$

$$= 1 \times 10^{-18} \text{ J}$$

The wavelength of the radiation associated with this energy change is given by equation (8.6), from which

$$\lambda = \frac{hc}{\Delta E} = \frac{6.6 \times 10^{-34} \times 3 \times 10^{-8}}{1 \times 10^{-18}} \text{ m}$$

$$= 2 \times 10^{-7} \text{ m} = 200 \text{ nm}$$

This indicates that electronic transitions will give rise to a spectrum in the visible/ultraviolet region. Both these results show the theory is consistent with the figures set out in Table 8.1. ∎

8.9 Atomic Spectrum of Hydrogen

Atomic spectra appear as a series of lines over a wide range from the infrared to the ultraviolet region. Balmer postulated that, in the case of the hydrogen atom, all the lines could be expressed by a formula of the form

$$\frac{1}{\lambda} = \bar{\nu} = R_{\text{H}} \left(\frac{1}{2^2} - \frac{1}{n_2^2} \right)$$

where n_2 is an integer greater than 2 and R_{H} is the Rydberg constant, which he found experimentally to be equal to 109 677.58 cm^{-1}. Subsequently other series were observed, all conforming to the general relationship

$$\bar{\nu} = R_H \left(\frac{1}{n_1^2} - \frac{1}{n_2^2} \right) \tag{8.11}$$

where $n_1 = 1$ is the Lyman series, $n_1 = 2$ is the Balmer series, $n_1 = 3$ is the Paschen series, and so on.

The Schrödinger equation can give an exact solution for a simple system like a hydrogen atom and predicts that the eigenvalues for the energy are given by

$$E_n = - \frac{m_e \, e^4 Z^2}{2(4\pi\epsilon_0)^2 \hbar^2 n^2} = - \frac{m_e \, e^4}{8\epsilon_0^2 \, h^2} \left(\frac{1}{n^2} \right) \tag{8.12}$$

where $\hbar = h/2\pi$. This is consistent with experiment in that the energy is inversely proportional to the square of the principal quantum number.

Example 8.5

Use the above expression to derive a value for the Rydberg constant, given that the reduced mass of an electron is 9.105×10^{-3} kg.

Using values for e, ϵ_0 and h given at the end of the book, we obtain

$$R_H = \frac{(9.105 \times 10^{-31}) \times (1.602 \times 10^{-19})^4}{8 \times (8.85 \times 10^{-12})^2 \times (6.626 \times 10^{-34})^2} \; \text{J}$$

$$= 2.180 \times 10^{-18} \; \text{J}$$

Normally, however, the Rydberg constant is expressed in terms of the corresponding wavenumber and this is calculated by dividing by hc; thus

$$R_H = \frac{2.180 \times 10^{-18}}{(6.626 \times 10^{-34}) \times (2.998 \times 10^8)} \; \text{m}^{-1}$$

$$= 1.097 \times 10^7 \; \text{m}^{-1} \qquad \blacksquare$$

8.10 Microwave (Rotational) Spectroscopy

8.10.1 Microwave Activity

Spectra in the microwave region arise from rotational energy changes within the molecule. For a molecule to be 'microwave-active', it must have a permanent dipole moment. As it rotates, the changing dipole moment interacts with the oscillating electric field of the electromagnetic radiation, resulting in absorption or emission of energy. This requirement means that homonuclear diatomic molecules are inactive, but heteronuclear diatomic molecules and polyatomic molecules can all be microwave-active.

8.10.2 The Rigid-Rotor Model of a Diatomic Molecule

The classical picture of a diatomic molecule is of two masses, m_1 and m_2, held a fixed distance r apart as illustrated in Fig. 8.4. The moment of inertia about the bond (x) axis is zero but the moment of inertia I about the other two axes is given by

$$I = m_1 r_1^2 + m_2 r_2^2 \tag{8.13}$$

where r_1 and r_2 represent the distance of the two masses, m_1 and m_2 respectively,

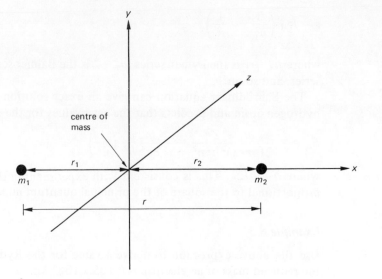

Figure 8.4 Centre of mass of a diatomic molecule.

from the centre of gravity of the molecule. If r is internuclear distance and equal to $r_1 + r_2$, the values of r_1 and r_2 are related by $r_1 m_1 = r_2 m_2$, giving

$$r_1 = \frac{m_2}{m_1 + m_2} r \quad \text{and} \quad r_2 = \frac{m_1}{m_1 + m_2} r$$

Substitution into equation (8.13) can be shown to give

$$I = \frac{m_1 m_2}{m_1 + m_2} r^2 = \mu r^2 \tag{8.14}$$

where μ is known as the **reduced mass** and for a diatomic molecule is given by

$$\mu = \frac{m_1 m_2}{m_1 + m_2} \tag{8.15}$$

Since the molecule is simultaneously vibrating, r is taken to be the equilibrium internuclear distance.

8.10.3 Rotational Energy

For the above rigid-rotor model of a diatomic molecule, the Schrödinger equation gives the eigenvalues for the energy of rotation E_J as

$$E_J = \frac{h^2}{8\pi^2 I} J(J + 1) \qquad J = 0, 1, 2, \text{etc.} \tag{8.16}$$

Since $\bar{\nu} = E_J/hc$, the above is usually written in the form

$$\bar{\nu} = \frac{E_J}{hc} = \frac{h}{8\pi^2 Ic} J(J + 1) \tag{8.17}$$

i.e.

$$\bar{\nu} = BJ(J + 1) \tag{8.18}$$

where $B = h/8\pi^2 Ic$ is called the rotational constant and has in equation (8.18) the same dimensions as $\bar{\nu}$ (e.g. units of cm^{-1} or m^{-1}).

However, equation (8.16) could equally be written as

$$E_J = BJ(J + 1) \tag{8.19}$$

in which case, B has dimensions of energy.

8.10.4 Rotational Energy Features

Some basic features of spectra arising from rotational energy changes are as follows:

(a) *Selection Rule*

The following relationship holds:

$$\Delta J = \pm 1$$

i.e. J values can only change by 1.

(b) *Degeneracy*

This term means the existence of two or more states with the same energy. Rotational states have a degeneracy of $2J + 1$. For example, in the second excited state ($J = 2$), there are five states of equal energy.

(c) *Population*

The number of molecules populating each rotational level shows a Boltzmann distribution (see Section 8.5.4), with the number of molecules N_J in any level being related to temperature by

$$N_J \propto \exp(-E_J/kT)$$

Taking degeneracy into account, the population of any individual J level is given by

$$N_J = K(2J + 1) \exp(-E_J/kT)$$

where K is a constant and E_J is given by equation (8.16). This is illustrated in Worked Example 8.13.5.

8.10.5 Rotational Energy Transitions

For successive transitions in absorption, substitution in equation (8.18) of the appropriate J values gives

for $J = 0 \rightarrow 1$	$\bar{\nu} = 2B$
for $J = 1 \rightarrow 2$	$\bar{\nu} = 4B$
for $J = 2 \rightarrow 3$	$\bar{\nu} = 6B$

i.e. the wavenumber of the absorbed radiation is directly proportional to the rotational quantum number of the final state. This produces very simple rotational spectra in which the **separation between successive rotational lines is always 2B**, i.e.

Separation $= \Delta \bar{\nu} = 2B$

This is illustrated in Fig. 8.5, which shows the energy levels and the spectrum produced. (The intensity peaking at about the $J = 3$ state is fairly typical and is a consequence of the Boltzmann distribution of energies at normal temperatures.)

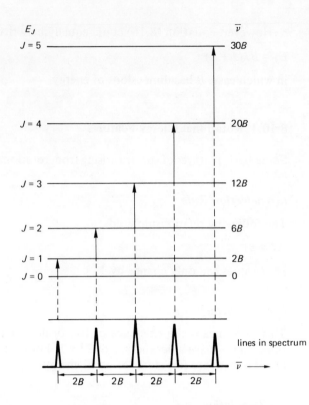

Figure 8.5 Rotational energy-level diagram leading to a rotational spectrum with equally spaced lines. (Intensity of spectral lines peaking at $J = 2 \rightarrow 3$ transition indicates these levels are the most populated.)

Example 8.6

Calculate the separation between the rotational lines of the spectrum of gaseous $^1H^{35}Cl$, given that its moment of inertia is 2.8×10^{-47} kg m^2.

The separation $\Delta\bar{\nu}$ between the rotational lines is $2B$, where $B = h/8\pi^2 Ic$. Therefore

$$\Delta\bar{\nu} = 2B = \frac{2 \times 6.626 \times 10^{-34}}{8\pi^2 \times (2.8 \times 10^{-47}) \times (2.998 \times 10^8)} \text{ m}^{-1}$$

$$= 2000 \text{ m}^{-1} = 20 \text{ cm}^{-1} \qquad \blacksquare$$

8.10.6 Applications of Microwave Spectroscopy

(a) Measurement of the separation between rotational lines (Worked Example 8.13.4) permits the determination of
   (i) moment of inertia,
   (ii) internuclear distance.
(b) Substitution of an isotope produces a different separation between rotational lines. This can be used to analyse mixtures of isotopes.
(c) Since in real molecules the rigid-rotor model breaks down, measurements can be used to determine distortion and anharmonicity effects.
(d) Polyatomic molecules can also be studied to give values of the three principal moments of inertia corresponding to the three planes of rotation and information about bond lengths.

8.11 Infrared (Vibrational–Rotational) Spectroscopy

8.11.1 The Simple Harmonic Oscillator Model for a Vibrating Molecule

The simplest model for the vibration of a molecule is the simple harmonic oscillator. In classical terms, the restoring force is directly proportional to the displacement x from the equilibrium position, i.e.

Force = $-kx$

where k is the force constant. The force is equivalent to the change of potential energy V with x, so that

Force = $-\partial V/\partial x = -kx$

which on integrating gives

$V = \frac{1}{2}kx^2$

Applying the Schrödinger equation to this model shows that the permitted energy levels E_v in a simple harmonic oscillator are given by

$$E_v = (v + \tfrac{1}{2})h\omega_e \qquad (8.20)$$

with ω_e being the fundamental vibration frequency and v being the vibrational quantum number, which can have values of 0, 1, 2, 3, etc.

Example 8.7

What is the zero-point energy of a diatomic molecule with a fundamental vibration frequency of 3×10^{14} Hz?

The energy of the diatomic molecule when its vibratory motion is considered to be that of a simple harmonic oscillator is given by

$E_v = (v + \tfrac{1}{2})h\omega_e$

For the lowest vibrational energy state, $v = 0$, giving the zero-point energy as

$E_v = (0 + \tfrac{1}{2})h\omega_e$

$\quad = (0.5 \times 6.626 \times 10^{-34} \times 3 \times 10^{14})$ J

$\quad = 9.94 \times 10^{-20}$ J ∎

8.11.2 Vibrational Energy Changes

At the wavenumbers in question, both rotational and vibrational spectra occur. The principles underlying the rotational changes are as discussed previously. As a first approximation, a vibrating molecule can be considered as a simple harmonic oscillator, but, in reality, it is necessary to take anharmonicity into account.

Therefore, for a diatomic molecule, the energy of vibration E_v is given by equation (8.20),

$E_v = (v + \tfrac{1}{2})h\omega_e$

where v is the vibrational quantum number and ω_e, the classical fundamental vibration frequency, is given by

$$\omega_e = \frac{1}{2\pi}\left(\frac{k}{\mu}\right)^{1/2} \qquad (8.21)$$

where k is the force constant and μ is the reduced mass. Alternatively, the **fundamental vibration wavenumber** is given by

$$\bar{\nu}_e = \frac{\omega_e}{c} = \frac{1}{2\pi c}\left(\frac{k}{\mu}\right)^{1/2} \tag{8.22}$$

The actual shape of the energy curve deviates considerably from the simple harmonic oscillator model especially at high values of v, as illustrated by Fig. 8.6, which is the familiar Morse curve. (This name arises from an empirical formula known as the Morse function which best describes its shape.) For this model, the Schrödinger equation gives an expression for the energy of vibration of an anharmonic oscillator as

$$E_v = (v + \tfrac{1}{2})h\omega_e - (v + \tfrac{1}{2})^2 x_e h\omega_e \tag{8.23}$$

where x_e is the anharmonicity constant. The wavenumber σ_v corresponding to E_v is given by

$$\sigma_v = \frac{E_v}{hc} = (v + \tfrac{1}{2})\bar{\nu}_e - (v + \tfrac{1}{2})^2 x_e \bar{\nu}_e \tag{8.24}$$

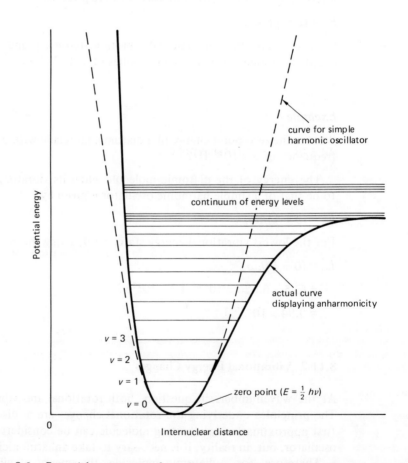

Figure 8.6 Potential-energy curve for a diatomic molecule showing vibrational energy levels.

Example 8.8

Calculate the fundamental vibration wavenumber of gaseous $^1H^{35}Cl$, given that the force constant for the stretching bond is 516 N m^{-1}.

The reduced mass μ of $^1H^{35}Cl$ is given by

$$\mu = \frac{m_H m_{Cl}}{m_H + m_{Cl}} = \frac{(34.969 \times 10^{-3}) \times (1.008 \times 10^{-3})}{(34.969 + 1.008) \times 10^{-3} \times (6.023 \times 10^{23})} \; kg$$

The fundamental vibration wavenumber is given by

$$\bar{\nu}_e = \frac{\omega_e}{c} = \frac{1}{2\pi c} \left(\frac{k}{\mu} \right)^{1/2}$$

Substituting,

$$\bar{\nu}_e = \frac{1}{2\pi \times (2.998 \times 10^8)} \left(\frac{516 \times 35.977 \times 6.023 \times 10^{23}}{34.969 \times 1.008 \times 10^{-3}} \right)^{1/2} m^{-1}$$

$$= 2990 \; cm^{-1} \qquad\qquad \blacksquare$$

8.11.3 Vibrational Energy Features

Some basic features of spectra arising from vibrational energy changes are as follows.

(a) *Selection Rules*

For the simple harmonic oscillator model, $\Delta v = \pm 1$. However, for the anharmonic model, it is found that at least three transitions occur which are named as indicated in order to distinguish them:

$\Delta v = \pm 1$ fundamental band
$\Delta v = \pm 2$ first overtone
$\Delta v = \pm 3$ second overtone

(b) *Population*

Boltzmann distribution applies for the population of vibrational levels, but degeneracy is not a complication in this case.

(c) *Energy Transitions*

The wavenumbers for the three transitions referred to above can be obtained by using the appropriate values of v in equation (8.24) thus:

- **fundamental transition**

$$\sigma_v = \sigma_{v=1} - \sigma_{v=0}$$

$$= (1 + \tfrac{1}{2})\bar{\nu}_e - (1 + \tfrac{1}{2})^2 \, x_e \bar{\nu}_e - \tfrac{1}{2}\bar{\nu}_e + (\tfrac{1}{2})^2 x_e \bar{\nu}_e$$

$$= \bar{\nu}_e (1 - 2x_e) \qquad\qquad (8.25)$$

- **first overtone**

$$\sigma_v = \sigma_{v=2} - \sigma_{v=0}$$

$$= (2 + \tfrac{1}{2})\bar{\nu}_e - (2 + \tfrac{1}{2})^2 x_e \bar{\nu}_e - \tfrac{1}{2}\bar{\nu}_e + (\tfrac{1}{2})^2 x_e \bar{\nu}_e$$

$$= 2\bar{\nu}_e (1 - 3x_e) \qquad\qquad (8.26)$$

- **second overtone**

$$\sigma_v = \sigma_{v=3} - \sigma_{v=0} = 3\bar{\nu}_e (1 - 4x_e)$$

It is important to appreciate that vibrational spectra will always have rotational transitions superimposed on them. This is illustrated in Fig. 8.7, showing that vibrational–rotational spectrum of gaseous hydrogen chloride. The vibrational transition is the fundamental one (i.e. $v = 0 \rightarrow 1$) but there is a transition between each rotational state, where $\Delta J = -1$ (producing the 'P branch') and where $\Delta J = +1$ (producing the 'R branch'); the gap in the centre arises from the fact that ΔJ cannot be zero as illustrated by Fig. 8.7. Under high resolution, double lines are seen due to the presence of the two isotopes, ^{35}Cl and ^{37}Cl, in the sample.

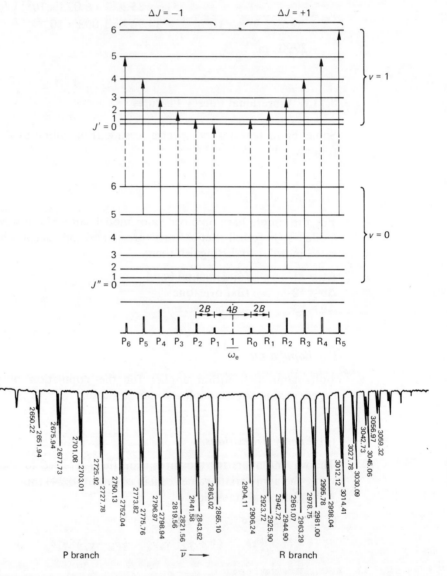

Figure 8.7 Fundamental absorption band of gaseous hydrogen chloride arising from transitions between the rotational states of first two vibrational states. (Double lines arise from the ^{35}Cl and ^{37}Cl isotopes.)

8.11.4 Applications of Infrared Spectroscopy

(a) Measurement of the wavenumber corresponding to the centre of the fundamental and first overtone band will enable both the fundamental wavenumber

250

and the anharmonicity constant for a molecule to be determined. This method is illustrated in Worked Example 8.13.8.

(b) Determination of the fundamental vibration wavenumber will also enable the force constant (i.e. a measure of the elasticity of the bond) to be obtained.

(c) In a mixture of isotopes, a shift in the position of the fundamental band is observed, enabling isotope effects to be studied as illustrated by Worked Example 8.13.7.

(d) These principles can be extended to polyatomic molecules, where each bond will vibrate. It is found that, for a molecule with N atoms, it will have $3N - 5$ such vibrational modes if linear and $3N - 6$ modes of vibration if non-linear. If the vibration in a particular mode produces a change in dipole moment, a vibrational spectrum will be observed.

This can be illustrated by reference to a triatomic linear molecule, which according to the above will have $(3 \times 3) - 5 = 4$ vibrational modes. These are illustrated in Fig. 8.8, showing that a molecule like carbon dioxide will have a symmetric stretching mode, an asymmetric stretching mode and two degenerate bending modes.

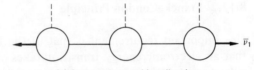

(a) Symmetric stretching vibration

(b) Asymmetric stretching vibration

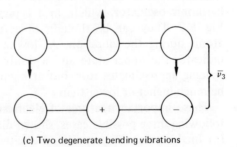

(c) Two degenerate bending vibrations

Figure 8.8   Vibrational modes of a linear triatomic molecule.

Clearly, the more complex a molecule, the more vibrational modes it will have and, as a consequence, infrared spectroscopy is a powerful analytical tool for the organic chemist.

(e) By using Raman spectroscopy (a technique that measures the scattered radiation), molecules that are infrared-inactive can be polarised, i.e. have a dipole moment induced in them. The above theory applies to Raman effects, so that these techniques can be extended to homonuclear diatomic molecules like nitrogen or to the vibrational modes in polyatomic molecules that are infrared-inactive. The selection rule for Raman effects is different, since $\Delta J = 0, \pm 2$.

8.12 Visible and Ultraviolet (Electronic–Vibrational) Spectroscopy

8.12.1 Electronic Energy Changes

At wavenumbers corresponding to the visible and ultraviolet regions of the spectrum, rotational, vibrational and electronic energy transitions occur. As a consequence, the spectra can be fairly complicated. Relative to the size of a typical electronic transition, any rotational change is very small and for our purposes will not be taken into account. In considering the vibrational transitions that occur during an electronic transition, the energy equations considered in the last section for an anharmonic oscillator apply.

All molecules will show electronic spectra as the change in electronic structure allows interaction to occur with the radiation. Also no selection rules in respect of the vibrational or electronic transitions are relevant. Instead the probability of a particular transition occurring depends solely on the relative positions of the two potential energy–internuclear distance curves (i.e. the Morse curves in the case of stable molecules). Three examples of electronic transitions will be referred to in the next section.

8.12.2 Franck–Condon Principle

One important requirement is that of the Franck–Condon principle, which states that an electronic energy transition takes place so rapidly that the vibrating molecule does not change its internuclear distance during the transition. This simply means that in the potential-energy diagrams, the electronic transitions between different vibrational states can be represented by vertical lines.

Consider a molecule in the lowest vibrational state of the ground electronic state. The probability of a transition to a particular vibrational level of the upper electronic state depends on the position of the oscillating atoms at the time of the transition. This can be deduced from the vibrational wavefunctions for the harmonic oscillator, which, in a typical diatomic molecule, are as illustrated in Fig. 8.9. They can be thought of as probability curves for the position of the atoms during the vibration. At low values of v' (conventionally a single prime indicates the upper state and a double prime the lower state), the internuclear spacing approximates to r, but at higher values of v', the internuclear spacing will be much higher or lower than r.

These important features of electronic spectra can be best represented by the following three possible cases, shown diagrammatically in Figs 8.10a, b and c.

(a) In this case, the ground and excited electronic states have approximately the same equilibrium internuclear distance. As a consequence, the $0 \rightarrow 0$ transition is the most probable one and the vibrational lines on the resulting spectrum indicate this.

(b) In this case, the minimum potential energy of the excited state is at a greater internuclear distance than that of the ground state and the most probable transition is now the $0 \rightarrow 2$ transition as shown.

(c) When the upper state has a significantly greater internuclear distance than the ground state, the dissociation limit of the excited state is likely to be exceeded. When dissociation occurs, the spectrum displays a continuum (i.e. no apparent separation between successive lines). The wavenumber at which the onset of this continuum occurs corresponds to the dissociation limit and enables dissociation energy values to be determined accurately.

Emission spectra or absorption from an excited vibrational level is much more complex as transitions can take place from either extreme of the vibration with

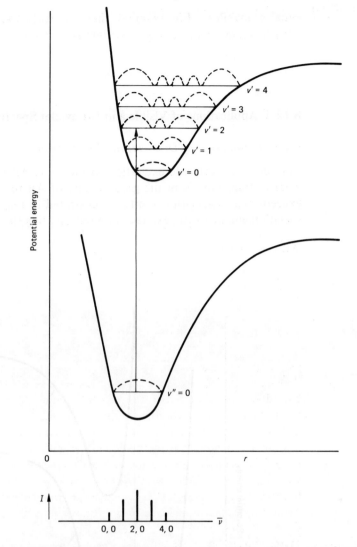

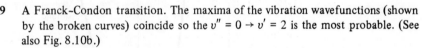

Figure 8.9 A Franck–Condon transition. The maxima of the vibration wavefunctions (shown by the broken curves) coincide so the $v'' = 0 \rightarrow v' = 2$ is the most probable. (See also Fig. 8.10b.)

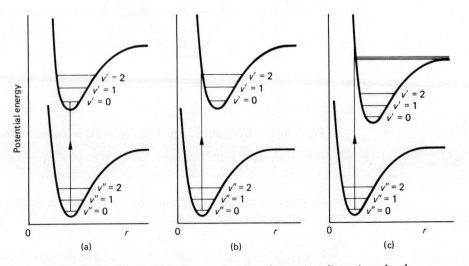

Figure 8.10 Electronic–vibrational energy changes in a diatomic molecule.

equal probability. (For example, there are two maxima for the $v' = 4$ state in Fig. 8.9.) In these circumstances, two intensity maxima are observed in the spectrum.

8.12.3 Applications of Visible and Ultraviolet Spectroscopy

(a) *Determination of Dissociation Energy from Dissociation Limits*

Consider the electronic excitation of molecule AB which can lead to dissociation when a transition from the ground state of AB to a stable excited state of AB* exceeds the dissociation limit, as illustrated in Fig. 8.11. Here D_0' gives the dissociation energy of the excited state representing the process

$$AB^* \rightarrow A + B^*$$

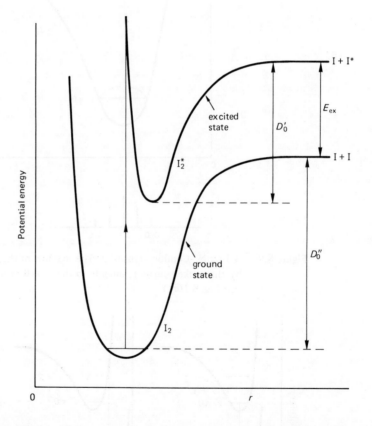

Figure 8.11 Electronic energy transition of iodine vapour leading to dissociation.

and D_0'' gives the dissociation energy of the ground state (the 'normal' dissociation energy) representing the process

$$AB \rightarrow A + B$$

The dissociation limit measures the energy transition represented by $D_0'' + E_{ex}$

where E_{ex} is the excitation energy of the atom B, which can usually be obtained from atomic spectra data. Therefore D_0'' can be determined from the dissociation limit and E_{ex}.

Example 8.9

The dissociation limit for iodine vapour is observed at 499.5 nm. Given that the excitation energy for an iodine atom is 90.7 kJ mol^{-1}, determine the dissociation energy of iodine.

The energy corresponding to 499.5 nm is given by

$$E = \frac{N_A hc}{\lambda} = \frac{(6.023 \times 10^{23}) \times (6.626 \times 10^{-34}) \times (2.998 \times 10^8)}{499.5 \times 10^{-9}} \text{ J mol}^{-1}$$

$$= 239.5 \text{ kJ mol}^{-1}$$

This is the energy needed for the process

$$I_2 \rightarrow I_2^* \rightarrow I + I^* \qquad E = 239.5 \text{ kJ mol}^{-1}$$

For the process

$$I \rightarrow I^* \qquad E = 90.7 \text{ kJ mol}^{-1}$$

Subtracting gives

$$I_2 \rightarrow I + I \qquad E = 148.8 \text{ kJ mol}^{-1}$$

This is the normal dissociation energy of iodine (see Table 2.1). ∎

(b) *Calculation of Dissociation Energies from Vibrational-Electronic Spectra*

In many molecules the electronic transitions are as those illustrated by Figs 8.10a and b in which no continuum is observed. Instead the limit can be calculated on the basis that at the limit, the separation between successive vibrational energy levels is zero. This means that at the limit, equation (8.24) is equal to zero, i.e.

$$\sigma_v = (v + \tfrac{1}{2})\bar{v}_e - (v + \tfrac{1}{2})^2 x_e \bar{v}_e = 0$$

giving

$$\sigma_v = \bar{v}_e [1 - 2x_e(v_{max} + 1)] = 0 \tag{8.27}$$

or

$$v_{max} = \frac{1}{2x_e} - 1 \tag{8.28}$$

Substitution of v_{max} into equation (8.27) gives the energy corresponding to the dissociation energy. This approach is illustrated in Worked Example 8.13.10.

8.13 Worked Examples

8.13.1 Lambert–Beer Law

A 10^{-3} mol dm^{-3} solution absorbs 10 per cent of the incident light of a certain wavelength in a cell of 1 cm path-length. What concentration of the same solution would be required to absorb 90 per cent of the light in the same cell?

Answer

From the Lambert–Beer law, the absorbance A is related to the intensity of the transmitted light I_t by

$$A = \log_{10}\left(\frac{I_0}{I_t}\right) = \epsilon c l$$

where the intensity of the incident light is I_0, ϵ is the molar decadic absorption coefficient, c is the concentration of the absorbing medium and l is the path-length.

For 10% absorbance, A is given by

$$A = \log_{10}\left(\frac{I_0}{I_t}\right) = \log_{10}\left(\frac{100}{90}\right) = \frac{\epsilon \times 10^{-3} \times 0.1}{\text{dm}^2 \text{ mol}^{-1}}$$

giving

$$\epsilon = \frac{0.04576}{10^{-4}} \text{ dm}^2 \text{ mol}^{-1} = 458 \text{ dm}^2 \text{ mol}^{-1}$$

For the second solution with 90% absorbance,

$$A = \log_{10}\left(\frac{100}{10}\right) = (458 \times c \times 0.1) \text{ dm}^3 \text{ mol}^{-1}$$

giving

$$c = \frac{1.000}{458 \times 0.1} \text{ mol dm}^{-3} = 2.18 \times 10^{-2} \text{ mol dm}^{-3}$$

8.13.2 Wavelength and Absorbance

A beam of monochromatic radiation of frequency 2.52×10^{15} s^{-1} produces a reading of 900 units on a linear detector. An optical cell of path-length 4.00 cm containing a 1.45×10^{-5} g cm^{-3} solution of an absorbing solute of relative molecular mass 300 in a transparent solvent provides a reading of 12.5 units. The same cell, containing solvent only, causes a loss of 10 per cent of the incident radiation on it. Calculate (a) the wavelength of the radiation used; (b) the decadic absorbance of the solution; (c) the molar decadic absorption coefficient for the solute.

(University of Salford, BSc, Hons)

Answer

(a) The wavelength λ is related to the frequency ν and the speed of light c by

$$\lambda = c/\nu$$

Substituting,

$$\lambda = \frac{2.998 \times 10^8}{2.52 \times 10^{15}} \text{ m} = 1.19 \times 10^{-7} \text{ m}$$

$$= 119 \text{ nm}$$

(b) The concentration c of the solution is given by

$$c = 1.45 \times 10^{-5} \text{ g cm}^{-3} = 1.45 \times 10^{-2} \text{ g dm}^{-3}$$

$$= \frac{1.45 \times 10^{-2}}{300} \text{ mol dm}^{-3}$$

$$= 4.833 \times 10^{-5} \text{ mol dm}^{-3}$$

The incident light produces a deflection of 900 units which is reduced by 10% to 810 units as a consequence of the presence of the solvent. In the presence of the absorbing solute and solvent, the deflection is 12.5 units, so that

$$I_0/I_t = 810/12.5 = 64.8$$

Decadic absorbance

$$A = \log_{10}(I_0/I_t) = \log_{10} 64.8$$

i.e.

$$A = 1.81$$

(c) The decadic absorbance A is related to the molar decadic absorption coefficient ϵ, the concentration c and the path-length l by

$$A = \epsilon c l$$

i.e.

$$\epsilon = \frac{A}{cl} = \frac{1.81}{4.833 \times 10^{-5} \times 0.4} \text{ dm}^2 \text{ mol}^{-1}$$

$$= 936 \text{ m}^2 \text{ mol}^{-1}$$

8.13.3 Atomic Hydrogen Spectrum

The first emission line of the Balmer series of the hydrogen atom is observed at 656.3 nm. Determine the value of the Rydberg constant and calculate the energy of the light quanta emitted during the transition.

Answer

The wavelength λ of the emission line in the Balmer series of the hydrogen atomic spectrum is given by

$$\frac{1}{\lambda} = R_H \left(\frac{1}{2^2} - \frac{1}{n^2} \right)$$

where R_H is the Rydberg constant and n is a constant having values of 3, 4, 5, etc. For the first emission line, $n = 3$, giving

$$\frac{1}{656.3 \times 10^{-9} \text{ m}} = R_H \left(\frac{1}{2^2} - \frac{1}{3^2} \right)$$

i.e.

$$R_H = 1.097 \times 10^7 \text{ m}^{-1}$$

The energy of the light quanta emitted per mole is given by

$$\Delta E = N_A hc/\lambda$$

where h is Planck's constant, c is the velocity of light and N_A is Avogadro's constant. Substituting,

$$\Delta E = \frac{(6.023 \times 10^{23}) \times (6.626 \times 10^{-34}) \times (2.998 \times 10^8)}{656.3 \times 10^{-9}} \text{ J mol}^{-1}$$

$$= 182 \text{ kJ mol}^{-1}$$

8.13.4 Bond Length

The microwave absorption spectrum of nitrogen oxide (NO) showed lines at the following wavenumbers:

3.405 cm^{-1} 6.810 cm^{-1} 10.215 cm^{-1} 13.620 cm^{-1}

Calculate the bond length.

Answer

The allowed rotational energy levels of a rigid diatomic molecule (see equation (8.16)) are given by

$$E_J = \frac{h^2}{8\pi^2 I} J(J+1)$$

where J is the rotational quantum number and has values of 0, 1, 2, etc. The selection rule for the above is that $\Delta J = +1$, so that for a transition between state J and state $J + 1$, the wavenumber is given by

$$\bar{\nu} = \frac{\Delta E_J}{hc} = B(J+1)(J+2) - B(J+1)$$

$$= 2B(J+1)$$

where $B = h/8\pi^2 Ic$ and is the rotational constant. The wavenumbers of the allowed transitions are (see Fig. 8.5) therefore given by

$$\bar{\nu} = 2B, 4B, 6B, 8B, \text{ etc.}$$

i.e. the separation between successive levels equals $2B$.

From the data, we see that the separation between successive levels is 3.405 cm^{-1}. Therefore $B = (3.405/2)$ cm^{-1} = 1.7025 cm^{-1}. Since

$$B = 1.7025 \times 10^2 \text{ m}^{-1} = \frac{h}{8\pi^2 Ic}$$

rearranging gives

$$I = \frac{6.626 \times 10^{-34}}{8\pi^2 \times (2.998 \times 10^8) \times 1.7025 \times 10^2} \text{ kg m}^2$$

$$= 1.644 \times 10^{-46} \text{ kg m}^2$$

The moment of inertia of a diatomic molecule is given by

$$I = \mu r^2 = \left(\frac{m_1 m_2}{m_1 + m_2}\right) r^2$$

where μ is the reduced mass, m_1 and m_2 are the masses of the nuclei and r is the internuclear distance. Therefore,

$$1.644 \times 10^{-46} = \left(\frac{14.007 \times 15.999 \times 10^{-3}}{(14.007 + 15.999) \times (6.023 \times 10^{23})}\right) r^2 / \text{m}^2$$

giving

$$r = 1.151 \times 10^{-10} \text{ m} = 0.1151 \text{ nm}$$

8.13.5 Population of Energy Levels

Estimate the population of carbon monoxide molecules at room temperature,

between
(a) the first and ground vibrational states separated by 25 kJ mol^{-1};
(b) the first and ground rotational states separated by 0.05 kJ mol^{-1}.
(Assume $RT = 2.5$ kJ mol^{-1}.)

Answer

(a) The population of molecules follows a Boltzmann distribution, giving

$$\frac{N_{v=1}}{N_{v=0}} = \exp\left(-\frac{(E_{v=1} - E_{v=0})}{RT}\right)$$

$$= \exp(-25/2.5)$$

$$= \exp(-10)$$

$$\approx 4.5 \times 10^{-5}$$

Therefore only one in about every 500 000 molecules is in the first vibrational state above the ground state.

(b) Ignoring degeneracy at first,

$$\frac{N_{J=1}}{N_{J=0}} = \exp\left(-\frac{(E_{J=1} - E_{J=0})}{RT}\right)$$

$$= \exp(-0.05/2.5)$$

$$= \exp(-0.02)$$

$$\approx 0.98$$

However, degeneracy = $2J + 1$, so the $J = 1$ state is three-fold degenerate, giving

$$\frac{N_{J=1}}{N_{J=0}} = 3 \times \exp(-0.02)$$

$$= 2.9$$

Therefore the distribution is approximately 3:1 between the $J = 1$ state and the ground state.

8.13.6 Infrared Absorption

Calculate the infrared frequency in wavenumbers at which the C=O group and the C≡N group would be expected to show an absorption band given that the force constant of the C=O group is 1230 N m^{-1} and the force constant of the C≡N group is 1750 N m^{-1}.

Answer

The wavenumber is related to the force constant by

$$\bar{v}_e = \frac{\omega_e}{c} = \frac{1}{2\pi c}\left(\frac{k}{\mu}\right)^{1/2}$$

For the C=O group

$$\mu = \frac{12.011 \times 15.099 \times 10^{-3}}{(12.011 + 15.099) \times (6.023 \times 10^{23})} \text{ kg}$$

$$= 1.111 \times 10^{-26} \text{ kg}$$

Therefore,

$$\bar{\nu}_e = \frac{1}{2\pi \times (2.998 \times 10^8)} \times \left(\frac{1230}{1.111 \times 10^{-26}}\right)^{1/2} \text{ m}^{-1}$$

$$= 1.766 \times 10^5 \text{ m}^{-1}$$

$$= 1766 \text{ cm}^{-1}$$

For the C≡N group

$$\mu = \frac{12.011 \times 14.007 \times 10^{-3}}{(12.011 + 14.007) \times (6.023 \times 10^{23})} \text{kg}$$

$$= 1.0736 \times 10^{-26} \text{ kg}$$

Therefore,

$$\bar{\nu}_e = \frac{1}{2\pi \times (2.998 \times 10^8)} \times \left(\frac{1750}{1.0736 \times 10^{-26}}\right)^{1/2} \text{ m}^{-1}$$

$$= 2.143 \times 10^5 \text{ m}^{-1}$$

$$= 2143 \text{ cm}^{-1}$$

8.13.7 Isotope Effect

Given that the fundamental vibration wavenumber of $^1\text{H}^{80}\text{Br}$ is 2650 cm^{-1}, calculate the shift in wavenumber when $^2\text{H}^{80}\text{Br}$ is used.

Answer

The fundamental vibration frequency ω_e of a rigid diatomic molecule, assumed to behave as a simple harmonic oscillator, is related to the force constant k by

$$\omega_e = \frac{1}{2\pi} \left(\frac{k}{\mu}\right)^{1/2}$$

The fundamental vibration wavenumber $\bar{\nu}_e$ is given by

$$\bar{\nu}_e = \frac{\omega_e}{c} = \frac{1}{2\pi c} \left(\frac{k}{\mu}\right)^{1/2}$$

Substituting gives

$$\bar{\nu}_e = \frac{1}{2\pi \times 2.998 \times 10^8} \times \left(\frac{80.928 \times 6.023 \times 10^{23}}{79.92 \times 1.008 \times 10^{-3}}\right)^{1/2} \left(\frac{k}{\text{N m}^{-1}}\right)^{1/2}$$

giving

$$k = 412 \text{ N m}^{-1}$$

Since the fundamental wavenumber is inversely proportional to the square root of the reduced mass μ,

$$\left(\frac{\bar{\nu}_{e,1}}{\bar{\nu}_{e,2}}\right)^2 = \frac{\mu_2}{\mu_1}$$

where subscripts 1 and 2 refer to $^1\text{H}^{80}\text{Br}$ and $^2\text{H}^{80}\text{Br}$, respectively. Substituting gives

$$\left(\frac{2650 \text{ cm}^{-1}}{\bar{\nu}_{e,2}}\right)^2 = \left(\frac{2.014 \times 79.92 \times 10^{-3}}{2.014 + 79.92}\right) \times \left(\frac{1.008 + 79.92}{1.008 \times 79.92 \times 10^{-3}}\right)$$

giving

$$\bar{\nu}_{e,2} = 1886 \text{ cm}^{-1}$$

Therefore, there is a shift of 764 cm^{-1} to a lower wavenumber.

8.13.8 Infrared Spectrum of Hydrogen Fluoride

The infrared absorption spectrum of excited hydrogen fluoride shows a series of lines centred at 3958.38 cm^{-1} and a weak overtone at 7736.63 cm^{-1}. Calculate (a) the fundamental vibration wavenumber; (b) the anharmonicity constant; (c) the force constant, given that the reduced molecular mass is 1.592 56 $\times$ 10^{-27} kg. Assume the moment of inertia of the molecule is the same in the upper and lower vibrational states.

Answer

(a) The fundamental band arises from transitions between $v = 0$ and $v = 1$ and the corresponding wavenumber (see equation (8.25)) is given by

$$\sigma_{v=0 \to 1} = \bar{\nu}_e(1 - 2x_e)$$

where $\bar{\nu}_e$ is the fundamental vibration wavenumber and x_e is the anharmonicity constant.

The wavenumber for the first overtone arising from transitions between vibrational levels $v = 0$ and $v = 2$ (see equation (8.26)) is given by

$$\sigma_{v=0 \to 2} = 2\bar{\nu}_e(1 - 3x_e)$$

Substituting the appropriate values in equations (8.25) and (8.26) gives

$$3958.38 \text{ cm}^{-1} = \bar{\nu}_e(1 - 2x_e) = \bar{\nu}_e - 2\bar{\nu}_e x_e \tag{1}$$

$$7736.63 \text{ cm}^{-1} = 2\bar{\nu}_e(1 - 3x_e) = 2\bar{\nu}_e - 6\bar{\nu}_e x_e \tag{2}$$

Multiplying equation (1) by 3, and subtracting equation (2) from it, gives

$$\bar{\nu}_e = 4138.51 \text{ cm}^{-1}$$

(b) Substituting this value of $\bar{\nu}_e$ in equation (1) gives

$$3958.38 \text{ cm}^{-1} = [4138.51(1 - 2x_e)] \text{ cm}^{-1}$$

so that

$$x_e = 0.02176$$

(c) The force constant k is related to the fundamental vibration wavenumber by

$$\bar{\nu}_e = \frac{\omega_e}{c} = \frac{1}{2\pi c} \left(\frac{k}{\mu} \right)^{1/2}$$

Rearranging,

$$k = 4\pi^2 \bar{\nu}_e^2 c^2 \mu$$

i.e.

$$k = 4\pi^2 (413\,851)^2 \times (2.998 \times 10^8)^2 \times 1.59256 \times 10^{-27} \text{ N m}^{-1}$$

$$= 968 \text{ N m}^{-1}$$

8.13.9 Carbon Monoxide Spectrum

The spectrum of the fundamental band of carbon monoxide under high resolution is given in Fig. 8.12. Comment on its features and describe what information can be obtained from it.

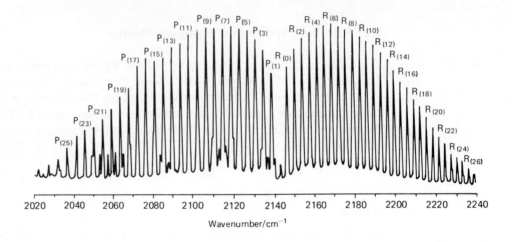

Figure 8.12

Answer

(a) The fundamental band represents the $v = 0$ to $v = 1$ vibrational energy transition.

(b) The fine structure arises from transitions between the rotational energy states of the $v = 0$ vibrational state and rotational energy states of the $v = 1$ vibrational state; those transitions for which $\Delta J = -1$ give rise to the P branch and those for which $\Delta J = +1$ give rise to the R branch.

(c) The gap at the centre of the band is a consequence of the fact that ΔJ cannot be zero.

(d) The relative population of the rotational states shows a Boltzmann distribution with $J = 5$, 6 and 7 being the most populated states.

The following information can be obtained from the spectrum:

(i) The fundamental band is centred at 2143 cm^{-1}. If the centre of the first overtone is also known, the fundamental vibration frequency, the force constant and the anharmonicity constant can all be determined (as in Worked Example 8.13.8 for HF). We can obtain the results

$$\bar{\nu}_0 = 2170 \text{ cm}^{-1}, \, k = 1900 \text{ N m}^{-1} \text{ and } x_e = 6.15 \times 10^{-3}$$

(ii) The average spacing between the rotational lines is 3.8 cm^{-1}, from which the moment of inertia and the internuclear distance can be determined (as in Worked Example 8.13.4 for NO). We get

$$I = 1.47 \times 10^{-46} \text{ kg m}^2 \text{ and } r = 1.14 \times 10^{-10} \text{ m.}$$

8.13.10 Hydrogen Chloride Spectrum

Analysis of the fundamental, first overtone and second overtone bands of HCl leads to the following equation for the vibrational energy levels in the ground state:

$$\bar{v} = 2990.6(v + \tfrac{1}{2}) - 52.63(v + \tfrac{1}{2})^2 \text{ cm}^{-1}$$

where v is the vibrational quantum number. (a) Calculate the wavenumber of the fundamental band; (b) show that $v = 27$ at the dissociation limit; (c) estimate a value for the dissociation energy; (d) calculate the zero-point energy.

(GRSC, Part II)

Answer

The separation between successive energy levels v and $v + 1$ is given by

$$\bar{v}/\text{cm}^{-1} = \sigma_{v+1} - \sigma_v$$
$$= 2990.6\,[(v + \tfrac{3}{2}) - (v + \tfrac{1}{2})] - 52.63\,[(v + \tfrac{3}{2})^2 - (v + \tfrac{1}{2})^2\,]$$
$$= 2990.6 - 105.26(v + 1)$$

(a) The fundamental band occurs at a wavenumber $\bar{v}_e$ corresponding to the transition $v = 0$ to $v = 1$. In the above equation for this transition, therefore, $v = 0$, giving

$$\bar{v}/\text{cm}^{-1} = 2990.6 - 105.26$$

i.e.

$$\bar{v} = 2885.3 \text{ cm}^{-1}$$

(b) At the dissociation limit, the separation between successive levels becomes zero and the maximum value of v, namely v_{max}, is given by

$$0 = [2990.6 - 105.26(v_{max} + 1)] \text{ cm}^{-1}$$

giving

$$v_{max} = \frac{2996.6}{105.26} - 1$$
$$= 27.4$$

showing that $v = 27$ at the dissociation limit.

(c) The dissociation energy D_e is the energy corresponding to $v = 27$, i.e.

$$\bar{v}/\text{cm}^{-1} = 2990.6(27 + \tfrac{1}{2}) - 52.63(27 + \tfrac{1}{2})^2$$
$$= 42\,440.1 \text{ cm}^{-1}$$

Since

$$D_e = N_A hc\bar{v}$$
$$D_e = [(6.023 \times 10^{23}) \times (6.626 \times 10^{-34}) \times (2.998 \times 10^8)$$
$$\times (4.2440 \times 10^6)] \text{ J mol}^{-1}$$
$$= 508 \text{ kJ mol}^{-1}$$

(d) The zero-point energy is given by the energy for $v = 0$ giving

$$\bar{v}/\text{cm}^{-1} = 2990.6(0 + \tfrac{1}{2}) - 52.63(0 + \tfrac{1}{2})^2$$
$$= 1482.1 \text{ cm}^{-1} = 1.4281 \times 10^5 \text{ m}^{-1}$$

giving

$$E = [(6.023 \times 10^{23}) \times (6.626 \times 10^{-34}) \times (2.998 \times 10^8)$$
$$\times (1.4821 \times 10^5)] \text{ J mol}^{-1}$$
$$= 17.7 \text{ kJ mol}^{-1}$$

8.13.11 Dissociation Energy

The dissociation limit which corresponds to the process

$$NO_2 \rightarrow NO + O(^1D)$$

where $O(^1D)$ is an excited oxygen atom, occurs at 245.9 nm. If the energy required to excite a ground-state $O(^3P)$ oxygen atom to an $O(^1D)$ atom is 163 kJ mol^{-1}, calculate the dissociation energy of the ON—O bond in NO_2.

Answer

For the transition

$$NO_2 \rightarrow NO + O(^1D)$$

the dissociation energy is the energy corresponding to the wavelength λ of the dissociation limit, i.e.

$$E = N_A hc/\lambda = \frac{(6.023 \times 10^{23}) \times (6.626 \times 10^{-34}) \times (2.998 \times 10^8)}{245.9 \times 10^{-9}} \text{ J mol}^{-1}$$

$$= 487 \text{ kJ mol}^{-1}$$

The dissociation energy of the ON—O bond is the energy required to dissociate NO_2 into NO and $O(^3P)$ atoms. This is obtained by subtracting the excitation energy for $O(^3P)$ to $O(^1D)$ from the above; thus

$$NO_2 \rightarrow NO + O(^1D) \qquad E = 487 \text{ kJ mol}^{-1} \qquad (1)$$

$$O(^3P) \rightarrow O(^1D) \qquad E = 163 \text{ kJ mol}^{-1} \qquad (2)$$

Subtracting (2) from (1) gives,

$$NO_2 \rightarrow NO + O(^3P) \qquad E = 324 \text{ kJ mol}^{-1}$$

8.14 Unworked Examples

8.14.1
The molar Napierian absorption coefficient of bromine in tetrachloromethane is 4480 dm^2 mol^{-1}. What percentage of incident light is absorbed by a 2 cm layer of solution containing 1.85 millimoles of bromine per dm^3?

8.14.2
The following concentrations of copper sulphate were added to excess '880' ammonia and the resulting solution diluted to 100 cm^3. The absorbance at each of the following concentrations at 600 nm was measured in a cell of 1 cm path-length with the following results:

$10^3[CuSO_4]$/mol dm^{-3}	2	4	6	8	10	12	14	16	18
Absorbance	0.120	0.205	0.309	0.413	0.509	0.630	0.706	0.818	0.902

Show that the Lambert–Beer law is obeyed and calculate the molar decadic absorption coefficient of the $Cu(NH_3)_4^{2+}$ ion at this wavelength.

8.14.3
The first four lines of the Lyman series in the atomic spectrum of hydrogen occur at wavelengths (nm) 121.57, 102.58, 97.25 and 94.98. Calculate the Rydberg constant.

8.14.4

The dissociation spectrum of the hydrogen atom consists of lines obeying the Rydberg equation

$$R_H = 1.097 \times 10^7 \left(\frac{1}{m^2} - \frac{1}{n^2} \right) \text{m}^{-1}$$

Deduce the value of the ionisation potential of the hydrogen atom.

(University of Manchester, BSc, Hons)

8.14.5

The microwave spectrum of hydrogen fluoride gives a series of lines whose separation is 40.5 cm^{-1}. Calculate the moment of inertia and the internuclear distance for the molecule.

8.14.6

Calculate the moment of inertia of (a) $^1H^{35}Cl$, (b) $^1H^{37}Cl$, (c) $^2H^{37}Cl$, all of which have an equilibrium bond length of 1.275×10^{-10} m. Using the results of the rigid-rotor approximation, calculate the positions of the first three rotational transitions for $^1H^{35}Cl$ and $^2H^{35}Cl$.

8.14.7

The separation between successive lines of the rotational spectrum of a molecule is 20 cm^{-1}. Assuming that all the molecules are in the ground vibrational state, calculate the relative population of molecules in the rotational states $J = 0$, 3 and 6 at 300 K.

8.14.8

Calculate the ratio of the populations of the $J = 5$ and $J = 0$ rotational energy states in HI at (a) 300 K and (b) 1000 K, given that the moment of inertia is 4.31×10^{-47} kg m^2.

8.14.9

Some lines near the centre of the vibration–rotation spectrum of $^1H^{35}Cl$ have wavenumbers 2927, 2906, 2866 and 2847 cm^{-1}. Calculate
(a) the rotational constant B;
(b) the moment of inertia;
(c) the bond length for the molecule.
The mass of the molecule is 1.6605×10^{-27} kg.

(University of Salford, BSc, Hons, 2nd year)

8.14.10

Calculate the zero-point energy of D_2 for which the fundamental vibration frequency is 9.25×10^{13} Hz.

(University of Leeds, BSc, 1st year)

8.14.11

The wavenumber of the O—H stretch in CH_3OH is 3300 cm^{-1}. Predict the wavenumber of the O—D stretch in CH_3OD.

8.14.12

From the wavenumbers 2885 cm^{-1} and 5679 cm^{-1} for the origins of the fundamental band and the first overtone in the infrared region of $^1H^{35}Cl$, calculate the anharmonicity constant, the fundamental vibration wavenumber and the force constant for the molecule.

(University of Nottingham, BSc, Part II)

8.14.13

The wavenumber corresponding to the zero-point energy of the hydrogen molecule is 4395 cm^{-1}. What is the wavenumber corresponding to the zero-point energy of the deuterium molecule given that the relative atomic mass of deuterium is 2.014?

8.14.14

Successive observed vibrational bands for ^{1}H^{35}Cl are centred at 2886.0 ($v = 1$), 5668.0, 8346.9, 10 923.0 and 13 396.5 cm^{-1}. Show that these bands fit the following expression for the vibrational energy for transitions from the ground vibrational state,

$$\sigma = \bar{v}_e(v + \tfrac{1}{2}) - x_e\bar{v}_e(v + \tfrac{1}{2})^2$$

and derive average values of $\bar{v}_e$ and x_e.

(University of Durham, BSc, Hons, Part I)

8.14.15

The wavenumber corresponding to a transition between vibrational levels of the chlorine molecule is given by

$$\bar{v}/cm^{-1} = 564.9(v + \tfrac{1}{2}) - 4.0(v + \tfrac{1}{2})^2$$

where v is the vibrational quantum number. Calculate the zero-point energy and a value for the dissociation energy of the molecule.

Answers to Unworked Examples

2.14.1 $w = -\dfrac{10}{64} RT = -580$ J

2.14.2 w(min) (reversible compression) = 1720 J
        w(max) (rapid compression) = 2480 J
        (compare with corresponding answers in first worked example)

2.14.3 p_2 = 2.8 atm

2.14.4 T_2(max) (rapid adiabatic compression) = 1040 K

2.14.5   (a) Yes — for a reversible change; no — for an irreversible change
        (b) T_2 = 575 K (cf. answer to 2.14.4)
           $\Delta H = \Delta G = 8.1$ kJ mol^{-1}

2.14.6   (a) 190 g
        (b) (i) 3.2 K, (ii) 150 g

2.14.7 $\Delta U = -1191$ kJ mol^{-1}, $\Delta H = -1195$ kJ mol^{-1}

2.14.8 $\Delta H = -\Delta_f H(C_2 H_2) = -226$ kJ mol^{-1}
        5230 K (assuming temperature-independent C_p and no heat losses)

2.14.9 $\Delta U = -726.5$ kJ mol^{-1}, $\Delta H = -725.3$ kJ mol^{-1}

2.14.10 $\Delta_f H^{\ominus}_{298\,K} (N_2 O(g)) = +82.0$ kJ mol^{-1}

2.14.11 $\Delta_f H^{\ominus}_{298\,K} (C_6 H_6(l)) = +49.0$ kJ mol^{-1}

2.14.12 $\Delta_f H(H_2 O_2(aq)) = -189.2$ kJ mol^{-1}

2.14.13 $\Delta H = -239.9$ kJ mol^{-1}, $\Delta U = -236.9$ kJ mol^{-1}

2.14.14 ΔH(298 K) (solution of NaOH) = -42 kJ mol^{-1}

2.14.15 $\Delta H^{\ominus}_{523\,K} = -82.3$ kJ mol^{-1} ($\Delta H^{\ominus}_{298\,K} = -80.8$ kJ mol^{-1})

2.14.16 $\Delta H^{\ominus}$(1300 K) = -284.0 kJ mol^{-1} ($\Delta H^{\ominus}$(300 K) = -283.0 kJ mol^{-1})

2.14.17 $\Delta H^{\ominus}_{1000\,K} = -35.9$ kJ mol^{-1}

2.14.18 E(C—Cl) = 329 kJ mol^{-1}

2.14.19 D(CH$_3$—H) = 427 kJ mol^{-1}, D(CH$_2$—H) = 481 kJ mol^{-1}
        D(CH—H) = 417 kJ mol^{-1}, D(C—H) = 335 kJ mol^{-1}
        Average = 415 kJ mol^{-1}. This illustrates the uncertainty attached to in-
        discriminate use of average bond enthalpies

2.14.20 $\Delta_f H^{\ominus}$(HS$^{\bullet}$) = $+138.5$ kJ mol^{-1}
        D(HS$^{\bullet}$) = $+356.5$ kJ mol^{-1}

2.14.21 Resonance energy = 182.2 kJ mol^{-1}

2.14.22 $-\Delta_c H$(CsF) = 750 kJ mol^{-1}

2.14.23 $\Delta_i H$(Br) = -336 kJ mol^{-1}
        i.e. Br$^-$ → Br + e $\Delta H = +336$ kJ mol^{-1}

2.14.24 (a) C_p = 38.0, 46.6 and 53.8 J K^{-1} mol^{-1} at 300, 600 and 1000 K,
        respectively
        (b) (i) $\Delta H = 33.0$ kJ mol^{-1}, (ii) $\Delta S = 48.0$ J K^{-1} mol^{-1}

2.14.25 (a) $\Delta S = 10.6$ J K^{-1} mol^{-1}

(b) $\Delta S = +19.1$ J K^{-1} mol^{-1}

2.14.26 $\Delta S = 20.0$ J K^{-1} mol^{-1}

2.14.27 $\Delta S = +2.8$ J K^{-1} mol^{-1}

2.14.28 $S^{\ominus}_{500\ K}(\text{Na}(l)) = 74$ J K^{-1} mol^{-1}

2.14.29 $S^{\ominus}_{298\ K}(\text{HCl}(g)) = 186$ J K^{-1} mol^{-1}

2.14.30 $w = -RT = -3.1$ kJ mol^{-1}, $\Delta H = +40.6$ kJ mol^{-1},

$\Delta U = +37.5$ kJ mol^{-1}, $\Delta S = 46\,000/373 = 109$ J K^{-1} mol^{-1},

$\Delta G = 0$, $\Delta A = -3.1$ kJ mol^{-1}

2.14.31 $K^{\ominus}_{298\ K} = 13.5$, $\Delta G^{\ominus}_{298\ K} = -6.5$ kJ mol^{-1}

2.14.32 $K^{\ominus}_{298\ K} = 0.167$, $\Delta G^{\ominus}_{298\ K} = +4.44$ kJ mol^{-1}

2.14.33 $K^{\ominus}_{298\ K} = 4.3$, $\text{CH}_3(\text{CH}_2)_2\text{CH}_3 : \text{CH}_3\text{CH}(\text{CH}_3)_2 = 19:81$

2.14.34 $p(\text{ICl}) = 0.78$ atm

2.14.35 $\Delta_f S^{\ominus} = -\text{d}(\Delta_f G^{\ominus})/\text{d}T = -51.3$ J K^{-1} mol^{-1}

$\Delta_f H^{\ominus} = -246$ kJ mol^{-1}

2.14.36 $\Delta G^{\ominus}(800\ \text{K}) = +68$ kJ mol^{-1}, $K^{\ominus}_p(800\ \text{K}) = 3.6 \times 10^{-5}$ atm^{-2}

(assuming ΔH and ΔS to be temperature-independent)

2.14.37 $D(\text{I—I}) = 156$ kJ mol^{-1}

2.14.38 $K^{\ominus}_p(800\ \text{K}) = 4.5 \times 10^{22}$ atm$^{-1/2}$

2.14.39 $K_p(693\ \text{K}) = 0.0196$ atm^3, $K_p(723\ \text{K}) = 0.181$ atm^3

$\Delta H = 309$ kJ mol^{-1}

2.14.40 $\text{CaCO}_3(s) \rightarrow \text{CaO}(s) + \text{CO}_2(g)$ $\Delta H^{\ominus} = 168$ kJ mol^{-1}

2.14.41 $\Delta H^{\ominus} = -116$ kJ mol^{-1}

2.14.42 For $\alpha = 0.9$, $K_p = 4.26$, $T = 605$ K

(assuming ΔH and ΔS to be temperature-independent)

2.14.43 $K^{\ominus}_p(550\ \text{K}) = 1.5 \times 10^{-3}$, which permits 50% equilibrium yield with $p = 50$ atm (assuming temperature-independent ΔH and ΔS, and no competing reactions)

2.14.44 $\Delta G^{\ominus}$ is negative (and the equilibrium constant greater than unity) above about 1000 K. However, having to maintain such a high temperature for this endothermic reaction would be costly

2.14.45 $p = 10$ atm, $f = 9.5$ atm

$p = 50$ atm, $f = 37.8$ atm

2.14.46 $p = 10$ atm, $f = 9.0$ atm

$p = 20$ atm, $f = 16.0$ atm

2.14.47 $p = 100$ atm, $f = 107$ atm

$p = 1000$ atm, $f = 1994$ atm

3.9.1 Similar to Fig. 3.3 (sulphur), but Y/liquid line has a negative slope. Pressure is best represented on a logarithmic scale

3.9.2 $C = 4$ (any four of the substances involved in the reaction)

$F = 3$ (any three of T, $p(\text{H}_2\text{O})$, $p(\text{HCl})$ and $p(\text{H}_2)$)

(assuming no solid solution formation)

3.9.3 (a) 230°C

(b) 0.4

(c) 0.5

3.9.4 $x(\text{C}_6\text{H}_5\text{NO}_2) = 0.73$, $x(\text{C}_6\text{H}_{14}) = 0.27$

3.9.5 1:1 compound formation with a congruent melting point of 105°C. Two eutectic points at $x_A = 0.23$, $\theta_C = 90$°C and $x_A = 0.67$, $\theta_C = 101$°C. For melt of $x_A = 0.35$, rate of cooling slows between 98 and 90°C and temperature halts for a time at 90°C

3.9.6 Transition point at 8.3°C, $x(\text{C}_2\text{H}_6\text{N}_2\text{O}) = 0.46$

Compound formation with an incongruent melting point

3.9.7   (a) $615°C$

          (b) Solid solution β ($x(CaCl_2) = 0.97$)

          (c) 42% β($x(CaCl_2) = 0.95$), 58% liquid ($x(CaCl_2) = 0.69$)

          (d) 44% eutectic ($x(CaCl_2) = 0.62$), 56% β ($x(CaCl_2) = 0.94$)

3.9.8 1.37×10^7 Pa (135 atm)

3.9.9 $dT/dp = -1.73 \times 10^{-6}$ K Pa^{-1}

3.9.10 $\ln(p/Pa) = 25.34 - 5153$ K$/T$

3.9.11 $\Delta_l^g H = 31.7$ kJ mol^{-1}, normal boiling point $= 56°C$

3.9.12 p(water, $90°C$) $= 70.5$ kPa

3.9.13   (a) 22.0 kJ mol^{-1}

          (b) 250 K

          (c) 88 J K^{-1} mol^{-1} (i.e. conforms with Trouton's rule)

3.9.14 $\Delta_l^g H = 61.0$ kJ mol^{-1}, $\Delta_l^g S$ (630 K) $= 97$ J K^{-1} mol^{-1}

        (high ΔS may reflect metal bonding in liquid mercury)

3.9.15   92 per cent (calculate input concentration at 193 K, use Clausius-Clapeyron equation to calculate vapour pressure at 193 K, calculate exit concentration as $n/V = p/RT$)

3.9.16   (a) $V(CCl_3COOH) = 92$ cm^3 mol^{-1}

          (b) 51.4 cm^3

3.9.17

$w(H_2SO_4)$	$V(H_2SO_4)$/cm^3 mol^{-1}	$V(H_2O)$/cm^3 mol^{-1}
0.25	42.4	17.9
0.5	45.8	17.5
0.75	49.3	16.3

3.9.18 $a(CH_3COCH_3) = 0.289$, $f(CH_3COCH_3) = 0.723$

        $a(CHCl_3) = 0.515$, $f(CHCl_3) = 0.858$

3.9.19 $x(Pb) = 0.40$, $f(Bi) = 0.886$

        $x(Pb) = 0.80$, $f(Bi) = 0.577$

3.9.20   (a) T(t.p.) $= 279$ K, p(t.p.) $= 4.9$ kPa

          (b) $K_f = 5.0$ K (mol kg^{-1})$^{-1}$

          (c) $\Delta_l^g S$ (353 K) $= 91$ J K^{-1} mol^{-1}

3.9.21 $M_r = 273$

        Comparison with $M_r(C_6H_5CH_2COOH) = 136$ suggests dimerisation

3.9.22 $K_b = 1.06$ K (mol kg^{-1})$^{-1}$

3.9.23 $K_f = 0.515$ K (mol kg^{-1})$^{-1}$, apparent molality of solution $= 0.292$ mol kg^{-1}, giving $\alpha = 0.46$ and $K_a = 0.054$

3.9.24 $M_r = 180$

3.9.25 $M_r = 60$

3.9.26   (a) 493 kPa

          (b) 494 kPa

          (c) 476 kPa

        i.e. Morse equation involves negligible approximation, whereas van't Hoff equation involves a small, but significant, approximation. The experimental value is slightly higher than the ideal value, which is consistent with a solute activity coefficient greater than unity (see Worked Example 3.8.4)

3.9.27 $M_r = 61\,000$ (number average)

3.9.28 $x(l)(C_7H_{16}) = 0.854$, $x(g)(C_7H_{16}) = 0.894$

3.9.29 $x(g)(C_3H_6Br_2) = 0.398$

3.9.30   (a) $p(C_2H_4)/p(C_2H_6) = 2.424$ at 170.9 K and 2.260 at 185.8 K

          (b) 256.7 K and 279.9 K

          (c) $p(C_2H_4)/p(C_2H_6) = 1.836$ at 256.7 K and 1.751 at 279.9 K

          (d) Separation by distillation decreases with increasing pressure

3.9.31   (a) $x(CCl_4) \approx 0.6$ in initial distillate

      (b) Best possible separation produces pure C_2H_5OH plus minimum boiling point mixture of $x(CCl_4) = 0.63$

3.9.32   571 g of steam

4.12.1 $k = 4.68 \times 10^{-2} \ h^{-1}$, $t_{0.5} = 14.8 \ h$

4.12.2 $k = 1.53 \times 10^{-4} \ dm^3 \ mol^{-1} \ s^{-1}$

4.12.3   Zero order indicating strong adsorption. $k = 1.61 \times 10^{-6} \ mol \ dm^{-3} \ s^{-1}$

4.12.4 $k = 0.107 \ dm^3 \ mol^{-1} \ s^{-1}$

4.12.5   Plot of $\ln(3p_0 - p)$ versus t is linear indicating a first-order reaction. $k = 1.44 \times 10^{-3} \ s^{-1}$

4.12.6   (a) Final pressure = 300 mmHg; $t_{0.5} = 3120 \ s$

      (b) As $t_{0.5} = 3120 \ s$ again, the rate is independent of pressure and, therefore, the reaction is first-order

4.12.7 $k_1 + k_{-1} = 2.43 \times 10^{-4} \ s^{-1}$

4.12.8 $E^{\ddagger} = 211 \ kJ \ mol^{-1}$; $A = 2.5 \times 10^{13} \ s^{-1}$

4.12.9 $k(325 \ K) = 1.39 \times 10^{-4} \ s^{-1}$; $k(335 \ K) = 6.93 \times 10^{-4} \ s^{-1}$; $E^{\ddagger} = 146 \ kJ \ mol^{-1}$

4.12.10 617 K

4.12.11 $k(0°C) = 0.667 \ dm^3 \ mol^{-1} s^{-1}$; $E^{\ddagger} = 59.0 \ kJ \ mol^{-1}$

4.12.12 $\Delta S^{\ddagger} = -42.7 \ J \ K^{-1} \ mol^{-1}$ indicating a loss of freedom in forming the transition state

4.12.13 Plot of $1/k'$ against $1/[A]$ gives intercept $= 1/k_{\infty} = 0.117 \times 10^4 \ s$ and hence $k' = 8.55 \times 10^{-4} \ s^{-1}$

4.12.14 $\dfrac{d[CO]}{dt} = k_2 \left(\dfrac{k_1}{k_6}\right)^{1/2} [I_2]^{1/2} [CH_3CHO]$

4.12.15 $-\dfrac{d[O_3]}{dt} = \dfrac{2k_1 k_2 [O_3]^2}{k_{-1}[O_2] + k_2}$

      Therefore reaction is second-order with respect to ozone and the rate is inhibited by oxygen

4.12.16 $z_A z_B = 2.0$; $k_0 = 1.40 \times 10^{-3} \ dm^3 \ mol^{-1} \ s^{-1}$

5.10.1 $\rho = 2.0 \times 10^{-1} \ \Omega \ m$

      $\kappa = 5.0 \ S \ m^{-1}$

      $\Lambda = 0.25 \ S \ m^2 \ mol^{-1}$

5.10.2   (a) $1.266 \ cm^{-1}$

      (b) $1.206 \times 10^{-3} \ S \ cm^{-1}$

      (c) $120.6 \ S \ cm^2 \ mol^{-1}$

5.10.3   (a) $\Lambda^{\infty} = 3.908 \times 10^{-2} \ S \ m^2 \ mol^{-1}$

      (b) $\alpha = 0.0417$

5.10.4 $\alpha = 1.33 \times 10^{-2}$

      $K_a = 1.79 \times 10^{-6} \ mol \ dm^{-3}$

5.10.5 $\alpha = 3.48 \times 10^{-2}$

      $K_a = 1.98 \times 10^{-5}$

5.10.6   Plot of Λc against $1/\Lambda$ is linear. Slope $1/(\Lambda^{\infty})^2$ gives $K_a = 1.81 \times 10^{-5}$ mol dm^{-3}

5.10.7 $1.28 \times 10^{-14} \ (mol \ dm^{-3})^2$

5.10.8 $2.56 \times 10^{-6} \ mol \ kg^{-1}$

5.10.9 $K_s = s^2 \gamma_{\pm}^2$ giving $\gamma_{\pm} = 0.828$

      Solubility in pure water $= 1.83 \times 10^{-3} \ mol \ kg^{-1}$

5.10.10 $\Lambda(SO_4^{2-}) = 8.0 \times 10^{-3} \ S \ m^2 \ mol^{-1}$

      $K_s(CaSO_4) = 4.03 \times 10^{-6}$

5.10.11 (a) pH 2.4
       (b) pH 3.6
       (c) pH 4.3

5.10.12 (a) $pK = 3.85$, $K_a = 1.4 \times 10^{-4}$ mol dm^{-3}
       (b) pH = 2.4
       (c) pH = 8.4

5.10.13 pH = 8.33

5.10.14 1.02×10^{-4} S m^{-1}

5.10.15 0.16

5.10.16 K_h(ammonium chloride) $= 5.71 \times 10^{-10}$; pH = 5.12
       K_h(sodium acetate) $= 5.77 \times 10^{-10}$; pH = 8.88

6.7.1   1.137 V

6.7.2   Applying the Nernst equation to each of the reduction reactions gives
$E(Ag^+ \mid Ag) = 0.68$ V; $E(Cu^{2+} \mid Cu) = 0.34$ V; $E(H^+ \mid \frac{1}{2}H_2) = -0.41$ V
Since the potential for the reduction of Ag^+ is the highest, Ag is therefore expected to discharge first at the cathode

6.7.3   At $-$ve electrode, $Zn(s) \rightarrow Zn^{2+}(aq) + 2e$
At $+$ve electrode, $Hg_2Cl_2(s) + 2e \rightarrow 2Hg(l) + 2Cl^-(aq)$
Overall reaction, $Zn(s) + Hg_2Cl_2(s) \rightarrow 2Hg(l) + Zn^{2+}(aq) + 2Cl^-(aq)$
$E_{cell} = 1.031$ V

6.7.4 $K = \dfrac{a_{Fe^{3+}} a_{Co^{2+}}}{a_{Fe^{2+}} a_{Co^{3+}}} = 5.4 \times 10^{17}$
Therefore, since the equilibrium constant is so high, Fe^{2+} ions can be titrated quantitatively with Co^{3+} ions

6.7.5 $E = -11.8$ mV

6.7.6   (a) $Zn \mid Zn^{2+}(aq) \parallel Ni^{2+}(aq) \mid Ni$
(b) $Pt, H_2(g) \mid HCl(aq) \parallel AgCl(s), Ag$
(c) $Cu(s) \mid Cu^{2+}(aq) \parallel Cl^-(aq) \mid Cl_2(g), Pt$
(d) $Hg, Na \mid NaOH(aq) \mid H_2(g), Pt$
(e) $Ag(s) \mid AgCl(s) \mid HCl(aq) \parallel HBr(aq) \mid AgBr(s), Ag$
(f) $Pb, PbSO_4(s) \mid H_2SO_4(aq) \mid PbSO_4(s), PbO_2, Pb$

6.7.7 $K_s = 2.36 \times 10^{-10}$ (mol dm^{-3})^2; $[Ag^+] = 1.54 \times 10^{-5}$ mol dm^{-3}

6.7.8 $E^{\ominus} = (RT/F) \ln K_s = -0.48$ V

6.7.9 $Zn + 2AgCl(s) \rightarrow 2Ag + Zn^{2+} + 2Cl^-$
$\Delta G = -196$ kJ mol^{-1}
$\Delta S = -95$ J K^{-1} mol^{-1}
$\Delta H = -224$ kJ mol^{-1}

6.7.10 $(\partial E/\partial T)_p = -0.000\,665$ V K^{-1}; $\Delta S = -62.7$ J K^{-1} mol^{-1}
$\Delta G = -FE = -21.8$ kJ mol^{-1} giving $\Delta H = -40.2$ kJ mol^{-1}

6.7.11 $E = 2 \times 0.329 \times 0.059 \log_{10}\left(\dfrac{0.90 \times 0.01}{0.97 \times 0.001}\right)$
      $= 0.0377$ V

6.7.12 From e.m.f. measurements, $\gamma_{\pm} = 0.514$
From Debye–Hückel law, $\gamma_{\pm} = 0.666$
The latter overestimates the inter-ionic attractions while the former does not take ion association in $CdCl_2$ into account

6.7.13 $E = 0.4686$ V

6.7.14 $E^{\ominus} = 0.2685$ V; $\gamma_{\pm} = 0.815$

7.8.1 $V_m = 25.5$ cm^3 (s.t.p.) g^{-1}, $b = 0.109$ kPa^{-1}

7.8.2 $A_m = 191 \times 10^{-20}$ m^2

7.8.3   146 m^2 g^{-1}

7.8.4 46×10^{-20} m^2

Comparison with the smaller value calculated from liquid density suggests adsorption at specific sites on the surface

7.8.5

V/V_m	0.25	0.75	1.25
ΔH_{ads}/kJ mol^{-1}	−10.8	−11.8	−7.4

Values suggest multilayer physical adsorption on a fairly homogeneous solid surface

7.8.6   2.03 nm (assuming zero contact angle, cylindrical pore shape, constancy of γ with r, equivalence of multilayer adsorption at flat and curved surfaces)

7.8.7   c.m.c. = 9×10^{-4} mol dm^{-3}

Γ (at c.m.c.) = 3.3×10^{-6} mol m^{-3}

$A_m = 1/\Gamma N_A = 50 \times 10^{-20}$ m^2

7.8.8 W_a = 53 mJ m^{-2}, $W_c = 2\gamma_{WA}$ = 144 mJ m^{-2}

7.8.9 ζ = 25.6 mV

8.14.1   81 per cent

8.14.2   Plot of $\log(I_0/I_t)$ versus c is linear; therefore, Lambert–Beer law is obeyed; ϵ = 500 dm^2 mol^{-1}

8.14.3 $R_H = 1.097 \times 10^7$ m^{-1}

8.14.4 $I(\text{H}^+)$ = 1312 kJ mol^{-1}

8.14.5 $I = 1.382 \times 10^{-47}$ kg m^2; r = 0.093 nm

8.14.6   For $^1\text{H}^{35}\text{Cl}$: $2B$ = 21.169 cm^{-1}, $4B$ = 42.338 cm^{-1}, $6B$ = 63.507 cm^{-1}

For $^1\text{H}^{37}\text{Cl}$: $2B$ = 21.136 cm^{-1}, $4B$ = 42.272 cm^{-1}, $6B$ = 63.408 cm^{-1}

For $^2\text{H}^{37}\text{Cl}$: $2B$ = 10.891 cm^{-1}, $4B$ = 21.782 cm^{-1}, $6B$ = 32.673 cm^{-1}

8.14.7 $N_0:N_3:N_6$ = 1:3.95:1.73 (allowing for degeneracy)

8.14.8   At 300 K, N_5/N_0 = 4.31

At 1000 K, N_5/N_0 = 9.02

8.14.9   (a) B = 10.0 cm^{-1}

(b) $I = 2.798 \times 10^{-47}$ kg m^2

(c) $r = 1.298 \times 10^{-10}$ m

8.14.10 $E = \frac{1}{2}h\omega_e = 3.065 \times 10^{-20}$ J

8.14.11 $\bar{\nu}_e(\text{O—D})$ = 2402 cm^{-1}

8.14.12 x_e = 0.0153, $\bar{\nu}_0$ = 2976 cm^{-1}, k = 511 N m^{-1}

8.14.13 $\bar{\nu}$ = 3109 cm^{-1}

8.14.14 $\bar{\nu}_e$ = 2990 cm^{-1}, x = 0.0174

8.14.15 E = 3.37 kJ mol^{-1}, D = 239 kJ mol^{-1}

Physical Constants and Conversion Factors

Physical constant	Symbol	Value
Molar gas constant	$R = N_A k$	8.3143 J K^{-1} mol^{-1}
Avogadro constant	N_A, L	6.0225×10^{23} mol^{-1}
Boltzmann constant	$k = R/N_A$	1.3805×10^{-23} J K^{-1}
Molar volume (ideal gas, 0°C, 1 atm)		2.2414×10^{-2} m^3 mol^{-1}
Elemementary charge	$e = F/N_A$	1.6021×10^{-19} C
Faraday constant	$F = N_A e$	9.6487×10^4 C mol^{-1}
Permittivity of a vacuum	ϵ_0	8.8542×10^{-12} F m^{-1}
Velocity of light in a vacuum	c_0	2.9979×10^8 m s^{-1}
Planck constant	h	6.6256×10^{-34} J s
Standard gravitational acceleration	g	9.8066 m s^{-2}

0°C = 273.15 K, 25°C = 298.15 K

1 atm = 760 mmHg = 760 Torr = 1.01325×10^5 Pa

$$\frac{RT \ln 10}{F} = 0.05916 \text{ V at } 298.15 \text{ K}$$

ln 10 = 2.3026

$\pi = 3.14159$

Periodic Table of the Elements and Relative Atomic Masses

I																	VIII
1 **H** 1.008	**II**											**III**	**IV**	**V**	**VI**	**VII**	2 **He** 4.003
3 **Li** 6.941	4 **Be** 9.012											5 **B** 10.81	6 **C** 12.01	7 **N** 14.01	8 **O** 16.00	9 **F** 19.00	10 **Ne** 20.18
11 **Na** 22.99	12 **Mg** 24.31			Transition elements								13 **Al** 26.98	14 **Si** 28.09	15 **P** 30.97	16 **S** 32.06	17 **Cl** 35.45	18 **Ar** 39.95
19 **K** 39.10	20 **Ca** 40.08	21 **Sc** 44.96	22 **Ti** 47.88	23 **V** 50.94	24 **Cr** 52.00	25 **Mn** 54.94	26 **Fe** 55.85	27 **Co** 58.93	28 **Ni** 58.70	29 **Cu** 63.55	30 **Zn** 65.38	31 **Ga** 69.72	32 **Ge** 72.59	33 **As** 74.92	34 **Se** 78.96	35 **Br** 79.90	36 **Kr** 83.80
37 **Rb** 85.47	38 **Sr** 87.62	39 **Y** 88.91	40 **Zr** 91.22	41 **Nb** 92.91	42 **Mo** 95.94	43 **Tc** (98)	44 **Ru** 101.1	45 **Rh** 102.9	46 **Pd** 106.4	47 **Ag** 107.9	48 **Cd** 112.4	49 **In** 114.8	50 **Sn** 118.7	51 **Sb** 121.8	52 **Te** 127.6	53 **I** 126.9	54 **Xe** 131.3
55 **Cs** 132.9	56 **Ba** 137.3	71 **Lu** 175.0	72 **Hf** 178.5	73 **Ta** 180.9	74 **W** 183.9	75 **Re** 186.2	76 **Os** 190.2	77 **Ir** 192.2	78 **Pt** 195.1	79 **Au** 197.0	80 **Hg** 200.6	81 **Tl** 204.4	82 **Pb** 207.2	83 **Bi** 209.0	84 **Po** (209)	85 **At** (210)	86 **Rn** (222)
87 **Fr** (223)	88 **Ra** (226.0)	103 **Lr** (260)	104 **Unq** (261)	105 **Unp** (262)	106 **Unh** (263)	107 **Uns**	108 **Uno**	109 **Une**									

Lanthanide series

57 **La** 138.9	58 **Ce** 140.1	59 **Pr** 140.9	60 **Nd** 144.2	61 **Pm** (145)	62 **Sm** 150.4	63 **Eu** 152.0	64 **Gd** 157.3	65 **Tb** 158.9	66 **Dy** 162.5	67 **Ho** 164.9	68 **Er** 167.3	69 **Tm** 168.9	70 **Yb** 173.0

Actinide series

89 **Ac** (227)	90 **Th** 232.0	91 **Pa** (231)	92 **U** 238.0	93 **Np** (237)	94 **Pu** (244)	95 **Am** (243)	96 **Cm** (247)	97 **Bk** (247)	98 **Cf** (251)	99 **Es** (252)	100 **Fm** (257)	101 **Md** (258)	102 **No** (259)

Index